INTEGRATED MATHEMATICS SCHEME

IMS

INTEGRATED MATHEMATICS SCHEME

Peter Kaner
Formerly Inspector for Mathematics
Inner London Education Authority

Bell & Hyman · London

First published 1983 by
Bell & Hyman Limited
Denmark Hose
37–39 Queen Elizabeth Street
London SE1 2QB

Reprinted 1984

Kaner, Peter
Integrated mathematics scheme, MI—(IMS)
1. Mathematics—1961–
I. Title
510 QA37.2

ISBN 0–7135–1368–3

Typeset by Polyglot Pte Ltd, Singapore

Printed and bound in Great Britain by
Blantyre Printing & Bindery Ltd, London & Glasgow

Acknowledgements

The publishers would like to thank the following for permission to reproduce the photographs on the pages indicated:

The British Tourist Authority, p. 38.
Indesit Limited, p. 168

Illustrations and design by Paul Allingham.

Contents

Unit M1 Calculating *without* a calculator

1·1 Constructing a multiplication table

The multiplication table for any number is formed by adding on.
Always watch for patterns to check and to make the work easier.

Example:
Construct the multiplication table for 62.

$1 \times 62 = 62$	←	start
$2 \times 62 = 124$	←	double
$3 \times 62 = 186$	←	add on
$4 \times 62 = 248$	←	double 2×62
$5 \times 62 = 310$	←	$620 \div 2$
$6 \times 62 = 372$	←	add on 62
$7 \times 62 = 434$	←	add $310 + 124$
$8 \times 62 = 496$	←	double 4×62
$9 \times 62 = 558$	←	add $248 + 310$
$10 \times 62 = 620$	←	add on 62 to check!

↑ Note the pattern: 2, 4, 6, 8, 0 . . . to check.

Once the table has been constructed all multiplication and division questions about 62 can be answered.

Example:
Use the multiplication table for 62 to find:
(a) 7×62 (b) 30×62 (c) 43×62

(a) $7 \times 62 = 434$ Read the table
(b) $30 \times 62 = 1860$ $30 \times 62 \rightarrow 3 \times 10 \times 62 \rightarrow 3 \times 62 \times 10 \rightarrow 186 \times 10 \rightarrow 1860.$
(c) $43 \times 62 = 2666$ $43 \times 62 \rightarrow 40 \times 62 = 2480$
add $3 \times 62 = 186$
$43 \times 62 = 2666$

Exercise 1·1

A Make the multiplication tables for the following numbers:
1 14 **2** 23 **3** 35 **4** 68 **5** 77

B Use the tables you have made to calculate the following products:

1	(a) 14×7	(b) 9×14	(c) 30×14	(d) 15×14	(e) 60×14	(f) 68×15
2	(a) 5×23	(b) 8×23	(c) 40×23	(d) 70×23	(e) 55×23	(f) 83×23
3	(a) 6×35	(b) 12×35	(c) 20×35	(d) 50×35	(e) 18×35	(f) 47×35
4	(a) 2×68	(b) 9×68	(c) 11×68	(d) 60×68	(e) 82×68	(f) 93×68
5	(a) 3×77	(b) 15×77	(c) 28×77	(d) 36×77	(e) 90×77	(f) 200×77

C Use your tables to check the following. Work out both sides of the = sign and compare the result.

1 $(3 \times 14) + (6 \times 14) = 9 \times 14$ **2** $(23 \times 12) + (23 \times 18) = 23 \times 30$
3 $(35 \times 7) + (35 \times 8) = 35 \times 15$ **4** $(68 \times 16) + (68 \times 34) = 68 \times 50$
5 $23 \times 14 = 14 \times 23$ **6** $14 \times 35 = (10 \times 35) + (4 \times 35)$
7 $68 \times 77 = (60 \times 77) + (8 \times 77)$ **8** $35 \times 68 = (40 \times 68) - (5 \times 68)$

1·2 Long multiplication

It is sometimes quicker to carry out multiplication using *long multiplication*. The idea is the same, but we do not work out the whole table. This method requires multiplication facts up to 10×10.

Example:

Multiply 27×53

```
                                                   53
                             tens                  27
                              ↓                   ----
7 × 3 = 21, 7 × 5 = 35 tens, add 21 = . . . 371 ← This is 7 × 53. It is worked out in your head.
                                          1060 ← This is 20 × 53, the product 2 × 53 is worked out in your head
                                          ----
                                          1431
```

Exercise 1·2

A Copy and complete the following long multiplication calculations:

1	**2**	**3**	**4**
42	37	47	57
35	54	28	44
. . . 0	. . . .	376	. . .
1260	1850	. . . 0	. . . 0
. . . .	. . . .	. . . .	. . . .

B Use long multiplication to find these products:

1 14×15 **2** 14×60 **3** 23×55 **4** 83×23
5 18×35 **6** 35×47 **7** 68×82 **8** 36×77

Compare your answers with those you found in Exercise 1·1B.

C Products may be checked by digital roots . . .

1∅. Find the digital roots of the numbers
2∅. Find the digital root of the product
3∅. Multiply the digital roots in 1∅
4∅. Find the digital root of the result in 3∅
5∅. Compare 2∅ and 4∅

Example:

```
                42 × 35 = 1470
Digital roots   ↓    ↓      ↓
                6    8      12
  6 × 8 = 48
          ↓
          12
```

Check the following products by digital roots:

1 $46 \times 25 = 1150$ **2** $37 \times 37 = 1369$ **3** $41 \times 66 = 2706$
4 $35 \times 40 = 1400$ **5** $39 \times 76 = 2964$ **6** $48 \times 54 = 2592$

1·3 Division

Multiplication tables are used to find the result of dividing one number by another. Dividing is the inverse of multiplying.
$144 \div 16 = ?$ and $16 \times ? = 144$ **ask the same question.**

Example:
Divide 510 by 3

1∅. We subtract the largest chunk of 3s that we can to start with. $3 \times 100 = 300$ ($3 \times 200 = 600$ is too large)
2∅. We now subtract as many 3×10s as possible from the remainder.
3∅. As soon as the remainder is less than 3 the calculation is finished.

3	510	
	300	100 ... $3 \times 100 = 300$
	210	
	210	70 ... $3 \times 70 = 210$
		since $3 \times 7 = 21$

$510 \div 3 = 170$

Note: As you know your 3 times table there is no need to construct it.

The process is exactly the same when you are dividing by a large number.

Example:
Divide 2145 by 17

1∅. Construct the × 17 table.
2∅. Subtract the largest chunk of 17s. In this case 17×100. The next (17×200) would be too large.
3∅. Now subtract as many 17×10s as possible.
4∅. Now subtract as many 17s as possible.

1	17
2	34
3	51
4	68
5	85
6	102
7	119
8	136
9	153
10	170

17	2145	
	1700	100 ... $17 \times 100 = 1700$
	445	
	340	20 ... $17 \times 20 = 340$
	105	
	102	6 ... $17 \times 6 = 102$
	3	

$2145 \div 17 = 126$ R3

5∅. The remainder is below 17 so the calculation is finished.

Note: A rough check is always useful to make sure you have not made a slip. In this case 17×126 could be checked as $17 \times 120 \rightarrow \left.\begin{matrix}1700\\340\end{matrix}\right\} \rightarrow 2040$

Exercise 1·3

A **1** Calculate these divisions (without a calculator):

(a) 36 ÷ 4 (b) 49 ÷ 5 (c) 64 ÷ 6 (d) 80 ÷ 5 (e) 100 ÷ 7
(f) 120 ÷ 5 (g) 150 ÷ 8 (h) 262 ÷ 9 (i) 346 ÷ 8 (j) 455 ÷ 7

2 Check each division in question 1 by another method. (If you have a favourite method of your own, use that.)

3 Find the results of these divisions, making a multiplication table each time.

(a) 480 ÷ 15 (b) 725 ÷ 14 (c) 692 ÷ 17 (d) 1488 ÷ 13 (e) 2843 ÷ 19

Check roughly each time.

B **1** Divide the following:

(a) 1685 ÷ 35 (b) 4285 ÷ 40 (c) 6419 ÷ 37
(d) 5300 ÷ 72 (e) 4293 ÷ 48 (f) 7112 ÷ 59

2 Check each of the divisions in question 1 by multiplying the divisor* by the result.

3 (a) Complete the multiplication table for 125 and use it to find 6948 ÷ 125.

1 125
2 250
3 375
4 500
5 625

(b) Use your completed table to divide these numbers by 125:

3600 15 672
4895 48 485

1·4 Double and divide

Division can be carried out by constructing a doubles table instead of a multiplication table. This is probably easier if you are dividing by a very large number.

Example:

490 ÷ 6
Use the doubles table to find 20, 40, 80 × 6 and also 200, 400, 800 × 6 if you need them.

Doubles table

1	6
2	12
4	24
8	48

6	490	
	480	80
	10	
	6	1
	4	

490 ÷ 6 = 81 R4

In the example the double method was very fast because 490 is just larger than one of the doubles times 10.

The following example is to be compared with the same calculation done earlier.

* The number you are dividing *by*.

Example:

2145 ÷ 17

1	17
2	34
4	68
8	136

17	2145	
	1700	100
	445	
	340	20
	105	
	68	4
	37	
	34	2
	3	

The working is slightly longer since
6 × 17 is subtracted as 4 × 17 and 2 × 17.

2145 ÷ 17 = 126 R3

Exercise 1·4
Use doubles tables to calculate these divisions:

1	(a) 63 ÷ 4	(b) 89 ÷ 5	(c) 106 ÷ 6	(d) 442 ÷ 7
2	(a) 365 ÷ 12	(b) 480 ÷ 16	(c) 535 ÷ 14	(d) 729 ÷ 19
3	(a) 782 ÷ 34	(b) 1041 ÷ 22	(c) 4253 ÷ 48	(d) 5849 ÷ 75
4	(a) 13 629 ÷ 135	(b) 62 634 ÷ 422	(c) 50 651 ÷ 331	

1·5 Decimals

Whenever you have to carry out multiplication or division involving decimals always change the problem to one involving whole numbers and tens.

Example:

35 × 1·2
→ 35 × 12 ÷ 10
→ 420 ÷ 10
→ 42

If you multiply 35 by 12 you will get a number 10 times larger than you require. So divide by 10 at the end.

Example:

3·5 × 1·2
→ 35 × 12 ÷ 100
→ 420 ÷ 100
→ 4·2

35 × 12 gives a result 100 times too large because 35 is 10 times too big and so is 12. So divide by 100 at the end.

Note: There is a rule to help in multiplication (but not division). Count the number of figures after the decimal point. They should be the same before and after the multiplication.

3·5 × 1·2 = 4·20

2 figs *2 figs*

Division is a little more complicated because if you enlarge the divisor by 10 times you decrease the result 10 times.

Example:

3·6 ÷ 12
→ 36 ÷ 10 ÷ 12
→ 36 ÷ 12 ÷ 10
→ 3 ÷ 10
→ 0·3

Increasing 3·6 to 36 has increased the result 10 times. So divide by 10 to get the correct result.

Example:

36 ÷ 1·2
→ 360 ÷ 12
→ 30

Since we make the divisor 10 times larger we must increase the first number 10 times to keep the result. So 36 becomes 360. This is the same as writing the division as a fraction; multiplying top and bottom by 10.

$$\frac{36}{1 \cdot 2} = \frac{360}{12}$$

Always check that the result of a division looks sensible. It is very easy to get the decimal point in the wrong place. Our last example divides and multiplies decimals where the numbers are a little more complicated. We have also continued the division into decimals.

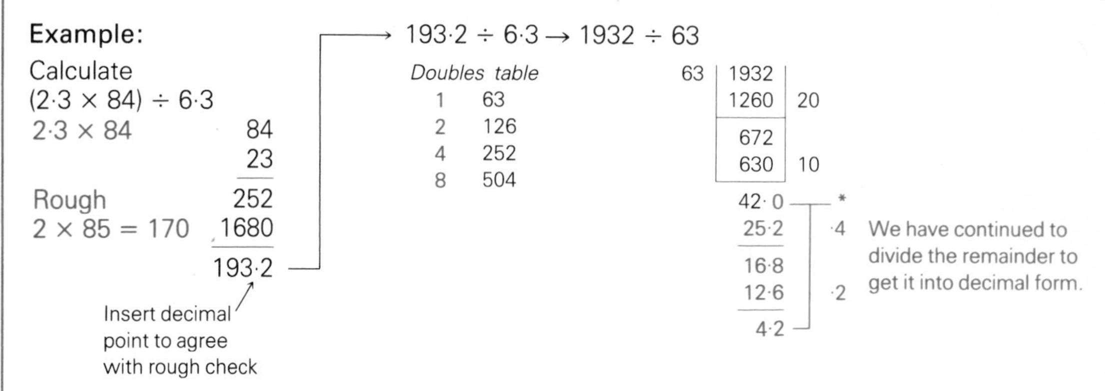

In the above example we used the decimal multiplication table which is found by dividing the ordinary table by 10.

·1	6.3	1	63	10	630	100	6300
·2	12·6	2	126	20	1260	200	12 600
·4	25·2	4	252	40	2520	400	25 200
·8	50·4	8	504	80	5040	800	50 400

* We know we are going to get a recurring decimal!

Exercise 1·5 (without calculator)

A Multiply these numbers:

1	$6 \times 0{\cdot}4$	**2**	$24 \times 0{\cdot}5$	**3**	$14 \times 0{\cdot}8$	**4**	$18 \times 0{\cdot}7$
5	$22 \times 0{\cdot}5$	**6**	$35 \times 0{\cdot}8$	**7**	$0{\cdot}4 \times 0{\cdot}5$	**8**	$0{\cdot}8 \times 0{\cdot}8$
9	$0{\cdot}2 \times 0{\cdot}2$	**10**	$1{\cdot}6 \times 2{\cdot}5$	**11**	$3{\cdot}4 \times 4{\cdot}2$	**12**	$6{\cdot}5 \times 1{\cdot}8$

B Divide these numbers:

1	$4{\cdot}8 \div 6$	**2**	$8{\cdot}4 \div 7$	**3**	$10{\cdot}8 \div 9$	**4**	$13{\cdot}2 \div 11$
5	$2{\cdot}8 \div 4$	**6**	$5{\cdot}1 \div 17$	**7**	$3{\cdot}6 \div 0{\cdot}9$	**8**	$4{\cdot}5 \div 0{\cdot}5$
9	$7{\cdot}2 \div 0{\cdot}8$	**10**	$100 \div 0{\cdot}1$	**11**	$15 \div 0{\cdot}3$	**12**	$18 \div 0{\cdot}6$

C Select the correct result from those suggested:

1 $2{\cdot}3 \times 85$ . . . select from 19·55, 195·5, 1955
2 $3{\cdot}8 \times 7{\cdot}3$ . . . select from 2·774, 27·74, 277·4
3 $45 \div 0{\cdot}6$ . . . select from 750, 75, 7·5
4 $6{\cdot}9 \div 1{\cdot}3$ . . . select from 53, 5·3, 0·53

D Calculate these:

1	$3{\cdot}9 \times 14{\cdot}5$	**2**	$0{\cdot}8 \times 11{\cdot}2$	**3**	$6{\cdot}5 \times 17{\cdot}2$	**4**	$0{\cdot}64 \times 85$
5	$14{\cdot}2 \div 17$	**6**	$308 \div 6{\cdot}1$	**7**	$50{\cdot}4 \div 0{\cdot}8$	**8**	$6{\cdot}6 \div 12$

E Calculate:

1 $3{\cdot}2 \times 0{\cdot}45$ given that $32 \times 45 = 1440$
2 $1{\cdot}76 \times 3{\cdot}42$ given that $176 \times 342 = 60192$
3 $82 \div 1{\cdot}45$ given that $82 \div 145 = 0{\cdot}5655$
4 $3{\cdot}77 \div 0{\cdot}28$ given that $377 \div 28 = 13{\cdot}464$

Note: Multiplication and division depend on quick and accurate addition and subtraction, so you should practice these skills.

Unit M2 Equations

2·1 Problems into algebra

Sometimes the first step in solving a problem is to put the facts into a simple clear form. This often means using letters to represent numbers.

Examples:

(a) The length of the pool was x metres ... this means that it was some number of metres but we are not saying how many.

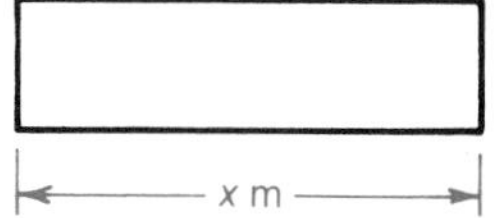

(b) The width of the pool was 5 metres less than its length ... length x metres, width $(x - 5)$ metres.

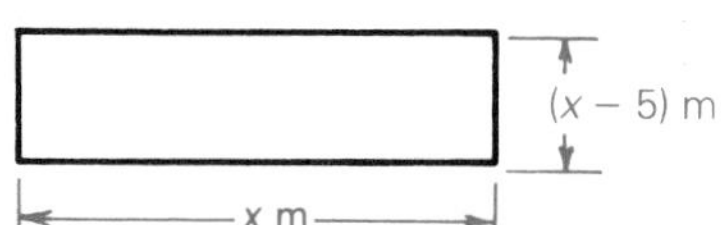

(c) One shirt cost £2 more than the other ... cheaper shirt £x
dearer shirt £$(x + 2)$

£ x

£(x + 2)

(d) One pen cost double the other ... cheaper pen cost x pence
dearer pen cost $2x$ pence

x p

2 x p

Note: $2x$ is short for $2 \times x$

Exercise 2·1

A State the following using n:

1 I think of a number (n) and add 5.
2 I think of a number and subtract 3.
3 I think of a number and double it.
4 I think of a number and multiply it by 6.
5 I think of a number and divide it by 2.
6 I think of a number, double it and add 5 to the result.
7 I think of a number, multiply it by 3 and subtract 4 from the result.
8 I think of a number, add 5 and then double the result.

B State the following using x

1 One number is 4 more than another.
2 One number is twice another.
3 One number is 5 less than another.
4 One number is 10 times another.
5 One dog weighed 2 kg more than another.
6 Today the temperature was 10° more than yesterday.
7 The car was travelling 17 km an hour faster than the lorry.
8 The woman earned twice as much as her husband.

C State these facts in symbol form using any letter you like.

1 A grandmother is 3 times as old as her grandson.
2 A Mercedes has a top speed 25 km per hour more than an Audi.
3 A garden is twice as long as it is broad.
4 A book has 42 pages less in part 1 than in part 2.
5 A class has 3 more boys than girls.
6 Three consecutive numbers.
7 Two consecutive odd numbers.
8 A large packet of soup cost 5p less than double the cost of a small packet.

2·2 Problems into equations

The second stage of solving a problem is often to form an equation. This puts the information in the form 'something' = a number. There will be an = sign and quantities on its left and right.

Example:

Problem When 3 is add to a number, the result is 8. What is the number?

Suppose x is the number

Equation then . . . $\underbrace{x+3}_{\text{left-hand side}} = \underbrace{8}_{\text{right-hand side}}$

Example:

Problem A bus had a certain number of passengers on board. At the next stop, the same number of new passengers got on and 3 got off. There were then 27 passengers on the bus. How many passengers were on the bus before it stopped?

Suppose there were n passengers before the bus stopped then . . .

Equation $\underbrace{n+n-3}_{\text{LHS}} = \underbrace{27}_{\text{RHS}}$

Exercise 2·2

Form equations from each of the following problems and solve them.

1 I think of a number (n), double it, subtract 3 and the result is 15.
2 A car travels a certain distance in 1 hour, 5 km more in the second hour and 39 km in the third hour. The total journey for the 3 hours was 80 km.
3 The three angles of a triangle are such that $\hat{B} = \hat{A} + 20°$ while $\hat{C} = \hat{B} + 20°$. Find the three angles of the triangle. (Remember all three angles add up to 180°.)

4 A girl was baby-sitting for her neighbour. The neighbour said, 'Add 50p to the money in your purse and I will give you three times as much as you then have in your purse'. The girl was paid £3·60. How much did she have in her purse to start?
5 A rectangle is 4·5 m wide and its area is 27 m^2. How long is the rectangle?
6 One quarter of a man's wages is deducted in tax. He takes home £80. How much are the wages before tax?

2·3 Solving equations

Finding the value of the letters in an equation is called solving the equation. This is done by arranging things so that the letter is isolated on one side of the equals sign with a number on the other side.

The equation is regarded as a balance and the following rules must be followed or the balance is upset and the two sides of the equation become unequal.

These rules are common sense

Rule (+, −) The same quantity may be added to both sides of the equation. The same quantity may be subtracted from both sides of the equation.

Rule (×, ÷) Both sides may be multiplied by the same quantity. Both sides may be divided by the same quantity.

Example:
Solve the equation $x - 5 = 8$

Add +5 to both sides of the equation →

$$x - 5 = 8$$
$$+5 = +5$$
$$x = 13$$

Check: LHS $13 - 5 = 8$
RHS 8

These should be the same if the solution is correct.

Example:
Solve the equation $2n + 3 = 17$

$2n + 3$ | 17

2n | 14

n | 7

$$2n + 3 = 17$$
$$-3 \quad -3$$
$$2n = 14$$
$$\div 2 \quad \div 2$$
$$n = 7$$

Check: LHS $(2 \times 7) + 3$
$14 + 3 = 17$
RHS 17

Example:

Solve the equation $2x + 3 = 9 - x$

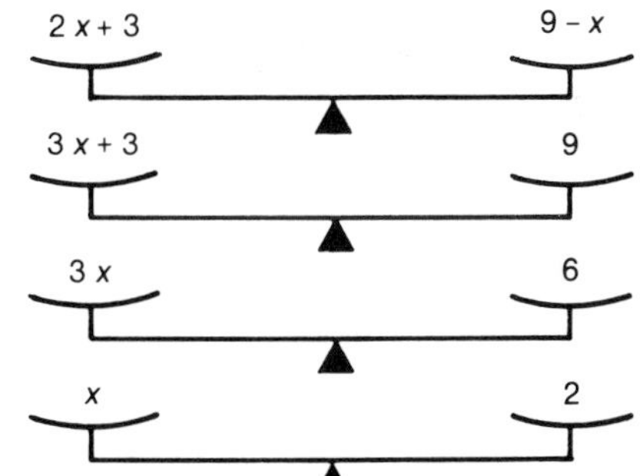

$$\begin{aligned} 2x + 3 &= 9 - x \\ +x \quad & \quad +x \\ 3x + 3 &= 9 \\ -3 \quad & \quad -3 \\ 3x &= 6 \\ \div 3 \quad & \quad \div 3 \\ x &= 2 \end{aligned}$$

Check: LHS $(2 \times 2) + 3$
$4 + 3 = 7$
RHS $9 - 2 = 7$

Exercise 2·3

A Solve the following equations: *Remember*: $-2 + 2 = 0$, $-3 + 3 = 0$, etc.

1 $x + 4 = 11$ **2** $x - 3 = 8$ **3** $x + 6 = 3$ **4** $x - 4 = 2$
5 $x + 5 = 0$ **6** $x - 7 = 0$ **7** $x + 5 = -2$ **8** $x - 6 = -3$

B Solve the following equations. Check the result, left-hand side against right-hand side.

1 $2x + 5 = 9$ **2** $3x - 2 = 7$ **3** $3x + 1 = 13$ **4** $4x + 3 = 17$
5 $5x - 7 = 3$ **6** $3x + 6 = 3$ **7** $2x + 7 = 7$ **8** $3x - 5 = -11$

C Solve the following equations. Check the result each time.

1 $2x + 3 = x + 2$ **2** $2x - 3 = x - 5$ **3** $3x - 2 = x + 4$ **4** $3x + 4 = 2x - 6$
5 $2x + 3 = 3 - x$ **6** $4x - 3 = 4 - 3x$ **7** $3x - 2 = x$ **8** $5x = 3x - 2$

2·4 Solving a problem

If you start off with a problem the steps to solution are:

1 Form equation
2 Solve equation
3 Check solution in problem

It is not sufficient to use LHS/RHS as a check as you may have made a mistake in forming the equation. This would not show up unless you checked in the original problem.

Example:

A rectangle is 4 cm longer than it is wide. Its perimeter is 36 cm. Find the sides of the rectangle.

1 *Form equation*
From the diagram,
width $= x$ cm
length $= x + 4$ cm

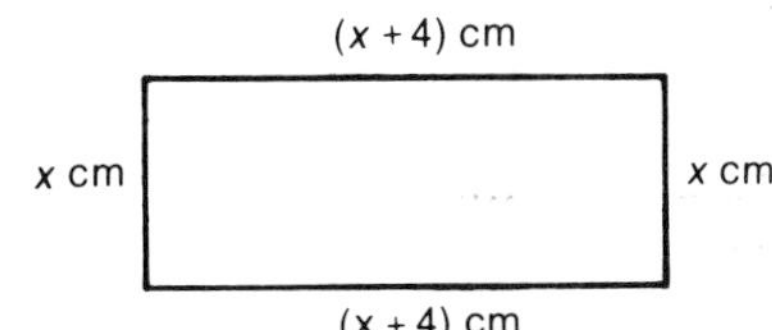

Therefore $x + x + x + 4 + x + 4 = 36$... the total perimeter.

2 *Solve equation*
By collecting x's and numbers we find the equation of the problem: $4x + 8 = 36$

$$\begin{aligned} 4x + 8 &= 36 \\ -8 \quad &-8 \\ \hline 4x &= 28 \\ \div 4 \quad &\div 4 \\ \hline x &= 7 \end{aligned}$$

3 *Check*
The width of the rectangle is 7 cm, length 11 cm and so the perimeter will be $2 \times 18 = 36$ cm. This agrees with the information.

Exercise 2·4

A *Numbers*

1 I think of a number, double it, add 7 and the answer is 17. What was the number?
2 I think of a number, subtract 5, double the result and the answer is 14. What was the number?
3 I think of a number, divide it by 3, subtract 2 and the answer is 7. What was the number?
4 I think of a number, halve it, add 6 and the answer is 14. What was the number?
5 The result of adding 24 to a number is the same as multiplying it by 4. What is the number?
6 The result of subtracting a number from 10 is the same as subtracting twice the number from 20. What is the number?
7 The result of adding a number to 12 is the same as subtracting twice the number from 20. What is the number?
8 Three consecutive numbers add up to 75. What are the numbers?

B *Rectangles and triangles*

1 The long sides of a rectangle are double the short sides. The perimeter is 100 m, find the lengths of the sides.
2 One side of a rectangle is 12 cm long. The perimeter is double the long sides plus an extra 14 cm. How long is the short side?
3 The difference between the long and the short sides of a rectangle is 8 cm. The perimeter is three times as long as the longest side. How long are the sides?
4 The short side of a rectangle is half of the long side. The perimeter is 32 cm, find the length of the sides.
5 The angles of a triangle add up to 180°. Two angles are equal and the third is 36°. Find the equal angles.
6 In a triangle $\hat{A} = \hat{B} = \hat{C} \times 2$. Find the angles.
7 In a triangle $\hat{A} = \hat{B} + 40°$, $\hat{C} = 50°$. Find $\hat{A}$, $\hat{B}$ and $\hat{C}$.
8 In a triangle the smallest angle is the same amount less than the middle-sized angle as that angle is less than the largest angle. Find the angles if the difference between the largest and smallest is 40°.

C *General*

1 One brother is three years older than the other. Their ages add up to 27. How old are the brothers?
2 A man is 36 years old when his son is 10. In how many years will the son be half his father's age?
3 The cost of a car increases by one fifth each year. If it now costs £720, what would have been the cost a year ago?
4 A bus with 42 seats is full when it arrives at a bus stop. x passengers get off and 12 passengers get on. At the next stop half the passengers get off the bus and 5 get on. There are now 20 passengers on the bus. Find x.

5 One sort of apple costs 12p a kilo more than another. Mrs Green buys 5 kilos of the cheap apples and 5 kilos of the dearer sort. The apples cost £2·40 altogether. How much are the apples per kilo?

6 A farm stock consists of a number of cows, twice as many sheep and 60 pigs. The total number of animals is 300. How many cows and sheep are there?

2·5 Numerical methods

Since the calculator is so fast, equations can be solved by trying a whole series of values for x and 'searching for a solution'. In the examples above the equations are very easy to solve, but often it would be easier to use a 'searching' method. Problems which occur in business and industry will usually lead to difficult equations. Solutions are found using a computer.

Example:

Solve $3x + 5 = 17$

We tabulate values of x, and $3x + 5$ from $x = 0$ to $x = 5$.

x	$3x$	$3x + 5$	
0	0	5	
1	3	8	
2	6	11	
3	9	14	
4	12	17*	$3x + 5 = 17$ here, so the solution is $x = 4$.
5	15	20	

(If we were asking a computer to solve this problem we could ask it to subtract each value of $3x + 5$ from 17 and **stop** when this was 0 or when the sign changed from positive to negative.)

Example:

Solve $2x + 3{\cdot}8 = 18{\cdot}4$

x	$2x$	$2x + 3{\cdot}8$	$18{\cdot}4 - (2x + 3{\cdot}8)$	
0	0	3·8	14·6	
1	2	5·8	12·6	
2	4	7·8	10·6	
3	6	9·8	8·6	
4	8	11·8	6·6	
5	10	13·8	4·6	
6	12	15·8	2·6	
7	14	17·8	0·6	
8	16	19·8	−1·4	⟵ *The difference has changed from +ve to −ve so we know the solution is between $x = 7$ and $x = 8$.*

We would now tabulate the value of $2x + 3{\cdot}8$ for $x = 7{\cdot}1,\ 7{\cdot}2,\ 7{\cdot}3\ldots$ etc.

Exercise 2·5

1 Tabulate $2x + 3{\cdot}8$ for the values 7·0, 7·1, 7·2 . . . 7·5 to find the exact solution of $2x + 3{\cdot}8 = 18{\cdot}4$.

2 Use tabulation to solve these equations:
(a) $3x + 2{\cdot}6 = 14{\cdot}9$ (b) $5x + 6{\cdot}2 = 27{\cdot}7$

3 Solve the equations of question 2 using the ordinary rules. We call this an algebraic method of solution.

4 Use a tabulation method to solve these equations:
(a) $2x + 3 = x + 2$ (b) $3x - 2 = x + 4$
(c) $3x + 4 = 2x - 6$ (d) $3x - 2 = x + \frac{1}{2}$

5 Compare the solutions in question 4 with the results you obtained by algebraic methods in Exercise 2·3C, questions 1, 3 and 4.

6 Which of the two methods do you prefer? Give your reasons.

Unit M3 Coordinates

3·1 The Cartesian grid

A set of equally spaced, perpendicular lines is called a **Cartesian grid**. The lines are numbered 0, 1, 2, . . . from left to right across the page and from bottom to top. The line across the page which is marked zero is called the x-axis while the zero line up the page is called the y-axis. The point where the x-axis meets the y-axis is called the **origin**.

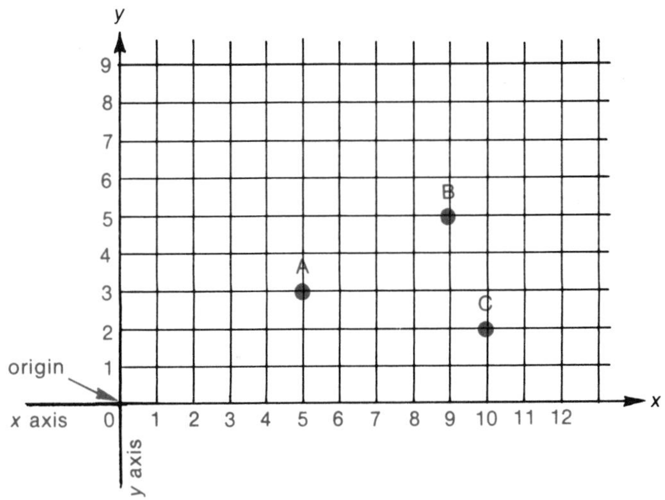

Points like A, B, C on the grid are given **coordinates**. These are pairs of numbers that tell you how to reach the point from 0.

Example:

The coordinates of A are (5, 3). This tells you that to reach A you go 5 places along the x-axis and then 3 places up to A. Remember you always go along first and then up. (It may help to think that A comes before U in the alphabet, along before up.)

Example:

Find the coordinates of B and C. B is 9 along and 5 up from the origin. Coordinates of B are (9, 5).
C is 10 along and 2 up from the origin. Coordinates of C are (10, 2).

Exercise 3·1

A **1** Write down the coordinates of all the points from A to J in the figure.

2 (a) H and G are on the same vertical line. How could you tell this from their coordinates?

(b) I, F and J are on the same vertical line. How could you tell this from their coordinates?

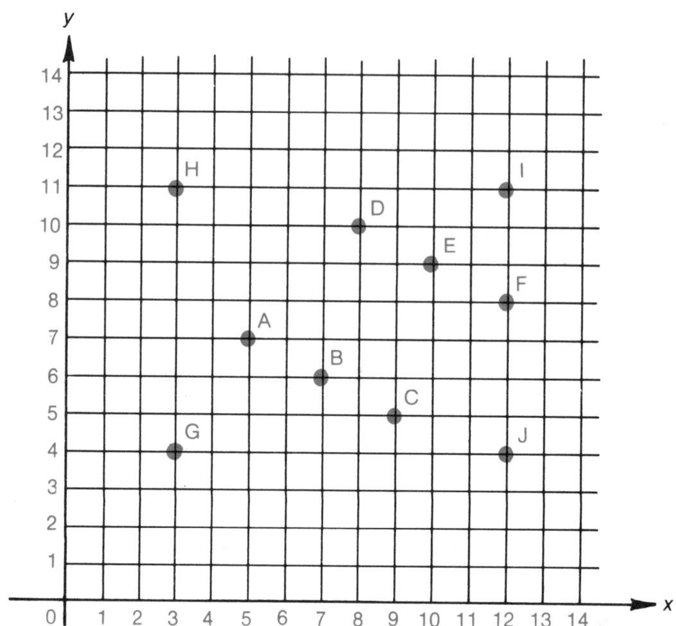

(c) G and J are on the same horizontal line. How could you tell this from their coordinates?

3 Write down the coordinates of these points (they are not marked on the figure):

(a) The point halfway between F and J.

(b) A point with the same *x*-coordinate as H and the same *y*-coordinate as A.

(c) Another point in line with A, B, and C.

(d) Another point in line with B, E, and I.

4 Measure the distance between

(a) A and D (b) B and E (c) C and F

(d) H and J (e) J and I (f) G and J

5 Which points would you join to form

(a) A rectangle? (b) A parallelogram?

(c) A right-angled triangle? (d) An isosceles triangle?

B Draw a Cartesian grid on graph paper. Mark the axes from 1 to 10.

1 Mark the points A (4, 1) and B (1, 4) on your grid.
What shape is formed by joining 0 (0, 0), A and B?

2 Mark the points C (2, 1); D (5, 1); E (2, 3) and F (5, 3).
What shape is formed by joining: (a) CDEFC? (b) CDFEC?

3 Mark the points G (3, 3); H (6, 4); I (7, 7); J (4, 6).
What shape is formed by joining GHIJG?

4 Mark the points K (4, 4); L (5, 5); M (6, 6); N (7, 7).
What shape is formed by joining K, L, M and N?

C **1** Write down the coordinates of:
(a) The centre of the circle.
(b) The vertices of the rectangle.
(c) The right-angled vertex of the triangle.
(d) The ends of the diagonal of the square.

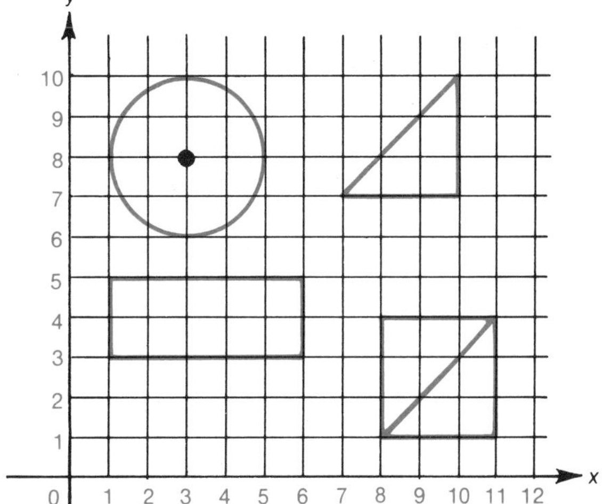

2 Which of these statements are true?
(a) The point (2, 8) is inside the circle.
(b) The point (9, 8) is inside the triangle.
(c) The point (4, 3) is on the rectangle.
(d) The point (8, 9) is on the triangle.
(e) The point (10, 2) is on the diagonal of the square.
(f) The point (7, 6) is outside the square and outside the circle.

3 Write down the coordinates of:
(a) 4 points inside the circle.
(b) 3 points inside the rectangle.
(c) 4 points on the square.
(d) 3 points outside the triangle.
(e) 3 points on the x-axis.
(f) 3 points on the y-axis.

3·2 Extending the grid

The grid can be extended in two ways:
(a) By taking points below zero on the axes, using negative numbers.
(b) By taking points between whole numbers, using decimals.

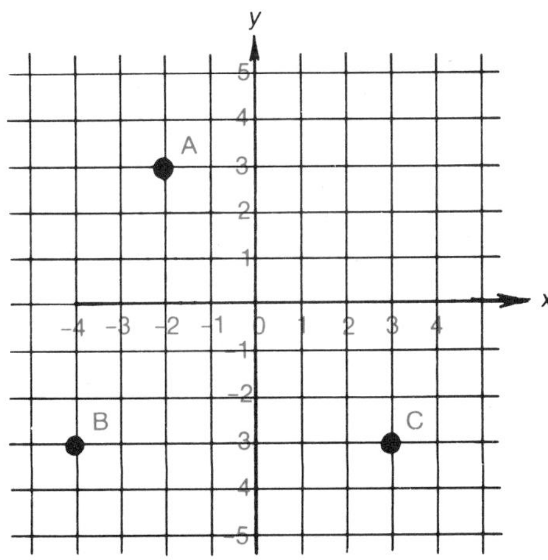

The grid is extended to negative numbers.
The coordinates of A are (−2, 3)
of B are (−4, −3)
of C are (3, −3)

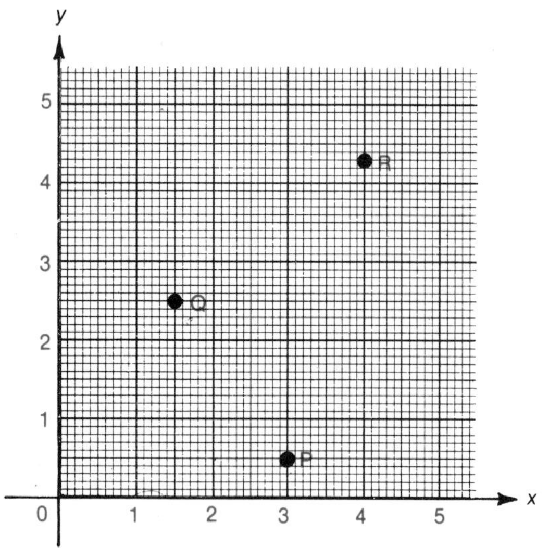

The grid extended to decimals.
The coordinates of P are (3, 0·5)
of Q are (1·5, 2·5)
of R are (4·0, 4·3)

The decimal grid can be extended to negative numbers, giving the complete grid.

This grid contains both negative and decimal coordinates.
The coordinates of W are (2·6, 1)
of X are (−1·5, 3·3)
of Y are (−2·7, −2)
of Z are (1·5, −2·4)

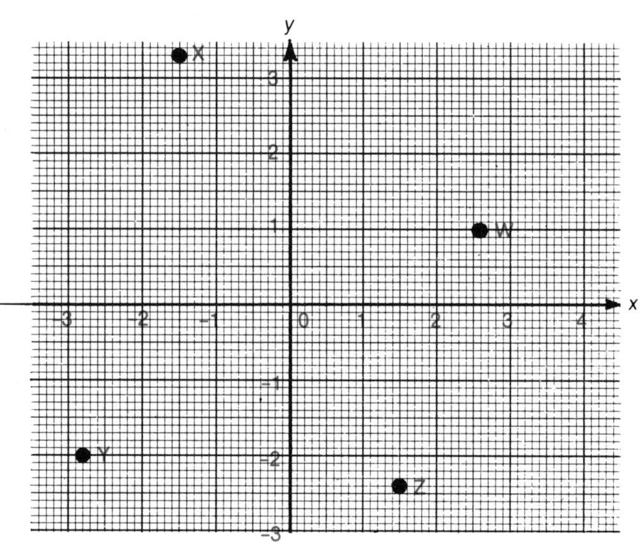

Exercise 3·2 (you need 1 mm^2 graph paper)

A 1 (a) Draw *x* and *y*-axes and mark them from −5 to +5 along the *x*-axis and from −3 to +5 up the *y*-axis.

(b) Mark these points and join them with straight lines.

(−2, 4) and (2, 4) . . . join them up
(−3, 3) and (3, 3)
(−3, 3) and (−2, −3)
(3, 3) and (−2, 3)
(−3, −2) and (3, −2)
(−2, 4) and (−3, 3)
(2, 4) and (3, 3)
(−2, 0·5) and (−1, 0·5)
(−2, −1) and (−1, −1)
(−2, 0·5) and (−2, −1)
(−1, 0·5) and (−1, −1)

Complete the picture however you like.

2 (a) Draw x and y-axes and mark them from −5 to +5 as before.
(b) Draw a circle, centre (0, 0) and radius 5 units, on the grid.
(c) Write down the coordinates of the 4 points at which the circle meets the axes.
(d) Which of the following points are inside the circle?
(3, 4); (5, 2·7); (4, 3·2); (3, −3·5); (4·5, −2); (−4, −3·5); (−5, −1); (−4·5, 2).
(e) Which of the following points are above the x-axis and inside the circle?
(4, 2); (3, −1); (2·5, −7); (−4, 2·3); (−4, 4·3); (−3, 4·2).
(f) The points (3, 4); (4, 3); (−3, 4); (−4, 3); (3, −4); (4, −3); (−3, −4); and (−4, −3) are *all* to be found on the circle. Find a similar set of 8 points one of which is (4·6, 2).
(g) Which of the following points are to the left of the y-axis and inside the circle?
(4, 5); (−4, 3); (−4, 2·5); (−2·5, −2·3); (−1·6, 5); (−2, −3·1); (2·3, −2·4); (−3, −4·3)
(h) Which of the following points are to the left of the y-axis and below the x-axis?
(7, 6); (−3, 4); (−2, −1·5); (3·6, −2·8); (−4, −7); (0, −7); (4, 0); (−4, 0); (−3·1, 2·2); (−1·8, −3·6).

3·3 Transformations (Translation)

When shapes are moved about, you can study the movement by looking at their coordinates on a grid. Changes in position will show as changes of coordinates. This is similar to the change of position on a map of an aircraft or ship.

Example:

The point A moves to a new position A′.
Coordinates of A . . . (1, 1)
of A′ . . (5, 3)

By looking at the coordinates we can see that the point moved 4 units in the x-direction and 2 units in the y-direction. The diagram agrees.

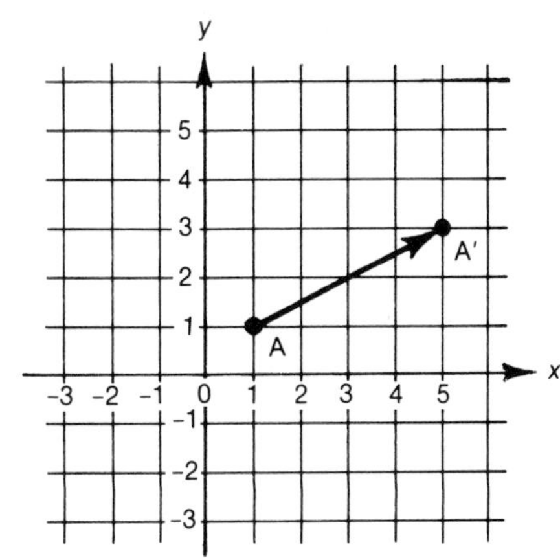

Example:

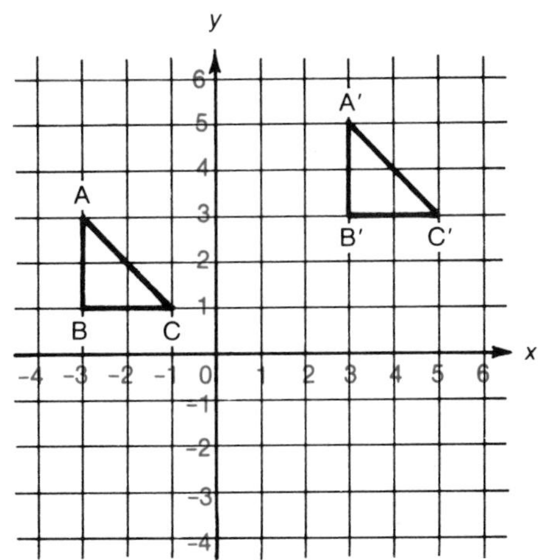

Every point of the triangle ABC has moved to a new position on triangle △A′B′C′.
Coordinates of A . . . (−3, 3)
of A′ . . . (3, 5)
of B . . . (−3, 1)
of B′ . . . (3, 3)

The points A and B have moved 6 units in the x-direction and 2 units in the y-direction.
Check that the same is true for the point C.

Exercise 3·3

A **1** Describe the movements that have taken place in the figures below.
2 Write down the coordinates of each point marked with a letter.
3 Show that, for each figure, the coordinates of each point change in the same way.

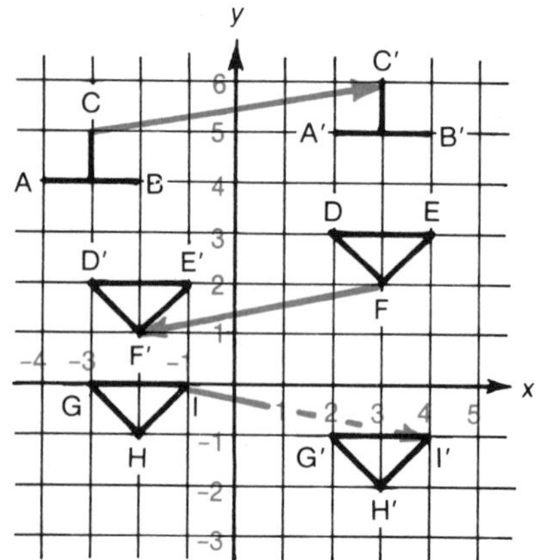

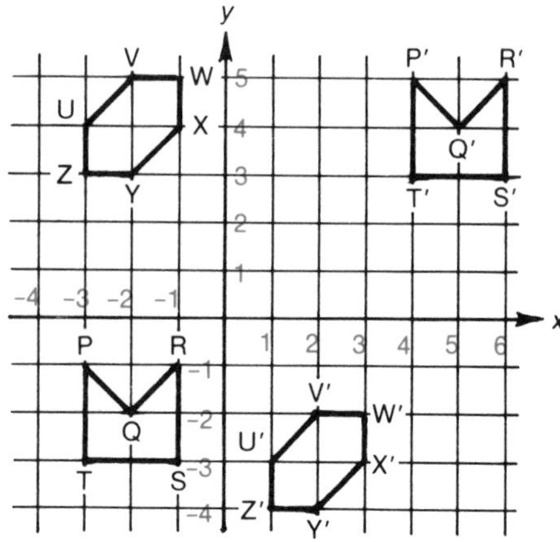

B Draw a grid on graph paper, x from -4 to 6, y from -4 to 6.
1 Draw the square whose coordinates are (1, 1); (2, 1); (2, 2) and (1, 2)
2 Draw the new position if the square is moved 2 units in the x-direction and 3 units in the y-direction. What are the coordinates of the 4 corners of the square in the new position?
3 Draw the triangle whose vertices are $(-3, 2)$; $(-1, 2)$ and $(-2, 4)$.
4 Draw the new triangles that are obtained if you:
(a) Add 2 to each y-coordinate.
(b) Add 4 to each x-coordinate.
(c) Subtract 2 from each y-coordinate.
(d) Subtract 1 from each x-coordinate.
(e) Add 4 to each x *and* 2 to each y-coordinate.
(f) Subtract 2 from each y-coordinate *and* subtract 1 from each x-coordinate.

C Draw a grid on graph paper, x from -5 to 5, y from -5 to 5.
1 Draw an L shape made from three unit squares, with the bottom left-hand corner at the point $(-4, -3)$.
2 Draw the images of the shape under the following translations:
(a) $x \rightarrow x$ $\quad$ This means that the x coordinate stays the same,
$y \rightarrow y + 3$ $\quad$ the y coordinate is increased by 3.
(b) $x \rightarrow x + 2$, $y \rightarrow y + 3$ $\quad$ (c) $x \rightarrow x + 5$, $y \rightarrow y + 4$ $\quad$ (d) $x \rightarrow x + 3$, $y \rightarrow y$
3 Describe each of the translations in question 2 in words . . .
'The figure is moved . . . in the x direction, . . .' etc.

3·4 Transformations (Reflection)

You may know that if you look in a mirror everything is switched round left to right. If you reflect your right hand in a mirror it looks like your left hand. (Try this with a mirror at home.) A transformation which turns left into right or top into bottom is called a **reflection**.

Example:

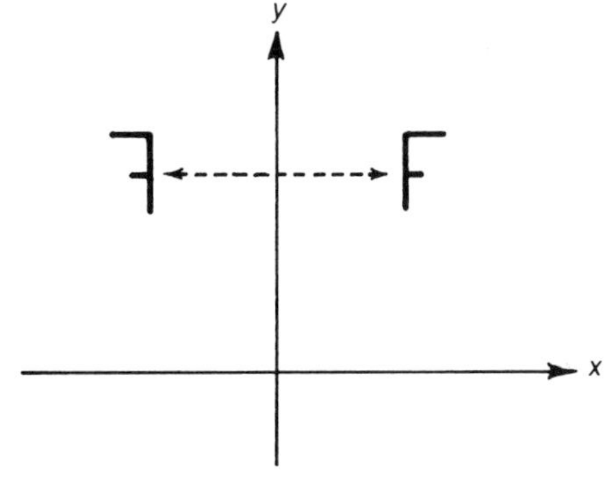

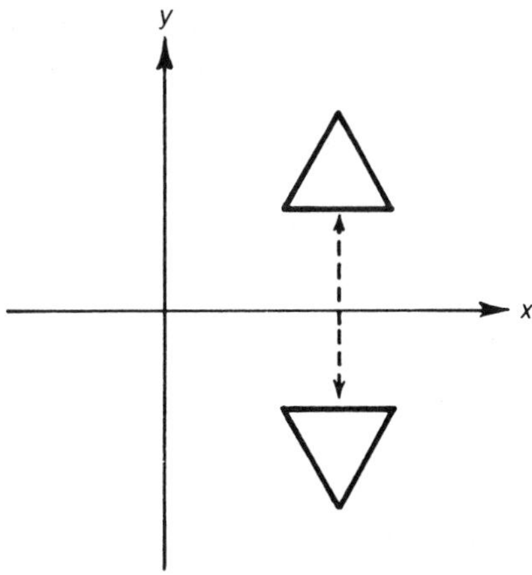

These two shapes are reflections of each other in the *y*-axis

These two shapes are reflections of each other in the *x*-axis.

(When a figure can be divided into two halves which are reflections it has an axis of symmetry, see Unit 9.)
You can tell when figures are reflections in the *x* or *y*-axes, from their coordinates.

Examples:

Coordinates:
X (−4, 4) X′ (4, 4)
Y (−2, 4) Y′ (2, 4)
Z (−4, 5) Z′ (4, 5)

Coordinates:
P(4, −1) P′ (−4, −1)
Q(2, −3) Q′ (−2, −3)

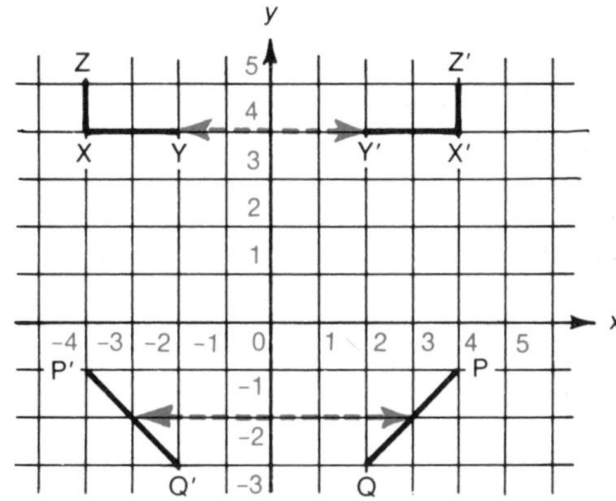

Reflection in *y*-axis
$x \to -x$
$y \to y$

Exercise 3·4

A Draw a grid on graph paper, *x* −5 to 5 and *y* −5 to 5.

1 Draw the triangle whoses vertices are P(2, 1); Q(4, 1) and R(4, 4).
2 Draw the reflection of the triangle in the *y*-axis.
3 Find the coordinates of the vertices of the reflection P′, Q′ and R′.
4 Do you agree that the *x*-coordinates add up to zero for each pair, point plus reflection?
5 Draw the reflection in the *x*-axis of △PQR
6 What do you notice about the coordinates of pairs of reflected points this time?

B The coordinates of the points ABCD in the figure below are: A(1, 7); B(4, 7); C(4, 6) and D(2, 6)

1. Write down the coordinates of the remaining vertices.
2. What are the coordinates of vertices of the figure which is the reflection of ABC . . . L in the *y*-axis?
3. What are the coordinates of the reflection in the *x*-axis?
4. What is the connection between the coordinates of corresponding points in the two reflections?

C 1 Draw the figure below, ABC . . . K, L on the graph paper.

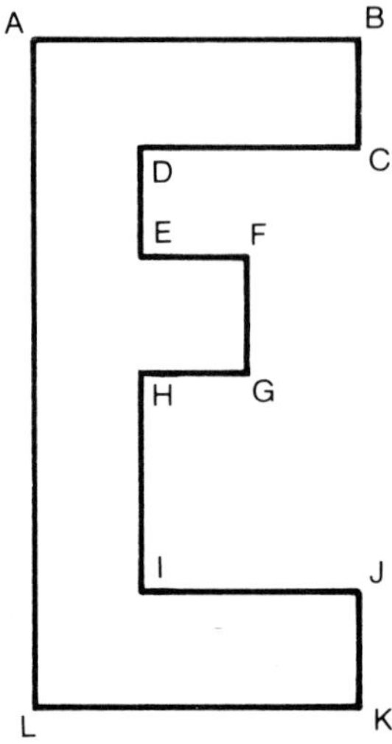

2. Draw the reflection in the line AL. Find the coordinates of A′, B′, . . . etc. under this reflection.
3. Draw the reflection in a line through B, C, J and K. Write down the coordinates of the vertices under this reflection.
4. Show, by considering the coordinates, that the reflection in question 3 is a translation of the reflection in question 2.

Unit M4 Straight line graphs

4·1 Tables of values

If we know that $y = 2x$ we can make a table showing values of y for different values of x.

Example:
Make a table of values for the function $y = 2x$ from $x = 0$ to $x = 5$.

$y = 2x$

x	0	1	2	3	4	5
y	0	2	4	6	8	10

If $x = 2$, $2x$ will be 4 therefore $y = 4$.
If $x = 4$, $2x$ will be 8 therefore $y = 8$.

Note: Draw the table carefully, fill in the values for x. Then work out the values for y.

Exercise 4·1

Make tables of values for the following functions:

1 $y = x$ for $x = 0$ to $x = 5$.
2 $y = 3x$ for $x = 0$ to $x = 6$.
3 $y = \frac{1}{2}x$ for $x = 0, 2, 4, 6, 8, 10$.
4 $y = -x$ for $x = -2, -1, 0, 1, 2$ and 3. *Note:* $-(-2) = 2$, etc.

4·2 Making a graph from a table of values

The table gives pairs of values for x and y.
If these pairs are used as coordinates on a grid, the graph of the function is obtained.

Example:
Draw the graph of $y = 2x$ from $x = 0$ to $x = 5$.
The table is the same as our first example.

$y = 2x$

x	0	1	2	3	4	5
y	0	2	4	6	8	10

(0, 0) (1, 2) (2, 4) (3, 6) (4, 8) (5, 10)

Each pair in the tables become coordinates for a point.

The points have been marked on the graph and a line drawn through them.
Note that the line is marked $y = 2x$
Note the line passes through (0, 0).
$y = 2x$ is the **equation** of the line.

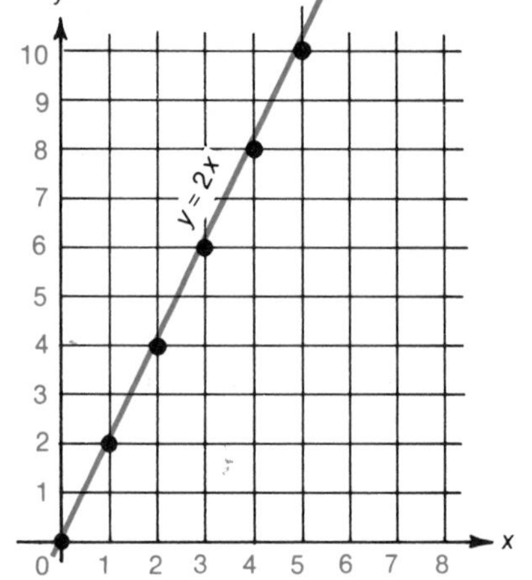

Exercise 4·2

Work on squared paper or graph paper.

1 Draw the graph of $y = x$ from $x = 0$ to $x = 5$
2 Draw the graph of $y = 1\frac{1}{2}x$ for $x = 0, 2, 4, 6$ and 8.
3 Draw the graph of $y = -x$ for $x = -2, -1, 0, 1, 2, 3$*
4 Draw the graph of $y = 3x$ for $x = -2, -1, 0, 1, 2$*
5 Draw the graph of $y = 0{\cdot}8x$ for $x = -2, -1, 0, 1, 2$ on 1 mm^2 graph paper.

4·3 The slope of a graph

The slope of a straight line is measured by the rise, as you go along the *x* direction. It can be found from any 2 points.

$$\textbf{Slope} = \frac{\text{distance moved in } y\text{-direction}}{\text{distance moved in } x\text{-direction}}$$

In moving up the line from O to P, you move 3 units **up** (in the y-direction) and 6 units **along** (in the x-direction).

$$\textbf{Slope} = 3 \div 6 = \tfrac{1}{2}$$

Note: We say the line has a positive slope because you go up the line as you move in the x-direction.

Example:

Find the slope of the line whose equation is $y = 3x$

$y = 3x$	x	−1	0	1	2	3
	y	−3	0	3	6	9

We can find the slope by choosing any pair of points on the line.

* You will need to extend your grid to negative numbers.

Using points B and C, C is 3 units above B and 1 unit along from B in the x-direction.

$$\text{Slope} = \tfrac{3}{1} = 3$$

Using points C and A, C is 6 units above A C is 2 units along from A in the x-direction.

$$\text{Slope} = \tfrac{6}{2} = 3$$

Using points B and D
B is 9 units above D
B is 3 units along from D
in the x-direction.

$$\text{Slope} = \tfrac{9}{3} = 3$$

Note: The quickest way is to choose the point (0, 0). This only works if the line passes through (0, 0). Not all lines will do this.

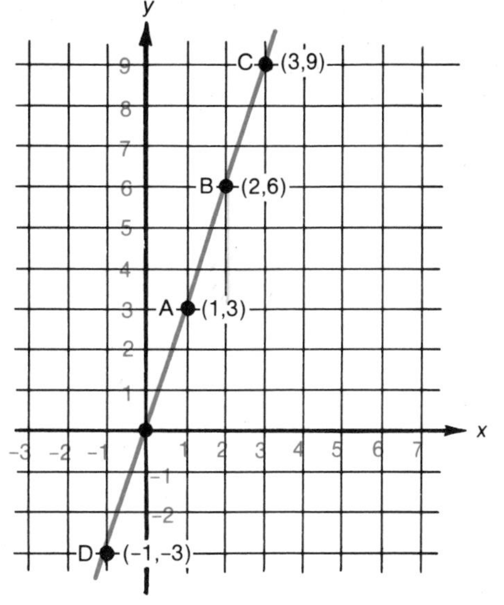

Exercise 4·3

1 Find the slope of each line in the figure. Check by using two **different** pairs of points each time.

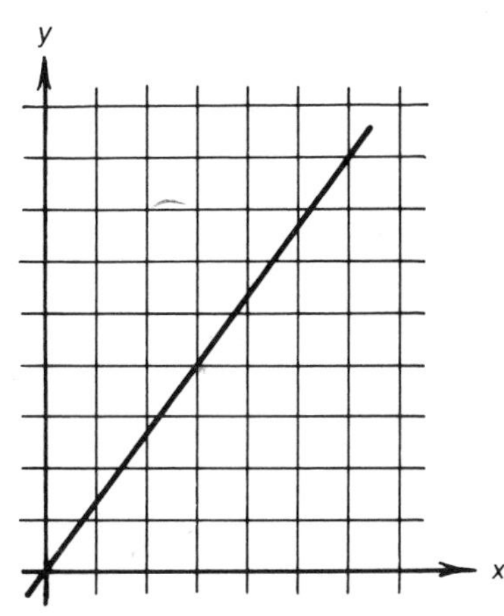

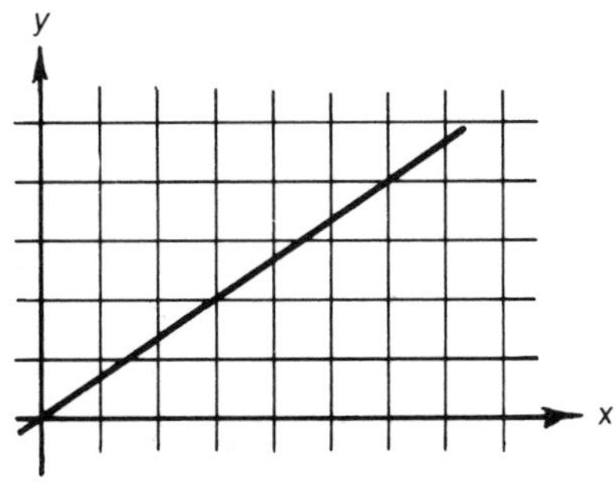

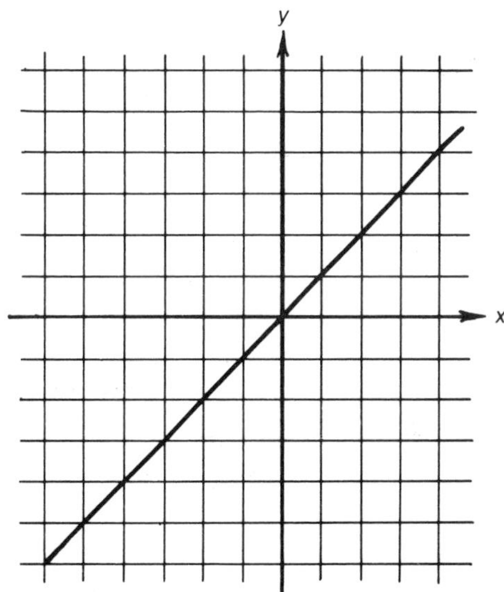

2 Find two points on each of these functions. Use the points to work out the slope of the graph of the function.
(a) $y = 4x$ (b) $y = 20x$ (c) $y = 0{\cdot}4x$ (d) $y = \frac{2}{3}x$

Example:
(1, 4) is a point on the graph of $y = 4x$ because when $x = 1$, $y = 4$.

3 Check the statements made about each of the functions below.
(a) $y = x$ The graph passes through (0, 0) and (4, 4).
The slope of the graph is 1.
(b) $y = 1\frac{3}{4}x$ The graph passes through (4, 7), (8, 14).
The slope of the graph is $1\frac{3}{4}$.
(c) $y = 2{\cdot}63x$ The graph passes through (0, 0) and (1, 2·63).
The slope of the graph is 2·63.
(d) $y = -2x$ The graph passes through (0, 0) and (2, −4).

The graph of $y = mx$ has slope m and passes through (0, 0).

4·4 Applications

The straight line graph through (0, 0) is very common in everyday life. It occurs whenever things change steadily and where none of one thing means none of the other. This situation is sometimes called **direct variation**.

Example:
John earns £1·25 an hour.

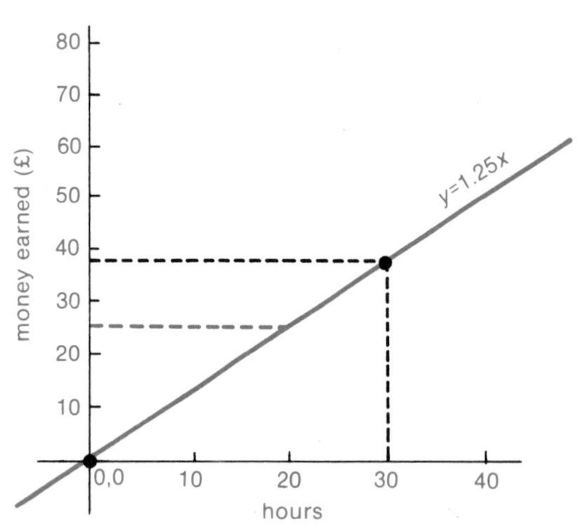

This is a typical $y = mx$ graph because
(a) if he works no hours he earns no money
(b) he earns a steady rate of pay.
$m = 1{\cdot}25$
x = number of hours
y = money earned

You only need 2 points to draw the graph (0, 0) and one other. We have used (20, 25). £25 for 20 hours work.
Note: (a) You choose a scale for the hours axis and for the wages axis which suits your information.
(b) The **slope** of the graph corresponds to the **rate** per **hour**.

Other points can be read from the graph, e.g. if he works 30 hours he will earn £37·50.

Exercise 4·4

A Draw $y = mx$ graphs for the following situations and use them to answer the questions.

1 Mary earns £2 an hour. How much would she earn in:
(a) 4 hours? (b) 7 hours? (c) 12 hours? (d) 45 hours?
What is the slope of the graph?

2 Jack earns £1·75 an hour. How much would he earn in:
(a) 20 hours? (b) 35 hours? (c) 80 hours? (d) 120 hours?

3 It costs £3·90 a week to hire a colour TV. How much would it cost to hire for:
(a) 20 weeks? (b) 45 weeks? (c) 120 weeks?

B These situations are also $y = mx$ type. Draw a graph for each one and explain how the slope of the graph gives information. Take care to choose a sensible scale for the y-axis.

1 A car is driven at 90 kmph on a motorway. How far will it travel in:
(a) 3 hours? (b) $4\frac{1}{2}$hours? (c) 5·4 hours?

2 A girl can swim 10 metres in 25 seconds. How long would it take her to swim:
(a) 40 m? (b) 65 m? (c) 300 m? (d) 1000 m?
How far would she swim in 10 minutes at this speed?

3 Sugar costs 35 p per kg. What would:
(a) 8 kg (b) 75 kg (c) 1800 kg cost?
What does the slope of the graph tell you?

4 Rail fares are calculated by the distance travelled. If a journey of 120 miles cost £8·50 single, find the cost of journeys of:
(a) 80 miles (b) 45 miles (c) 160 miles (d) 250 miles

5 Pure gold weighs 19·64 g per cubic centimetre. What would:
(a) 25 cm^3 (b) 300 cm^3 (c) 550 cm^3
of pure gold weigh?

C Graphs can be used to compare prices.

Example:

One type of TV costs £85 for 30 weeks hire. Another type costs £125 for 50 weeks hire. Which is dearer?

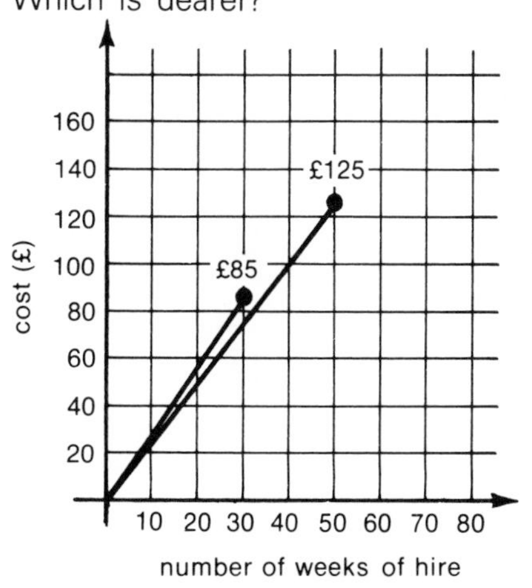

The £85 set has a *steeper slope.*
This means that the rate per week is higher.

Note: The rate per week can be calculated without drawing the graph.
First type: £85 ÷ 30 = £2·83 per week.
Second type: £125 ÷ 50 = £2·50 per week.

1 A soap powder is sold in packets of 400 g (46 p) and 750 g (80 p).
Which packet is better value?

2 Oil is sold in three sized cans: 1 litre (£1·36), 2 litre (£2·36) and 5 litre (£5·00). Use a graph to compare the costs. All three lines can be drawn on the pair of axes.

3 Gold weighs 19·64 grams per cm^3.
(a) How much would 10 cm^3, 25 cm^3, 60 cm^3 of pure gold weigh?
(b) What would be the volume of 100 g, 250 g, 600 g of pure gold?

4 Silver weighs 11·08 grams per cm^3.
(a) What would 10 cm^3, 25 cm^3, 60 cm^3 of pure silver weigh?
(b) What would be the volume of 100 g, 250 g, 600 g of pure silver?

5 Mary and John bought gold rings when they were engaged. How could they find out whether their rings are pure gold or a mixture of gold and silver, using graphs?

4·5 The graph of $y = mx + c$

We have seen that the graph of $y = mx$ has slope equal to m, and passes through the point (0, 0).

$$m = \frac{\text{up}}{\text{along}} = \frac{AB}{BC}$$

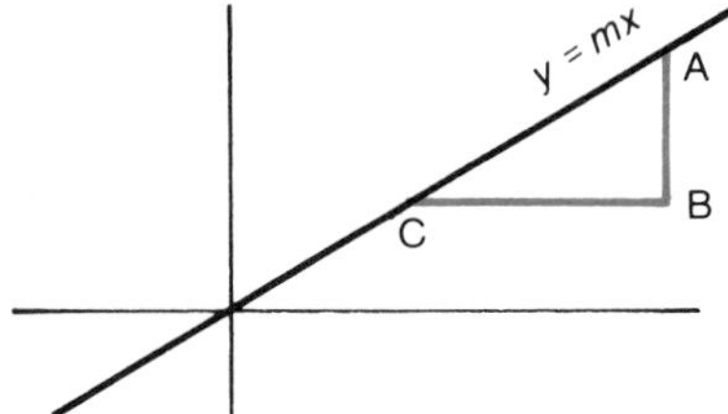

The graph of $y = mx + c$ has the same slope as $y = mx$ but is moved up (if c is positive). This line passes through the point (0, c) instead of (0, 0).

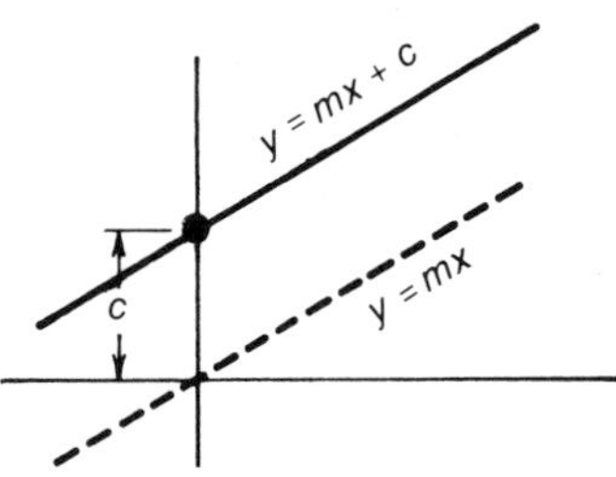

Example:

Draw the graph of $y = 2x + 3$.
(a) Find the coordinates of the points at which the line cuts the x-axis and the y-axis.
(b) Do the points (2, 3); (5, 8) or (4, 11) lie on the line?

First make a table of values.

$y = 2x + 3$	x	0	1	2	3	4	5
	y	3	5	7	9	11	13
		↓ (0, 3)	↓ (1, 5)	↓ (2, 7)	↓ (3, 9)	↓ (4, 11)	↓ (5, 13)

The line is parallel to $y = 2x$. The coordinates where the line meets the axes are: (0, 3) and $(-1\frac{1}{2}, 0)$. (2, 3) and (5, 8) are *not* on the line. (4, 11) *is* on the line.

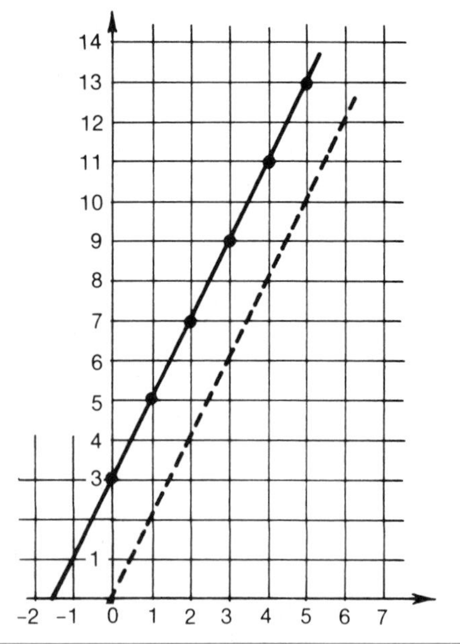

Exercise 4·5

A Draw graphs for each of these functions ($x = 0, 1, \ldots, 5$)

1 $y = 2x - 1$ **2** $y = 2x + 1$ **3** $y = x + 3$

4 $y = x + 6$ **5** $y = 3x - 2$ **6** $y = 3x + 4$

Find the points at which each line meets the x-axis and y-axis.

B Use your calculator to make a table of values for these functions ($x = 0, 1, 2, \ldots, 6$).

1 $y = 0{\cdot}8x + 2{\cdot}3$ **2** $y = 1{\cdot}7x - 3{\cdot}4$

3 $y = 4{\cdot}2x - 4{\cdot}8$ **4** $y = 0{\cdot}35x + 1{\cdot}45$

Check that the graph of each function is a straight line.

C The graph $y = mx + c$ is very common in everyday life. It happens when things change steadily but y is not 0 at the same time as x.

Example:

A self-drive car hire firm charges £7 per day plus 10 p a mile. Draw a graph showing the cost for different mileages.

Miles	0	10	20	30	40	50	60	70
Cost (£)	7	8	9	10	11	12	13	14

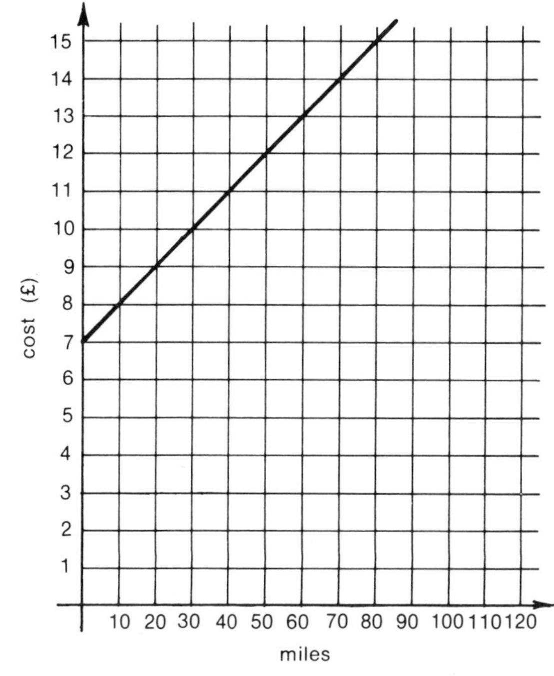

Notes: (a) There would not be much point in hiring the car for 0 miles, but it would still cost £7.

(b) The negative part of the graph has no meaning.

(c) If £y is the cost, and x miles are driven $y = \frac{1}{10}x + 7$.

The slope of the graph looks like the slope of $y = x$ but this is because the scale of miles is in 10s.

1 The use of a computer is charged at £75 the first hour and then £5 per hour after that. Draw a graph to show the costs of using the computer for 1 to 20 hours.

2 A spring is 25 cm in length. Each 10 g hung from it stretches it 0.4 cm. Draw a graph to show the length of the spring when weights from 10 g to 200 g are hung on it.

3 A man is paid £125 for a 38-hour week and then £4 per hour for extra time. How much does he earn if he works 5, 10, 15 and 20 hours overtime?
Draw a graph to show this. What does the slope of the graph represent?

Unit M5 Metric units of length

5·1 History

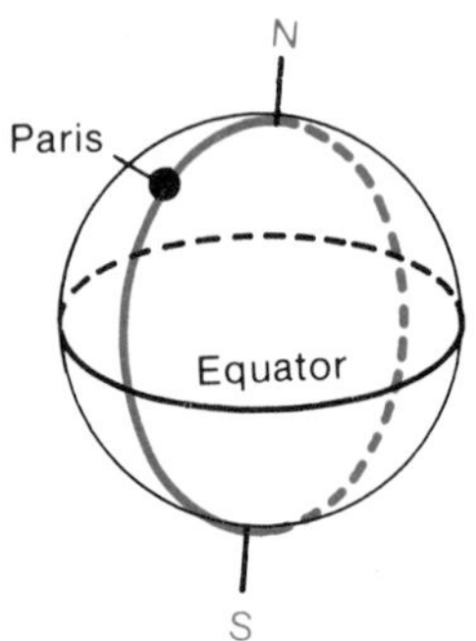

The metric system was invented by a French scientist in the year 1799. The starting point of the whole system was the size of the Earth. The picture shows a circle drawn through the North Pole, the South Pole and Paris. One quarter of this circle was taken to be 10 000 000 metres = 10 million metres. They were then able to make a standard metre, from which all others were measured.

Larger units consist of multiples of tens, hundreds and thousands of the standard metre. Smaller units are formed by dividing the metre into 100 or 1000 equal parts.

1 kilometre = 1000 metres . . . abbreviation for kilometre is km
1 hectometre = 100 metres . . . abbreviation for hectometre is hm
1 dekametre = 10 metres . . . abbreviation for dekametre is dam
METRE = 1 metre . . . abbreviation for metre is m
decimetre = $\frac{1}{10}$, 0·1 metre . . . abbreviation for decimetre is dm
centimetre = $\frac{1}{100}$, 0·01 metre . . . abbreviation for centimetre is cm
millimetre = $\frac{1}{1000}$, 0·001 metre . . . abbreviation for millimetre is mm

The main units → kilometre, METRE, millimetre

Exercise 5·1

A Copy and complete these statements:

1 1000 metres = 1 . . .
2 100 centimetres = 1 . . .
3 1000 millimetres = 1 . . .
4 10 millimetres = 1 . . .
5 100 metres = 1 . . .
6 100 millimetres = 10 . . .

B Which unit of length would be best for measuring:

1 The length of a hockey pitch?
2 The thickness of a fingernail?
3 The thickness of a piece of paper?
4 The length of material needed to make a shirt?
5 The distance across the channel from England to France?
6 The height of a glider?
7 The height of a kite?
8 The distance from the Earth to the Moon?

C Measure the following as accurately as,you can. (You will need a metre ruler or tape measure.) Record the measurements carefully.

1 Your height.
2 The circumference of your head.

3 The length, breadth and thickness of this book.
4 The distance from the door to the windows.
5 The length of your shoe.
6 The diagonal of the door frame.

5·2 Changing units in the metric system

Changing units is very simple in the metric system because the system is based on 10.
This means that changing units is a simple matter of moving the decimal point, or adding zeros to the end of a number.

Example:
Express 248 centimetres as: (a) millimetres, (b) metres.
(a) Since 1 cm = 10 mm
248 cm = 2480 mm
(b) Since 100 cm = 1 m
248 cm = 2·48 m

Exercise 5·2

A Change to centimetres:

1 48 m	**2** 3·7 km	**3** 0·4 hm	**4** 2·91 m
5 395 mm	**6** 2·72 dm	**7** 4·4 dam	**8** 2·03 m

B Change to metres:

1 14·6 km	**2** 2·9 dam	**3** 119 mm	**4** 0·32 hm
5 3 cm	**6** 2·9 dm	**7** 0·33 km	**8** 2·03 m

C Change to millimetres:

1 6·423 m	**2** 19 cm	**3** 5·3 hm	**4** 1·55 km
5 41·7 dm	**6** 55 m	**7** 0·38 m	**8** 5·5 dam

D Change to kilometres:

1 4500 m	**2** 8506 m	**3** 750 m	**4** 44 hm
5 504 hm	**6** 365 dam	**7** 29·5 dam	**8** 460 000 cm.

5·3 Estimating in metric units

Since metric units are so easy to change, it is simple to estimate a length.

Example:
(a) 1236 metres → 1·236 kilometres.
Thus 1236 metres is a bit more than 1 kilometre.
(b) 0·036 metre → 3·6 centimetres.
Thus 0·036 metre is nearly 4 centimetres.
(c) The length of my finger is 94 mm → 9·4 cm.
Thus 9 cm gives a good estimate.

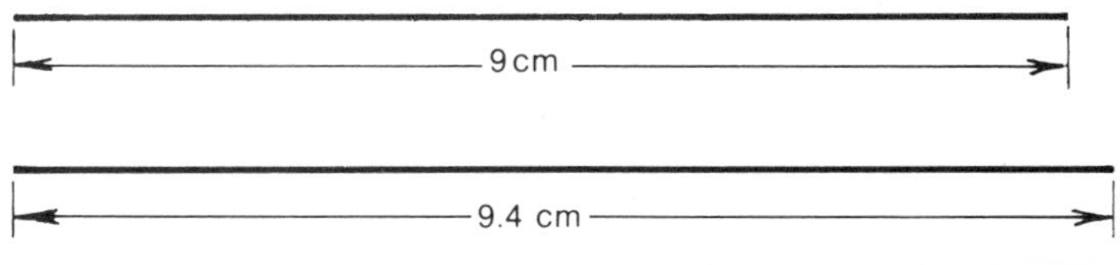

Exercise 5·3

A Which of these lengths seem about right?

1 The height of William the Conqueror was . . . 2 m, 20 cm, 20 m.
2 The width of the English Channel at Dover is . . . 40 m, 400 m, 40 km.
3 The length of the Cabbage White grub is . . . 3 mm, 3 cm, 3 dm.
4 Your pace is about . . . 1 m, 1 dm, 1 dam.
5 A jet usually flies at a height of . . . 12 km, 1200 m, 120 km.
6 The circumference of a bicycle wheel is . . . 150 cm, 1·5 m, 15 m.

B Pick out the true statements from these:

1 294 cm > 2 m
2 294 m > 2 km
3 1 hm > 1000 dam
4 245 km < 2450 m
5 702 m < 700 cm
6 100 dam = 1 km

C Measure all the lines in the two figures. Find a line in (b) which is the same length as one of the lines of (a).

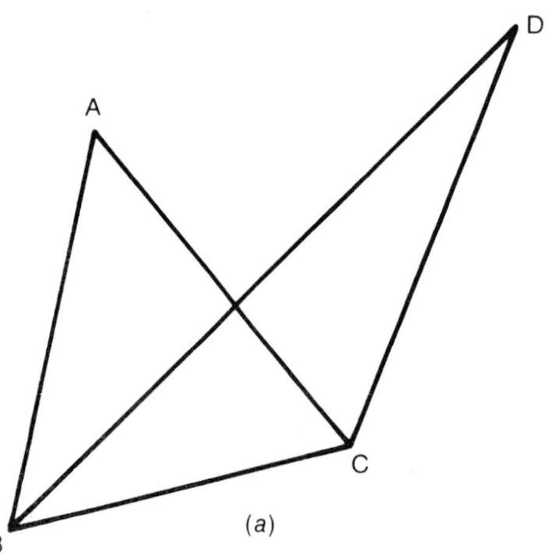

(*a*)

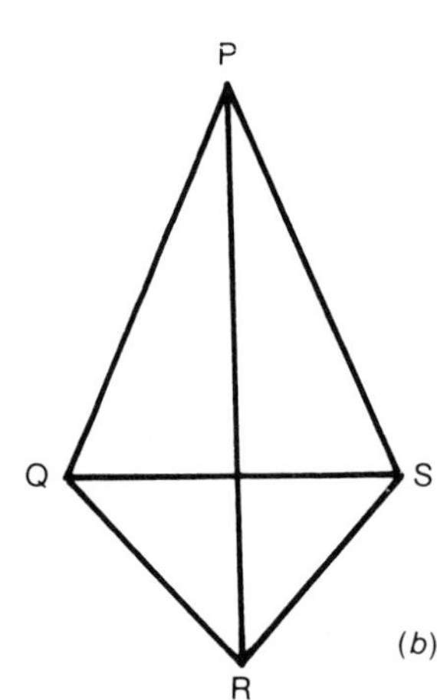

(*b*)

D The table below has been printed with two mistakes. Find them.

km	hm	dam	m	dm	cm	mm
1		100	1 000			
		0·24	2·4		240	
0·0043		0·43		4·3		
	0·27			270	2 700	
			0·045		45	450
1·63			1630		16 300	
0·42						420 000

Measurements in the same horizontal line should be equal.

E The figure below is part of an airline map of Europe drawn to scale. 1 cm on the map corresponds to a flying distance of 200 km.
Use the map to estimate the following distances:

1	Paris–Rome	**2**	Frankfurt–Lisbon	**3**	Paris–Madrid
4	Hamburg–Marseilles	**5**	Milan–Stockholm	**6**	Geneva–Vienna

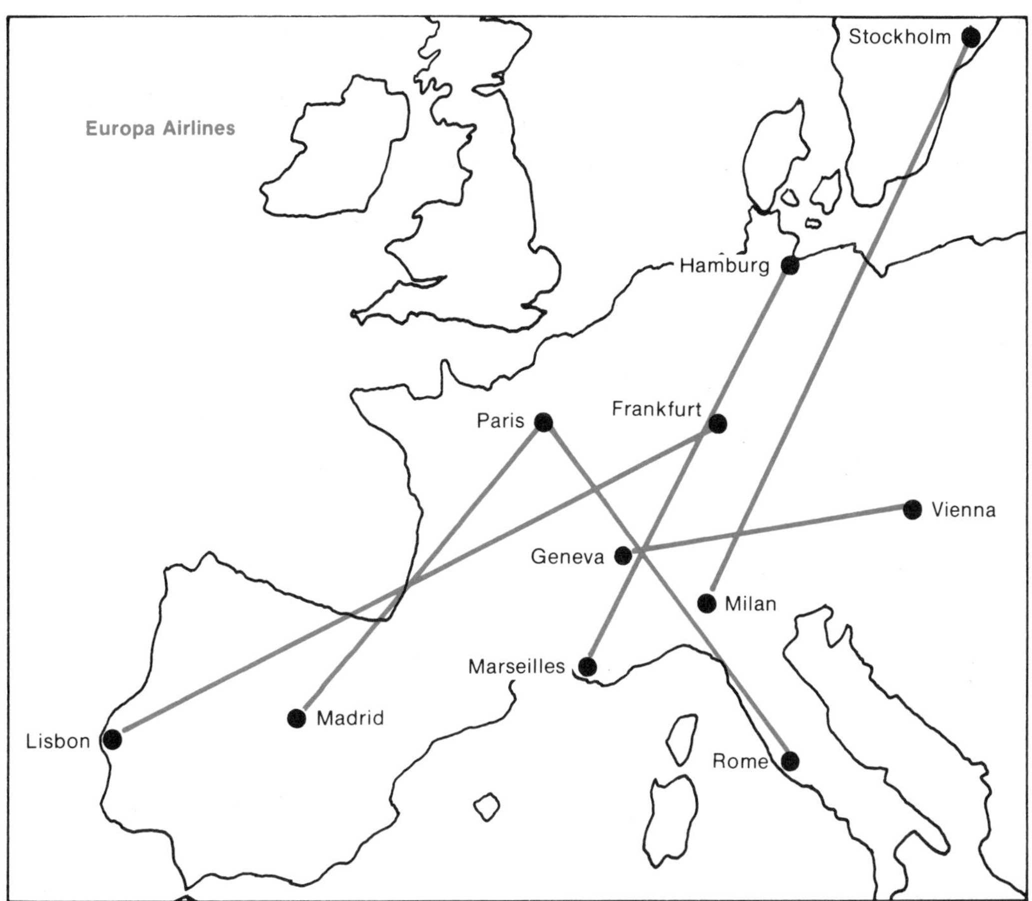

Unit M6 The rectangle

6·1 Properties

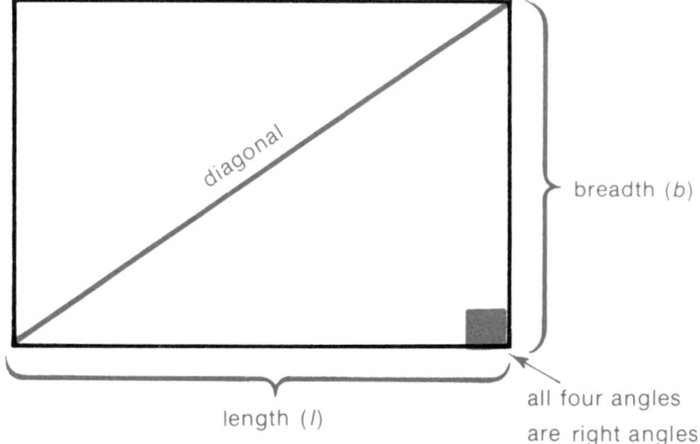

The **perimeter** runs round the edge of the rectangle.

If the rectangle were made of wire and the wire opened out, the length of the wire would be the length of the perimeter.

Length of perimeter $= 2l + 2b$

The **area** is the *space* inside.
It is found by multiplying the length by the breadth.

Area of rectangle $= l \times b$

A rectangle has four equal angles, all right angles.

A four-sided figure:

(a) With four equal angles must be a rectangle.
(b) With opposite sides equal and one right-angled corner, must be a rectangle.
(c) With opposite sides equal and equal diagonals must be a rectangle.

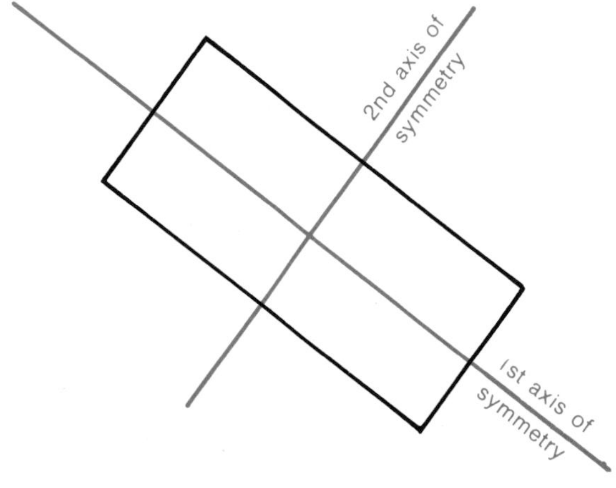

Every rectangle has two axes of symmetry.

They are lines which divide the rectangle into two matching halves.

If the rectangle is made of paper it can be folded along an axis of symmetry. Each half will then fit over the other.

Every rectangle has **rotational symmetry**. The rectangle can be turned around its centre. After a turn of 180° the rectangle will fit over its old position, but A will be where C was and B will be where D was. A further turn of 180° will bring the rectangle back to its first position.

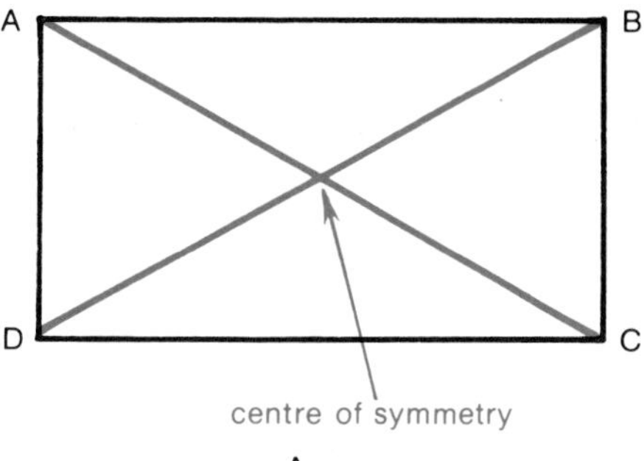

Exercise 6·1

A **1** ABCD is a figure in which $\hat{A} = \hat{B}$ and $\hat{C} = \hat{D}$. Does this mean that ABCD must be a rectangle? Draw an example.

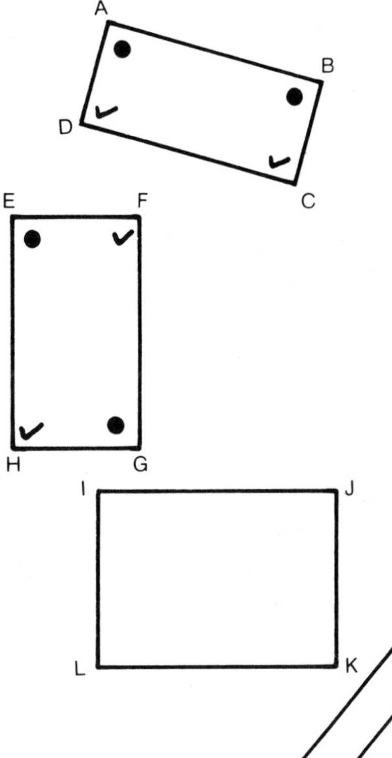

2 EFGH is a figure in which $\hat{E} = \hat{G}$ and $\hat{F} = \hat{H}$. Does this mean that EFGH must be a rectangle? Draw an example.

3 IJKL is a figure in which IJ = LK and IL = JK. Also $\hat{K} = 90°$. Does this mean that IJKL must be a rectangle? Draw an example.

4 MNOP is a figure in which MN = OP and MP = ON and MO = NP. Does this mean that MNOP must be a rectangle? Draw an example.

N
O
M
P

B **1** Measure the perimeters of the rectangles in section A above.
2 Calculate the areas of the rectangles to the nearest mm^2.
3 Is it true that the rectangle with the longest perimeter has the largest area?

C **1** Calculate the areas and perimeters of rectangles ABCD where:

(a) AB = 5 cm BC = 9 cm
(b) AB = 6·2 cm BC = 3·8 cm
(c) AB = 0·4 cm BC = 2·3 cm
(d) AB = 91 cm BC = 2 cm
(e) AB = 27 cm BC = 36 cm

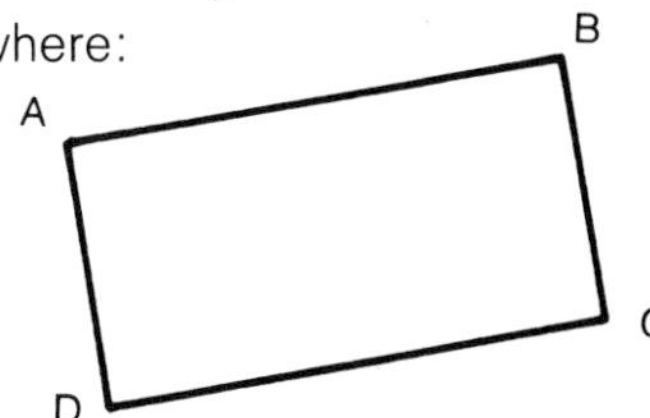

Record your results as a table.

AB	BC	*Perimeter* (cm)	*Area* (cm^2)
5	9	28	45

Do you agree with your answer to question B3 now?

2 Calculate the perimeters and areas of the rectangles in the diagram. Each unit is 5 mm in length. Give your answer in mm^2.

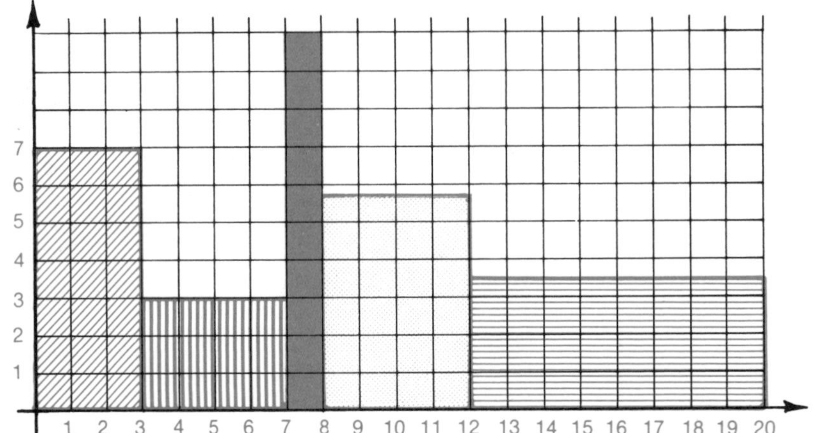

3 A swimming pool is 25 m long and 15 m wide. A boy runs round the perimeter of the pool while his friend swims one length. It takes them both 25 seconds.

(a) What are their speeds?

(b) What is the area of water surface of the pool?

(c) If every swimmer needs 4 m^2 of space to swim safely, what is the largest number of people that can be allowed in the pool at the same time?

D Copy the figure below on to 1 mm^2 graph paper.

1 For each rectangle mark: (a) axes of symmetry, (b) the centre of symmetry.

2 Measure the sides of each rectangle and calculate their perimeters and areas.

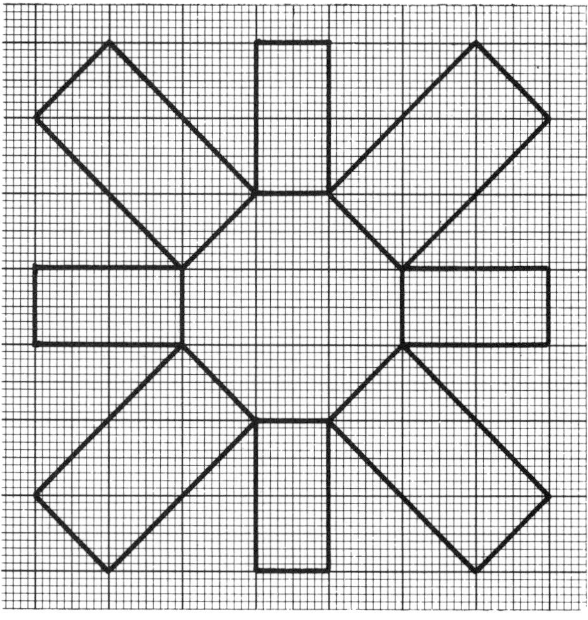

E Use your knowledge of the rectangle to find the following:

1 ABCD is a rectangle. Its perimeter is 42 cm. AD is 7 cm. Find AB.

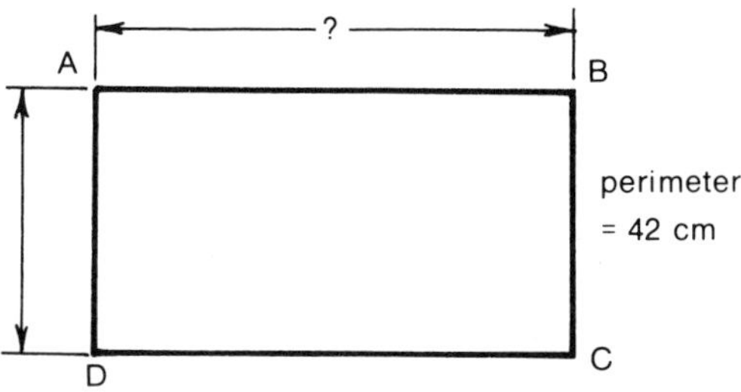

2 ABCD is a rectangle. One axis of symmetry is drawn. The distance from A to the axis of symmetry is 8·5 mm. Find AD.

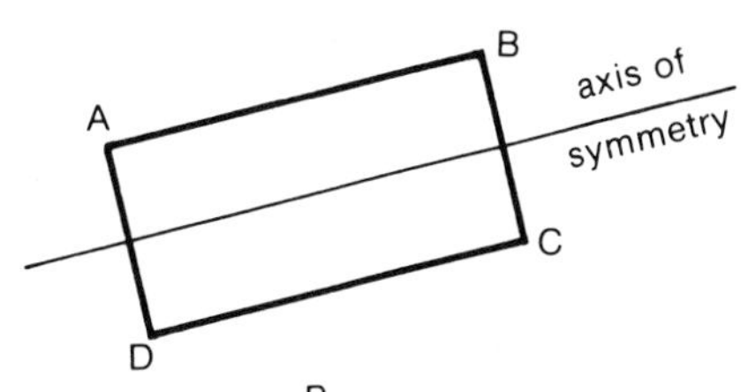

3 PQRS is a rectangle. PS is 1 cm longer than PQ. The area of PQRS is 16·56 cm^2. Find PS and PQ. (Use a calculator to find the answer.)

P Q S R

4 The perimeter of a rectangle WXYZ is 60 cm.

(a) Find the length of WX if:

(i) WZ = 1 cm (v) WZ = 5 cm
(ii) WZ = 2 cm (vi) WZ = 6 cm
(iii) WZ = 3 cm (vii) WZ = 9 cm
(iv) WZ = 4 cm (viii) WZ = 15 cm

(b) Make a table of results for question (a).

Perimeter	WZ	WX
60 cm	1	

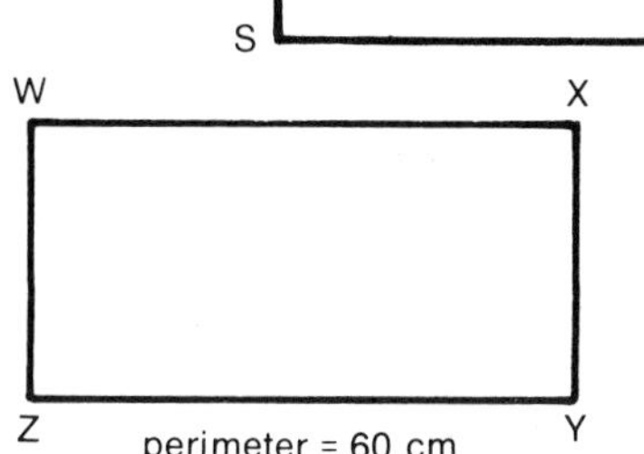

(c) Extend your table to show the area of WXYZ in each case. What is the largest area you have found?

(d) (i) Do you agree with the following statement?
'Of all the rectangles with a perimeter 60 cm the largest in area is the square whose side is 15 cm.'

(ii) Write a similar statement about the rectangles with perimeter 100 m.

(e) A farmer is making a rectangular enclosure for his cattle.

(i) What is the largest area he can enclose with 100 m of wire?

(ii) If each cow needs at least 1 m^2 to stand comfortably, how many could he keep inside the wire?

6·2 Use of rectangles

Rectangles are widely used in buildings, packaging, and in many man-made objects. The shape is not often found in nature, however. This is because the rectangle is a shape made by cutting rather than growing.

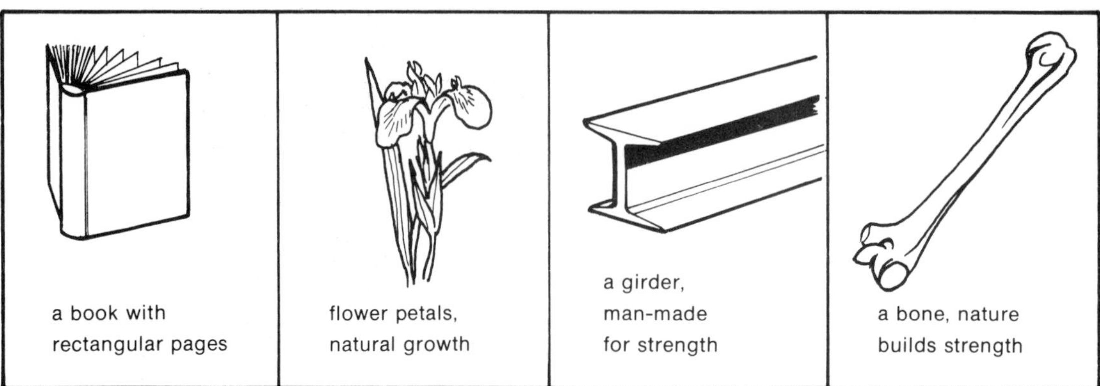

Exercise 6·2

1 Make a list of all the rectangles you can think of in everyday use.

2 Rectangles pack together to form tessellations. This property is used in tiling (though the rectangle is often a square). Many different patterns can be made.

(a) Draw two different tiling patterns made from 2 × 1 rectangles. (Rectangles whose length is twice their width.)

(b) Draw two different tiling patterns for 3 × 2 rectangles.

3 Pick out the different rectangles in this building. Where else in the building would rectangles be used?

4 Make a larger copy of this design which uses two different sizes of rectangle.

6·3 Special rectangles

The 'shape' of a rectangle

All rectangles have opposite sides equal, diagonals equal and four right angles. Special rectangles have all these properties but there is also an interesting relationship between the long and the short sides.

Examples:

1 *The square.* A square is simply a rectangle in which the longer side equals the shorter side.

2 *The golden rectangle.* When a square is cut from a golden rectangle, the piece remaining is the *same shape* as the original rectangle.

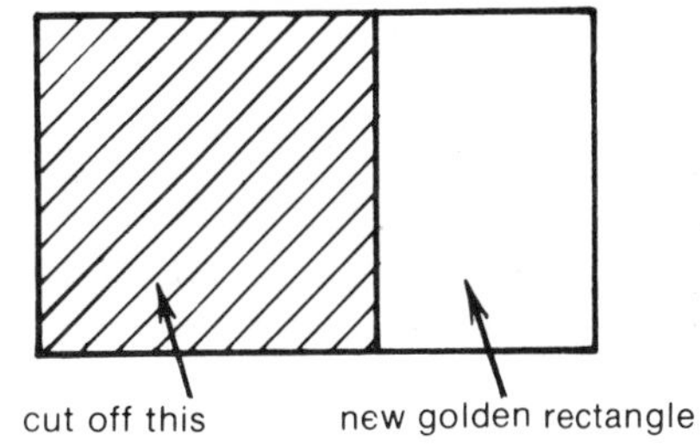

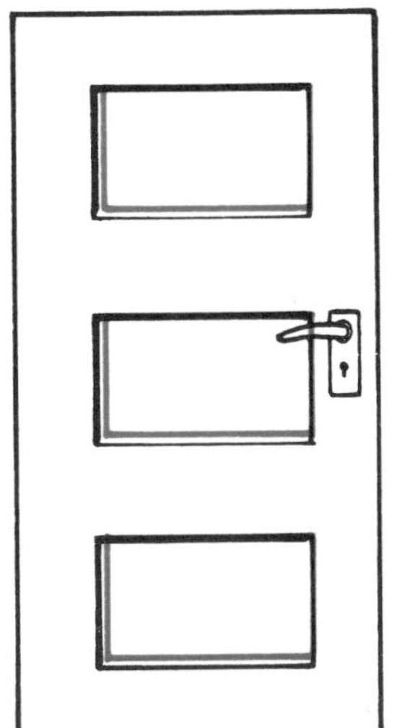

The golden rectangle has been used in designing pictures and buildings.

In all golden rectangles long side = 1·618 × short side.

Door with panels that are golden rectangles.

Exercise 6·3

1 Make a list of all the *squares* you can find that are used in everyday life.

2 Find six different rectangles in your home or classroom.
  (a) Measure their sides.
  (b) Calculate their **ratio** ... long side ÷ short side.

3 The ratio of the sides of all golden rectangles is 1·618 to 1.
  (a) Use your calculator to find 1 ÷ 1·618.
  What do you notice?
  (b) The fractions $\frac{1}{1}$, $\frac{2}{1}$, $\frac{3}{2}$, $\frac{5}{3}$, $\frac{8}{5}$... are made by a simple rule. Each fraction is made from the previous one.
  ... The top of the new fraction is the *sum* of the top and bottom of the previous one.
  ... The bottom of the new fraction is the *top* of the previous one.

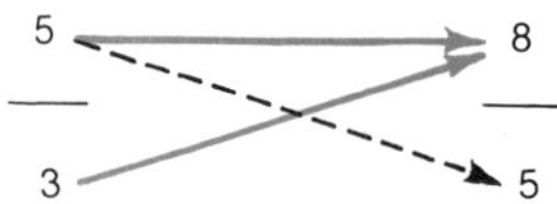

  (c) Find the next three fractions in the set, by following the same rules.
  (d) Work out each fraction in decimal form using the calculator.
  For example $\frac{1}{1} \rightarrow 1{\cdot}0$ $\frac{2}{1} \rightarrow 2{\cdot}0$ $\frac{3}{2} \rightarrow 1{\cdot}5$... and so on.
  (e) What do you notice about the decimal form of the fractions as you continue along the set?

6·4 The A-system of paper sizes

Drawing paper, typing paper and many books are rectangles with the same shape. This means that *long side* : *short side* is the same. The basic shape of the system is a rectangle which divides into two rectangles of the same shape as the one you started with.

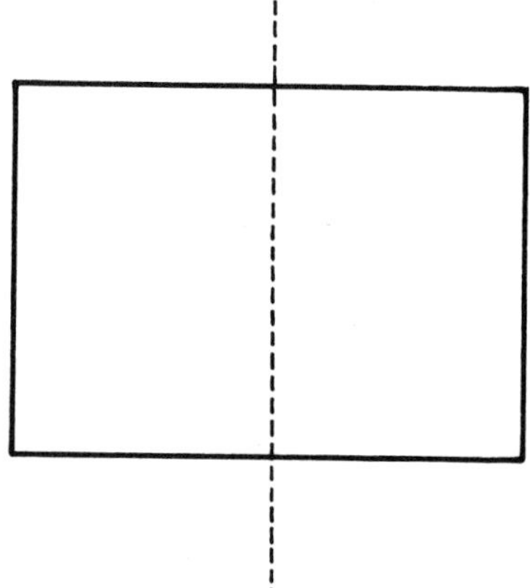

Each **half** has the same shape as the whole rectangle. The ratio

$$\frac{\text{long side}}{\text{short side}} = 1{\cdot}414$$

The largest piece of paper in the system has an area of $1\ \text{m}^2 = 10\,000\ \text{cm}^2$

The sides are 118·9 and 84·09 cm. This is A0 size. A1 size is obtained by cutting an A0 piece of paper in half. A2 size is obtained by cutting A1 in half, . . . etc.

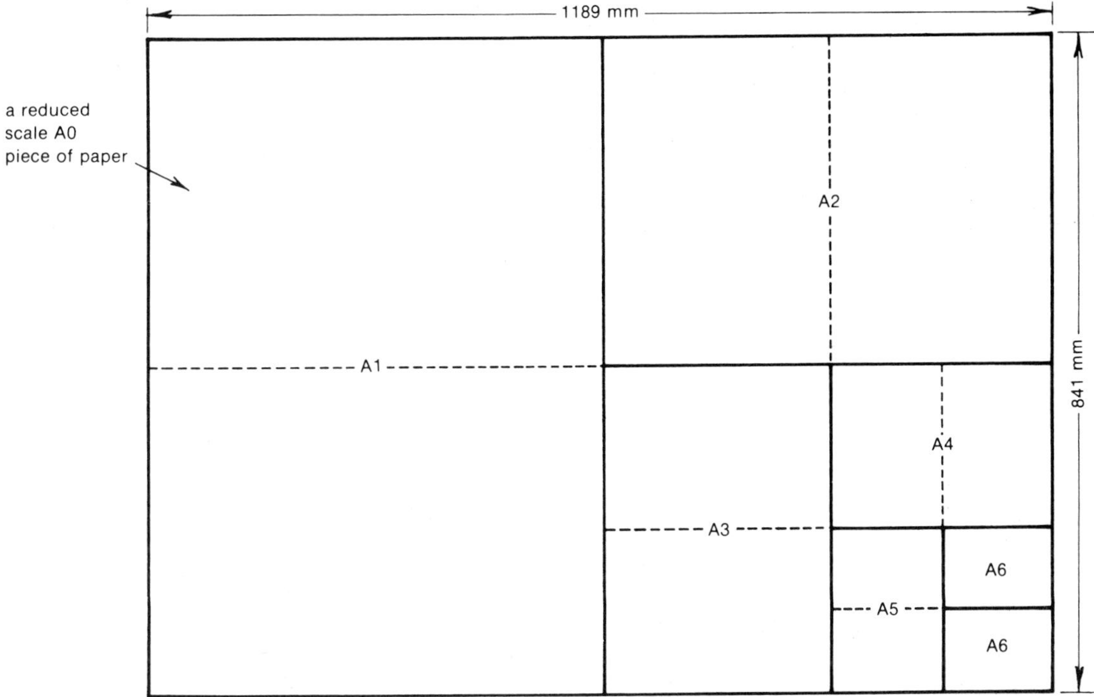

Exercise 6·4

1 Calculate the length of the long and short sides for A1, A2, A3, A4 and A5 paper.
2 Find a book which is exactly A5 size.
3 Which of these are exact A size? (Check by measurement): A telephone directory, a small newspaper, a large newspaper, your favourite magazine, a colour supplement from a Sunday paper.

6·5 Puzzles

Exercise 6·5

A 1 Start off with a rectangle of paper. Fold along any line you like.
2 Fold it again carefully so that the first fold is doubled.
3 Open out the paper. Cut along the fold lines to obtain four pieces. The problem is to arrange the pieces into a rectangle again.

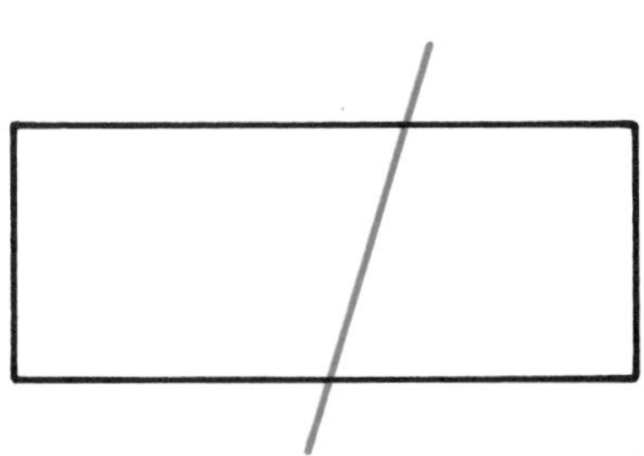 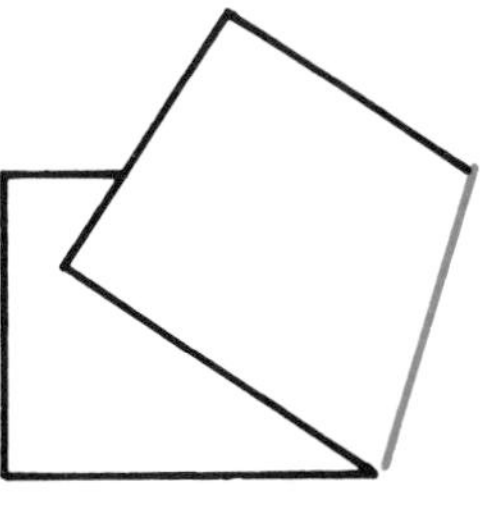 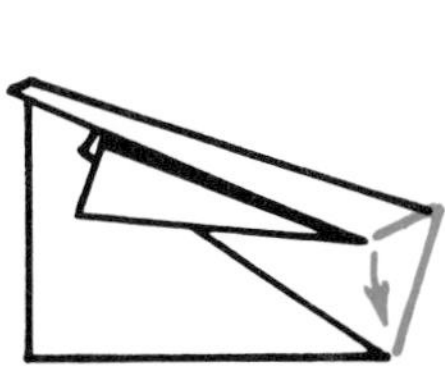

B Count the rectangles that may be found in this figure. Do not forget those made up of more than one smaller rectangle. It may help to letter the nine basic rectangles A, B, C, etc.

A B

C (Work with a partner)
Cut out the following 11 rectangles from graph paper.

1 25 cm × 4 cm
2 18 cm × 18 cm
3 15 cm × 10 cm
4 14 cm × 5 cm
5 13 cm × 6 cm
6 12 cm × 3 cm
7 11 cm × 9 cm
8 10 cm × 2 cm
9 8 cm × 7 cm
10 7 cm × 7 cm
11 2 cm × 2 cm

These rectangles can be formed into one large rectangle. What is its area?
Which rectangle is completely surrounded by others when the large rectangle has been constructed?

Unit M7 Variation

7·1 Direct variation

When one quantity increases steadily with another the situation is called **direct variation**.
Usually the rate of increase is written as . . . per . . .

Examples:

Apples cost 35p per pound
Silk costs £4 per metre
The car travels 180 km per hour
The rate of exchange is \$2·3 per pound

These rates enable us to calculate costs etc.
(a) The cost of 6 lb of apples is 6 × 35p
(b) The cost of 10 m of silk is 10 × £4
(c) In half an hour the car travels 180 km × $\frac{1}{2}$
(d) The value of £8 in dollars is \$2·3 × 8.

Exercise 7·1

1 Petrol costs 45p per litre. How much does 10 litres cost?
2 Grapes cost £1·40 per kilo. How much does 5 kilos cost?
3 Butter costs 60p per packet of 250 g. How much will 7 packets cost?
4 The rate of exchange for francs is 10·50 to the pound. How many francs could you buy for £4·50?
5 I can average 16 km per hour on my bike. How far can I travel in $2\frac{1}{2}$ hours?
6 Baby sitting pays 75p per hour. How much does Sheila earn in $3\frac{1}{2}$ hours?
7 A light aircraft uses 2·4 gallons of fuel per mile. How much fuel is needed for a journey of 50 miles?
8 A goldfish eats 0·25 g of food per day. How much food does it eat in a week? (If the fish weighs 10 g does it eat more than a human being, weight for weight? A person weighing 70 kg might eat 2 kg of food per day.)

7·2 Finding the rate

If you know that two quantities *vary directly* it is easy to find the **rate**. You simply divide one quantity by the other.

Examples:

FACT	RATE
10 gallons of petrol cost £35	Cost per gallon = £35 ÷ 10 → £3·50 per gallon
Jim earns £36 in 9 hours	Rate of pay = £36 ÷ 9 → £4 per hour
400 cm^3 of pure silver weighs 4400 g	Weight per cm^3 = 4400 ÷ 400 → 11 g per cm^3
A light bulb uses 2000 kJ of energy in 10 hours	Rate of using energy = 2000 ÷ 10 → 200 kJ per hour

Note: It is easy to tell which numbers to divide.

Cost per gallon is the same as $\frac{\text{cost}}{\text{gallons}} = \frac{£35}{10}$ ← *cost* / ← *gallons*

$= £3{\cdot}50$

In the same way, rate of pay is $\frac{\text{pay}}{\text{hours}}$

Exercise 7·2

A Find the rate per pound or rate per kg for these foods:

1 4 lb of beef costs £4·60.
2 10 kg of sugar costs £7·50.
3 14 kg of cod costs £35.
4 7 lb of potatoes costs 56p.
5 8 lb of damsons costs £1·80.
6 $\frac{1}{2}$ lb of ham costs £1·40.

B Find the hourly rate of pay for these jobs:

1 Charles earns £120 for a 40-hour week.
2 Jean earns £110 for a 35-hour week.
3 Mac earns £180 for a 45-hour week.
4 Sara earns £75 for a 25-hour week.
5 Wayne earns £20 for 8 hours on Saturday.
6 Marie earns £36 for 12 hours over the weekend.

C Find the speeds (rate of travel) for these:

1 650 miles in 15 hours.
2 27 miles in 2 hours.
3 136 km in 10 hours.
4 200 metres in 24 seconds.
5 150 metres in 1 minute.
6 1000 metres in 2·5 minutes.

D Find the density of these substances. (How many grams per cm^3?)

1 4 cm^3 of stone weighs 10 g → density of stone is 2·5 g per cm^3.
2 6 cm^3 of gold weighs 114 g.
3 9 cm^3 of steel weighs 70·65 g.
4 15 cm^3 of clay weighs 32·4 g.
5 20 cm^3 of glass weighs 53 g.
6 24 cm^3 of cork weighs 5·76 g.

Put the six substances in order of density, most dense first.

7·3 Finding a new pair of values

If two quantities vary directly and one pair of values is known, we can find another pair. First calculate the rate.

Example:

A piece of beef weighing 2·5 kg costs £8. How much would 4 kg of the same beef cost?*

2·5 kg costs £8 → cost is £8 ÷ 2·5 per kg
→ £3·20 per kg
Cost of 4 kg is £3·20 × 4 = £12·80

Exercise 7·3

A **1** A 10 litre can of oil costs £8·50. What would be the cost of a 15 litre can at the same rate per litre?
2 400 g of beef cost £1·20. What would be the cost of 1000 g?
3 15 litres of petrol cost £6·50. What would 36 litres cost?
4 90 cm of ribbon cost £1·35. What would 1.5 metres cost?
5 12 litres of paint cost £7·20. What would 20 litres cost?
6 45 kg of nitrate cost £18·50. What would 100 g cost?

B **1** Mary works in a shop part-time. She is paid £60 for a 25-hour week. What would she earn if she worked: (a) 35 hours, (b) 40 hours at the same rate of pay?
2 Tom works full-time on a farm. He is paid £140 for a 40-hour week. What would he earn if he only worked 25 hours in one week?
3 David is paid £75 a week for a part-time job of 22 hours. If he increases his hours to 36, what will he be paid?
4 Helen works 20 hours in a shop and is paid £36. She also helps in an old persons' home for 18 hours a week at the same rate of pay. What does she get paid altogether?
5 Peter works 38 hours a week as a bus conductor for £102. He does another 12 hours in the garage at the same rate of pay. How much does he earn altogether?

C **1** A man drives 240 km in 3 hours. How far would he travel in 5 hours at the same speed?
2 An aircraft flies London – Moscow (1200 miles) in $2\frac{1}{2}$ hours. How long would it take the same aircraft to fly from London to Lagos (3600 miles)?
3 A long distance runner runs 18 km in 100 minutes. If he ran at the same speed all through, how far did he travel in the first hour?
4 12 cm^3 of gold weigh 228 g. How much would 20 cm^3 weigh?
5 150 ml of mercury weigh 2100 g. How much would 1 litre weigh?

7·4 Comparisons

To compare 'value for money' it is often best to compare cost per unit.

Example:

The giant size packet costs £1·85 for 900 g or $\frac{185p}{900}$ per gram.

→ 0·2056p per gram (calculator).
The small size packet costs £0·70 for 250 g or $\frac{70p}{250}$ per gram.

→ 0·2800p per gram (calculator).
The giant size is considerably cheaper per gram.
(About three-quarters of the baby-size price.)

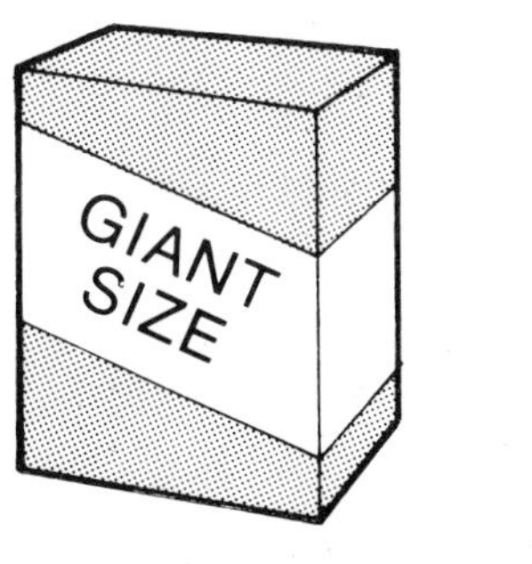

* We assume that the cost increases steadily with the quantity of beef. (Direct variation.)

Exercise 7·4

A Which of these are better buys?:

1 2lb of sugar for 84p or 7lb of sugar for £2·20

2 Large cornflakes (£1·40 for 500 g) or average cornflakes (85p for 325 g).

3 5 litres of oil for £4·40 or 12 litres of oil for £9·60.

4 750 ml of wine for £2·85 or 1·5 litres for £4·00.

5 250 miles of rail travel for £26 or 600 miles for £70·00.

6 125 g of tea for 45p or $\frac{1}{2}$ kilo of tea for £1·60.

B The questions above can be solved by finding how much you get for 1p or £1 and then comparing.

Example:

Giant size £1·85 for 900 g — you get $\frac{900}{185}$ g per penny

→ 4·864 g per penny (calculator).

Baby size 70p for 250 g — you get $\frac{250}{70}$ g per penny

→ 3·57 g per penny.

Thus you get about one third as much again per penny if you buy giant size.*

1 (a) If a 2 lb bag of sugar costs 84p, how much sugar is this per penny?
(b) If a 7 lb bag of sugar costs £2·20, how much is this per penny?
(c) Which is better value, the 2 lb bag or the 7 lb bag? Why?
(d) Compare your answer with question A1 above.

2 Go through the rest of section A above, comparing values by finding quantity per £ or quantity per penny. Find which is the best buy in each case and compare with your previous results.

3 Use either method to find which of the following pairs is of better value:
(a) $\frac{1}{2}$ kilo (500 g) of butter at 88p or 1 lb of butter at 79p (454 g)
(b) A gallon of oil (4·55 litres) at £7·80 or 5 litres at £8·50
(c) 500 g of coffee for £2·80 or 225 g of coffee for £1·80
(d) 125 ml of toothpaste for 85p or 50 ml for 40p.

4 In most cases the larger package is better value. Why do you think this is so?

C Other things beside cost are often compared.

Example:

A motorist compares the miles he travels with two different brands of petrol, brand A and brand B. With brand A he travel 200 miles on 6 gallons (27 litres). With brand B he travels 250 miles on 8 gallons (36 litres). Which is the most economical?

A. 200 miles on 6 gallons → $\frac{200}{6}$ miles per gallon

→ 33·33 miles per gallon

B. 250 miles on 8 gallons → $\frac{250}{8}$ miles per gallon

→ 31·25 miles per gallon

Brand A is more economical. (*Note:* It may also be more expensive.)

* The giant or large size is not *always* the cheaper.

1 Which of these are more economical? Brand X on which the car travels 150 km on 22 litres or brand Y on which the car travels 280 km on 36 litres.

2 Which of these two materials is more dense? (more grams per cm^3)
(a) 450 cm^3 of oak weighing 416 g.
(b) 625 cm^3 of pine weighing 343 g.

3 Which of these two countries is more heavily populated?
(a) England ... 46 million people in 130 400 km^2
(b) Japan ... 110 million people in 370 526 km^2

4 Which of these jobs is paid best?
(a) £85 per week (b) £350 per month (c) £4600 per year.

7·5 The graph of direct variation

The graph can be found from one pair of values. It is a straight line passing through (0, 0). Other pairs of values can be found once the graph has been drawn.

Example:
3 lb of lamb cost £4·50 (a) What is the rate per pound?
(b) How much lamb can you buy for £3?

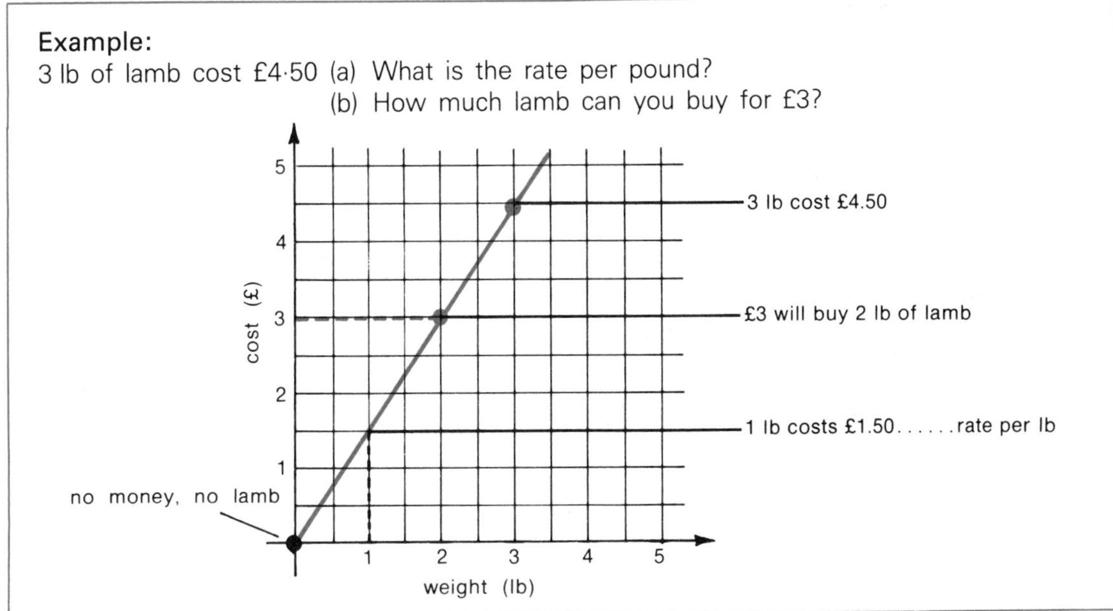

Exercise 1·5

A Draw graphs for each of the following, and use them to answer the questions.

1 Potatoes cost 80p for 12 lb.
(a) What would 25 lb cost?
(b) What weight could you buy for £2?

2 A taxi charges £3·60 for a journey of 4 miles.
(a) What would a journey of 10 miles cost at the same rate?
(b) How far could you go for £15?
(c) Would £20 be enough for 40 miles?

3 400 g of tea cost £1·40.
(a) What would 1 kg of the same tea cost?
(b) How much of the tea could you buy for 75p?
(c) Is this tea cheaper than 30p for 125 g?

4 50 kg of cement cost £3·80.
   (a) What is the cost per kg?
   (b) What would 1 tonne (1000 kg) of cement cost?
   (c) What weight of cement could be bought for £20?

B Draw graphs for each of the following situations. Use the graphs to answer the questions.

1 A jumbo-jet travels at 1040 km per hour.
   (a) How far does it travel in $3\frac{1}{2}$ hours?
   (b) How long would a 5000 km flight take?

2 A factory making shirts can make a shirt from 2·50 metres of cloth.
   (a) How many metres would be needed for 500 shirts?
   (b) How many shirts could be made from 300 metres of cloth?

3 The rate of exchange dollars/pounds was $2·30 = £1.
   (a) How many dollars would be worth £25?
   (b) Would 40 dollars be enough to buy a coat costing £38?
   (c) A shop offers to change a 50 dollar note for a £20 note. Is this reasonable?

4 12 g of carbon was burnt in oxygen to form carbon dioxide. The weight of carbon dioxide was found to be 44 g.
   (a) What weight of oxygen had combined with the 12 g of carbon (to form the 44 g of carbon dioxide)?
   (b) What weight of oxygen would combine with 1 g of carbon?
   (c) What weight of carbon would combine with 16 g of oxygen?

7·6 Use of calculator

Questions on direct variation can be done very quickly on the calculator. We can miss out the step that finds the rate of variation.

Example:
72 bags of flour cost £180. What would 50 bags cost at the same rate?

We start with £180 . . . for 72 bags.
→ £180 ÷ 72 for 1 bag
→ £180 ÷ 72 × 50 for 50 bags.

[C] [1] [8] [0] [÷] [7] [2] [×] [5] [0] [=] will now give the answer.

0 180 180 72 2·5 50 125

Exercise 7·6 (Use calculator)

1 A 50 Deutschmark note is worth £12·20. What are the following worth in British money:
(a) 80 DM
(b) 95 DM
(c) 106 DM
(d) 255 DM

2 A superjet flies 150 km in 8 minutes. How far will it fly in:
(a) 20 minutes?
(b) 1 hour?
(c) 1 hour 35 minutes?

3 How long will the jet in question 2 take to travel:
(a) 600 km?
(b) 950 km?
(c) 1400 km?
4 A girl earns £35 in 4 hours overtime. How much would she earn for:
(a) 7 hours overtime?
(b) 12 hours overtime?
(c) $14\frac{1}{2}$ hours overtime?
5 How much overtime would the girl need to do in order to earn:
(a) £20?
(b) £45?
(c) £65?

Unit M8 Scale, maps and plans

8·1 Enlargement

When an enlargement is made of a photograph, all the details stay the same. It is easier to see things on the larger print but there is nothing there that was not to be found in the smaller print.

When we form an enlarged image of the stamp by using a magnifying glass, we can see more details and read the letters more easily.

contact

enlargement

Exercise 8·1

A Fig. 1 shows two drawings of a church. The bigger drawing is an enlargement of the smaller one.

1 (a) Which point corresponds to 'b' on the enlargement?

(b) Which point corresponds to F on the smaller drawing?

2 Which of the following are the same in both drawings:

(a) The height of the steeple?

(b) The length of the roof?

(c) The distance from a to d and from A to D.

(d) The angles of the steeple.

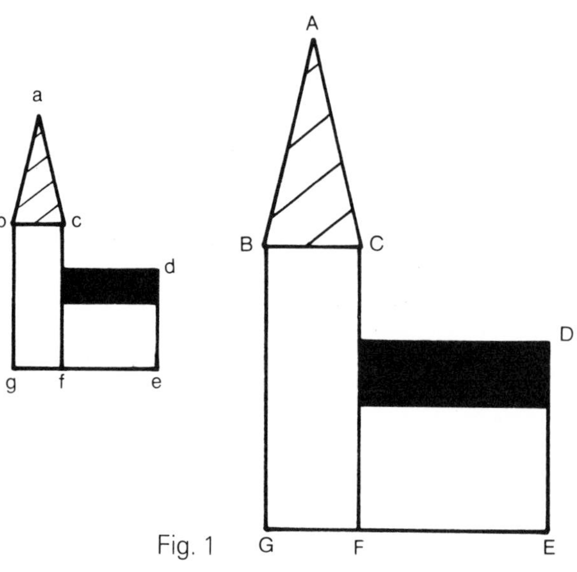

Fig. 1

3 (a) The distances ab and ac are equal in the smaller drawing. Which two distances would you expect to be equal in the enlargement?
(b) fg = dg in the small drawing. What corresponds in the enlargement to this pair of equal lines?

4 (a) The height of the tower (not including the steeple) is three times its base in the small picture. Is this proportion the same in the enlargement?
(b) Is the proportion of the steeple (height to base) the same in both drawings?

5 Do you agree with these statements about enlargements?
(a) Lengths change, but all lengths are changed in the same proportion.
(b) Angles do not change.
(c) Proportions do not change.
(d) Pairs of equal lines become pairs of equal lines in the enlargement.

8·2 Repeating shapes

Triangle abc is enlarged to triangle ABC.
Angles are unchanged.

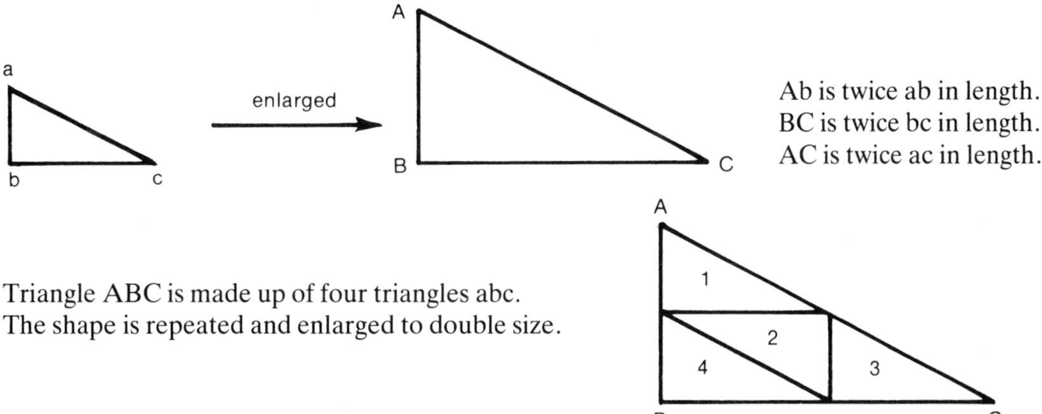

Ab is twice ab in length.
BC is twice bc in length.
AC is twice ac in length.

Triangle ABC is made up of four triangles abc.
The shape is repeated and enlarged to double size.

Exercise 8·2

1 Show that four equal squares can be fitted together to make one large square.

2 Show that four equal rectangles can be fitted together to form a larger rectagle of the same shape. (The large rectangle will be an enlargement of the smaller ones.)

3 Find a special shape of rectangle such that two of them make a larger rectangle of the same shape.

4 (a) Show, by drawing, that any parallelogram can be divided into four equal parts, each part being the same shape as the original parallelogram.
(b) Show how the parallelogram could be divided into six equal parts. Would the whole parallelogram be an enlargement of the parts in this case?

5 Four of the hexagons (Fig. 2) can be fitted together to make an enlargement. Cut out four hexagons of this shape and fit them together to form the enlarged hexagon. Can you find more than one way to do this?

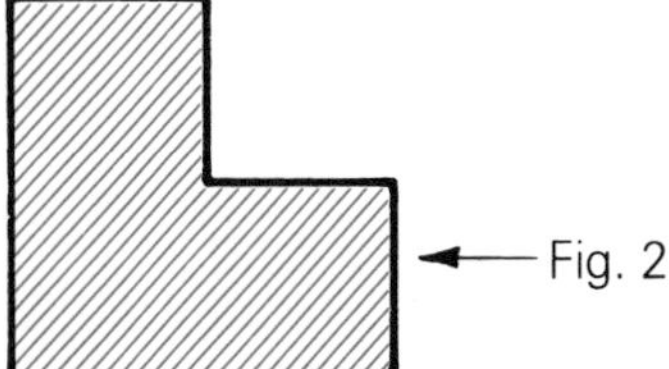
Fig. 2

6 The large hexagon (Fig. 3) is made up of three smaller hexagons and three rhombuses. Show that the three rhombuses would make up another hexagon.

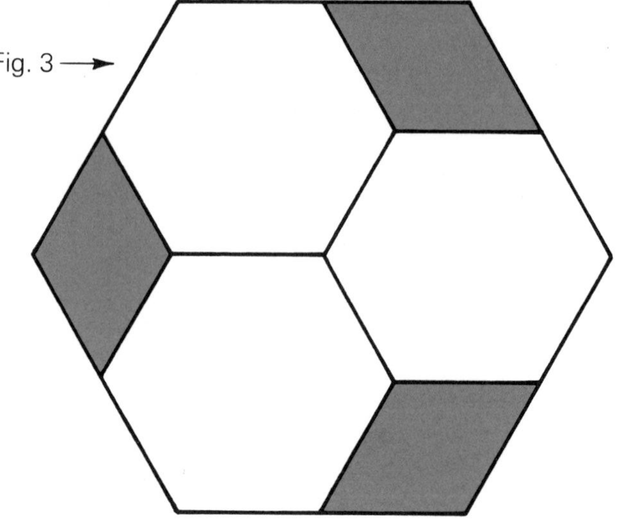
Fig. 3

8·3 Scale factor

When a shape is enlarged, all lengths are changed in the same way. For example, lengths could be doubled or increased by 25%.

The ratio of $\frac{\text{enlarged length}}{\text{original length}}$ is called the scale factor.

Example:

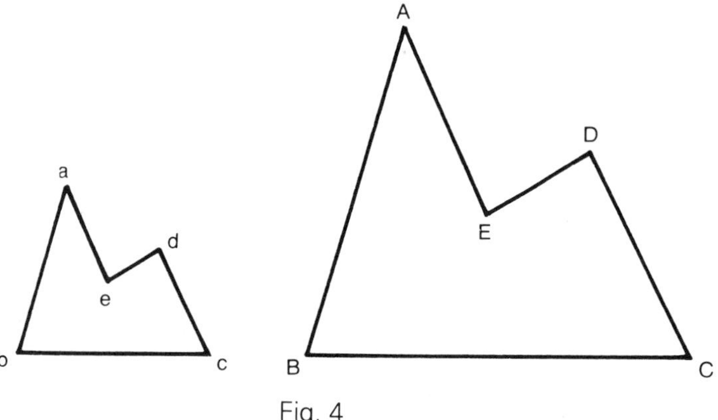

Fig. 4

All lengths are doubled in this enlargement.

Thus AB = 2ab CD = 2cd EA = 2ea
BC = 2bc DE = 2de

Lengths across the figure are also doubled.

AC = 2ac
EC = 2ec, etc.

The scale factor of this enlargement is 2.

You can find the scale factor by measuring any pair of corresponding sides.

If you know the scale factor and the length of a line you can calculate the length of the corresponding line.

Example:

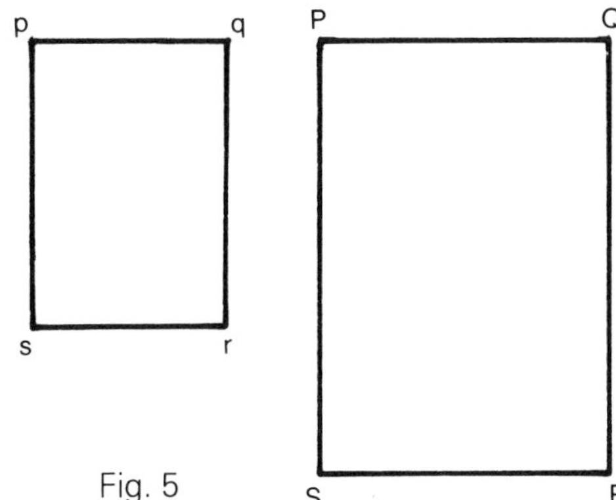

Fig. 5

pqrs is enlarged with a scale factor of 1·5.
PQ = 1·5pq, PR = 1·5pr, etc.

The scale factor 1·5 can be found by comparing any pair of corresponding sides.

Examples of calculations:

(a) Suppose in 8·2 ab = 5 cm, calculate AB.
The scale factor is 2. AB = 2 × ab = 2 × 5 cm
AB = 10 cm

(b) Suppose QS is 4.3 cm, calculate qs. (Fig. 5)
The scale factor is 1·5. QS = 1·5 × qs
4·3 = 1·5 × qs   qs = 4·3 ÷ 1·5
qs = 2·87 cm

Exercise 8·3

1 Find the scale factor for each of the enlargements in Figs. 6, 7 and 8.

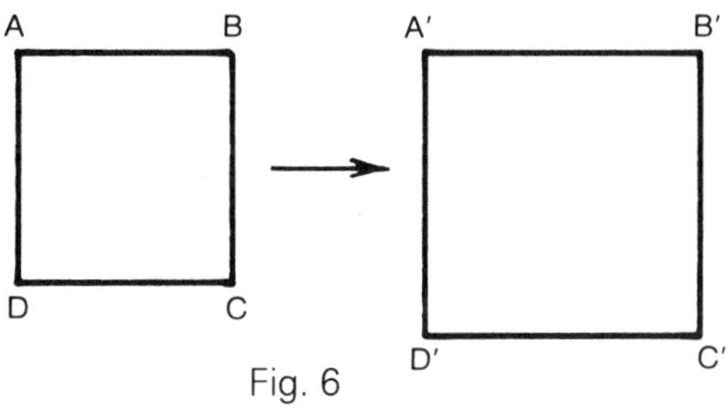

Fig. 6

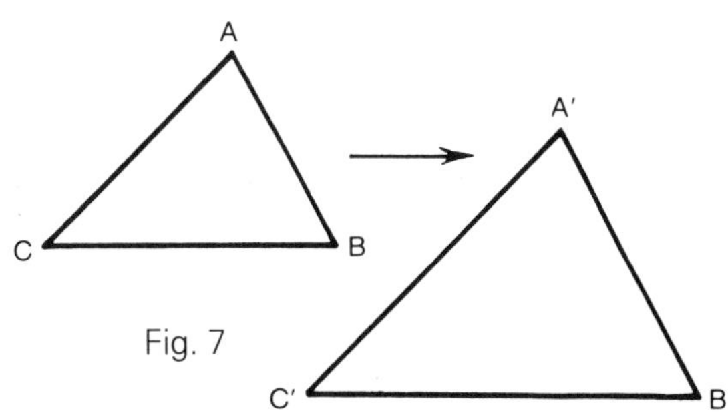

Fig. 7

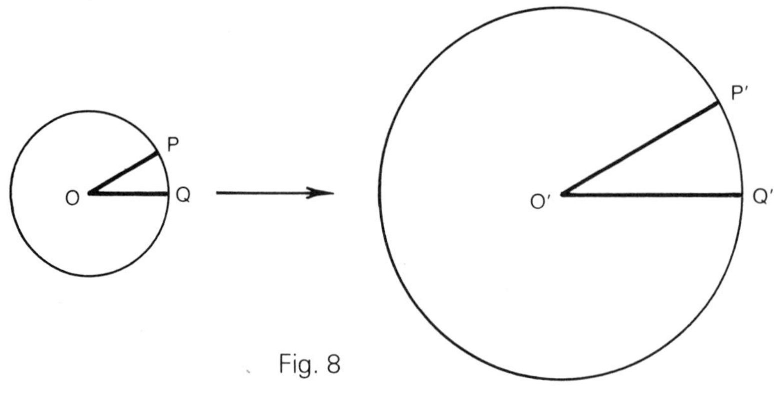

Fig. 8

2 Calculate the lengths marked ? in the enlargements of Figs. 9, 10 and 11.

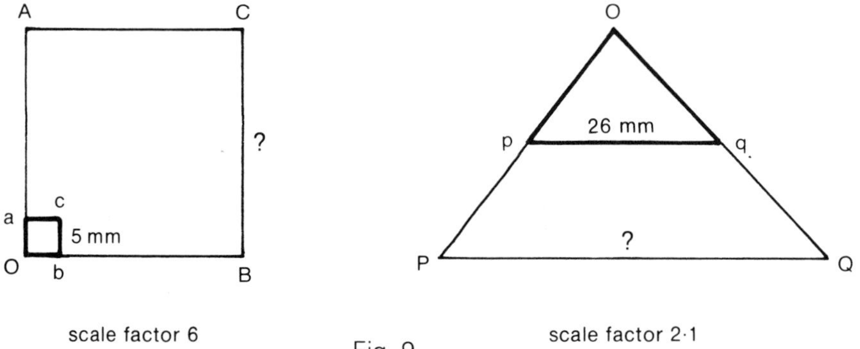

scale factor 6

scale factor 2·1

Fig. 9

scale factor abcde → ABCDE is 2

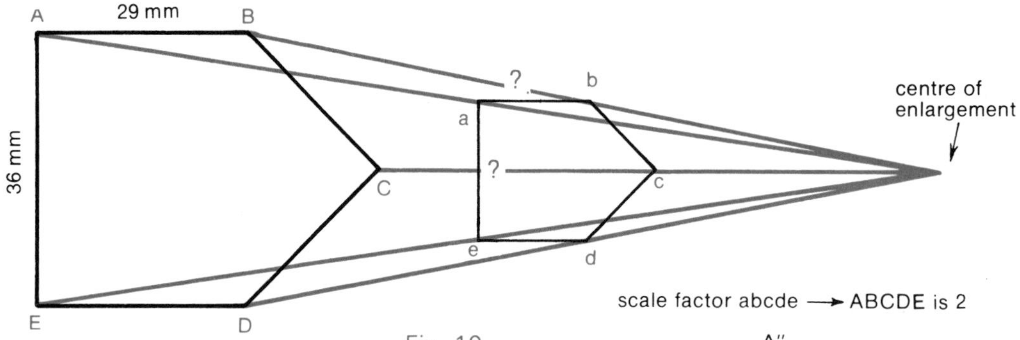

Fig. 10

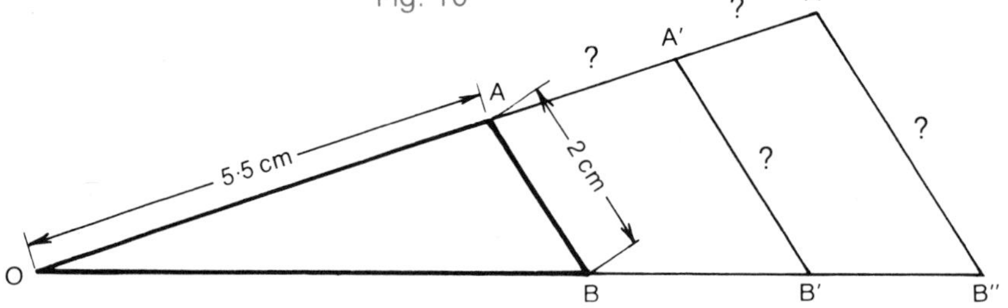

Fig. 11

Enlargement factor OAB → OA′B′ is 1·4
Enlargement factor OAB → OA″B″ is 1·7

8·4 Scale factor and coordinates

It is possible to make an enlargement on a grid by changing the coordinates.

Example:

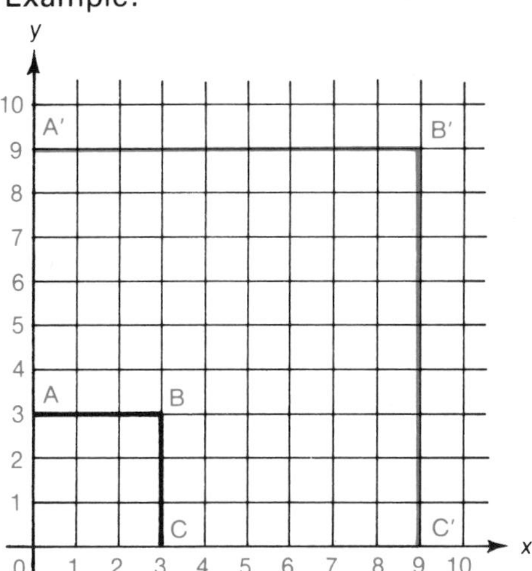

The square OABC is enlarged to the square OA′B′C

Coordinates of O . . . (0, 0)
A . . . (0, 3)
B . . . (3, 3)
C . . . (3, 0)

Coordinates of O . . . (0, 0)
A′ . . . (0, 9)
B′ . . . (9, 9)
C′ . . . (9, 0)

The square is enlarged by scale factor 3 and the coordinates are multiplied by 3.

Exercise 8·4 (use squared paper or graph paper)

A 1 Triangle OAB has coordinates (0, 0); (3, 1) and (2, 3).
(a) Draw triangle OA′B′ with coordinates (0, 0); (6, 2) and (4, 6).
(b) Is △OA′B′ an enlargement of △OAB? If so, what is the scale factor?

2 △ABC has its vertices at (1, 1); (1, 2); (3, 1). The coordinates of △A′B′C′ are (2, 2); (2,4); (6, 2). Is △A′B′C′ an enlargement of △ABC? What is the scale factor? What is the centre of enlargement?

3 △ABC has its vertices at (1, 2); (1, 1); (3 ,1). △PQR has vertices (2, 6); (2, 4); (5, 4) (Fig. 12). Show that the coordinates of P, Q and R are not obtainable from the coordinates of A, B, C by multiplying by a scale factor. (You can see that there is no centre of enlargement as the lines PA, QB and RC do not meet in one point.)

4 Use the coordinates of △ABC to find the coordinates of △XYZ given that:
(a) △XYZ is an enlargement of △ABC.
(b) The scale factor is 1·5.

Draw the triangle XYZ and find the centre of enlargement.

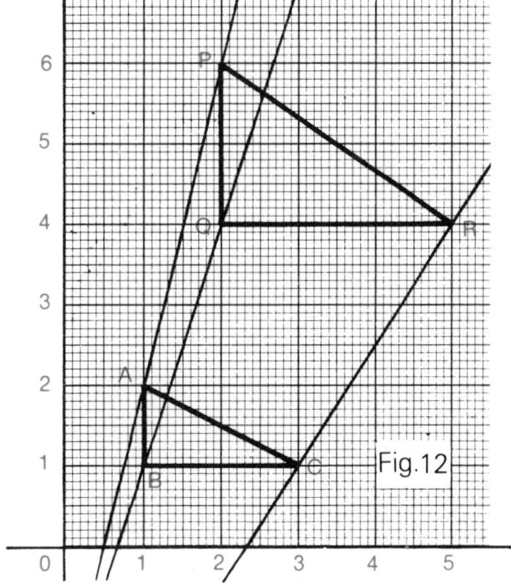

Fig. 12

B 1 Fig. 13 shows $\triangle ABC$ enlarged into $\triangle A'B'C'$ with centre of enlargement at (0, −3).

(a) Write down the coordinates of $\triangle ABC$ and of $\triangle A'B'C'$.

(b) Can you see any connection between the pairs of coordinates A, A′; B, B′; C, C′?

(c) Do you agree that this enlargement doubles the x-coordinate and doubles the y-coordinate, then adds 3?

(d) What are the coordinates of P and P′? Are they changed by the same rule?

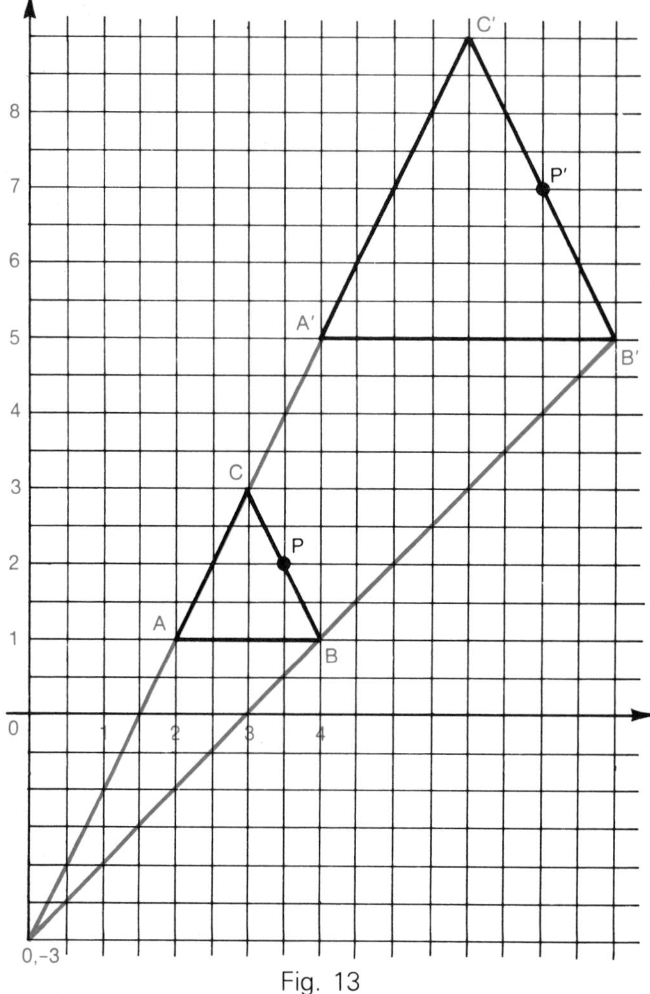

Fig. 13

2 (a) Use the coordinates to draw an enlargement, scale factor 2·5, of the little house in Fig. 14

(b) Check that the width of the roof and the sloping edges of the roof are enlarged 2·5 times.

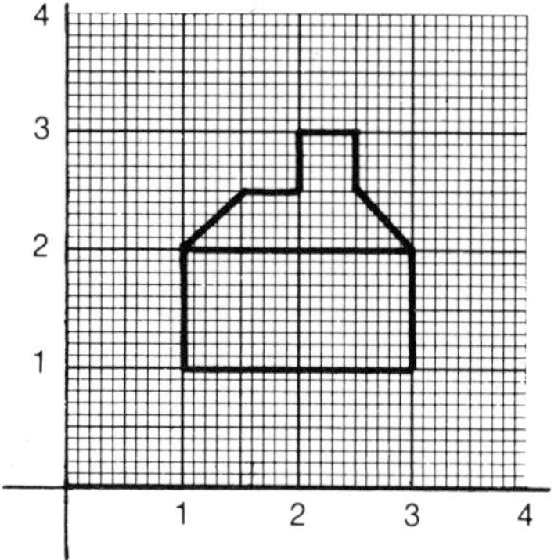

Fig. 14

3 (a) By choosing key points and noting their coordinates, make an enlargement of the insect in Fig. 15, three times as big as the original.

(b) Measure the wing-span of the insect on the enlargement and on the original.

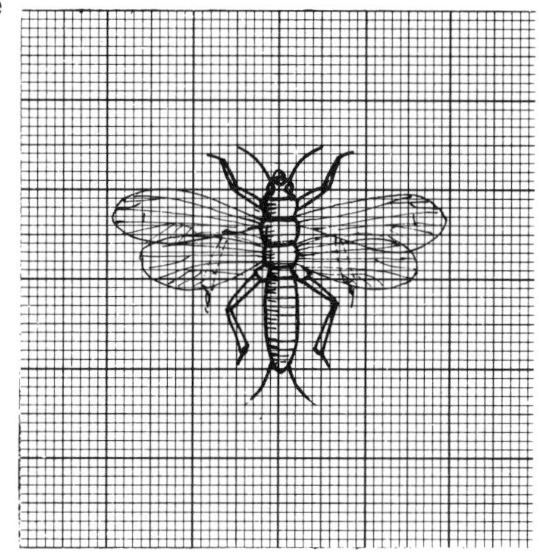

Fig. 15

8·5 Maps and plans

Maps and plans are usually enlargements in reverse. The small plan or map is related to a larger object or piece of land by a *scale factor*. If we know the scale factor and measure lengths on the plan or map we can calculate lengths on the object or piece of land.

Example:

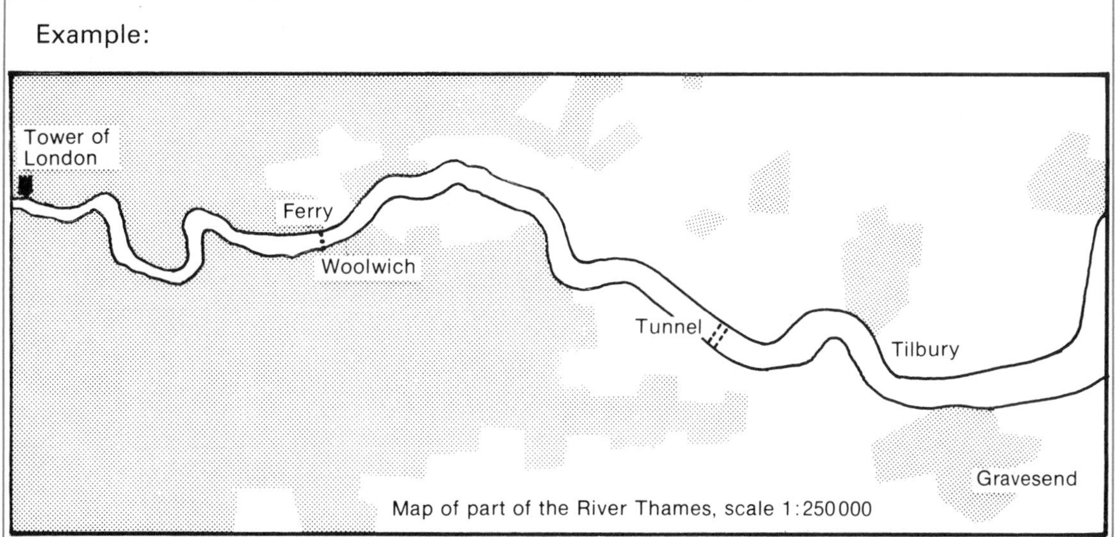

Map of part of the River Thames, scale 1:250 000

The scale factor of the map is 1 : 250 000. This means that 1 cm on the map will correspond to 250 000 cm = 2500 m = 2·5 km in real distance. *Find the distance* from the Woolwich ferry to the Dartford tunnel direct.

Distance on the map = 5·5 cm = Actual distance = 5·5 × 2·5 km

= 13·75 km

Example:

The scale factor of the drawing of the whale is 1 : 500. This means that 1 cm on the drawing corresponds to 5 m of real whale.

Find the real length of the whale and its 'depth' from top to bottom.

Measuring the diagram . . . length = 72 mm = 7·2 cm

real length = 7·2 × 500 cm = 3600 cm = 36 m

depth = 16 mm = 1·6 cm

real depth = 1·6 cm × 500 = 1·6 m × 5 = 8 m

Exercise 8·5

A 1 Find the following distances using the map of the Thames given above.

(a) Tower of London to Gravesend direct.

(b) Woolwich ferry to Tilbury direct.

(c) Tower of London to Dartford tunnel along the river.

(Use a strip of 1 mm^2 graph paper to measure the curves.)

2 (a) What is the distance from the whale's eye to the tip of its tail?

(b) What would the whale's 'waist measurement' be? (Remember the circumference of a circle is roughly three times its diameter.)

(c) If a whale 48 m long was drawn to the same scale, what would the length of the drawing be?

3 This is a ground plan of Durham cathedral. The full length of the cathedral is 159 m.

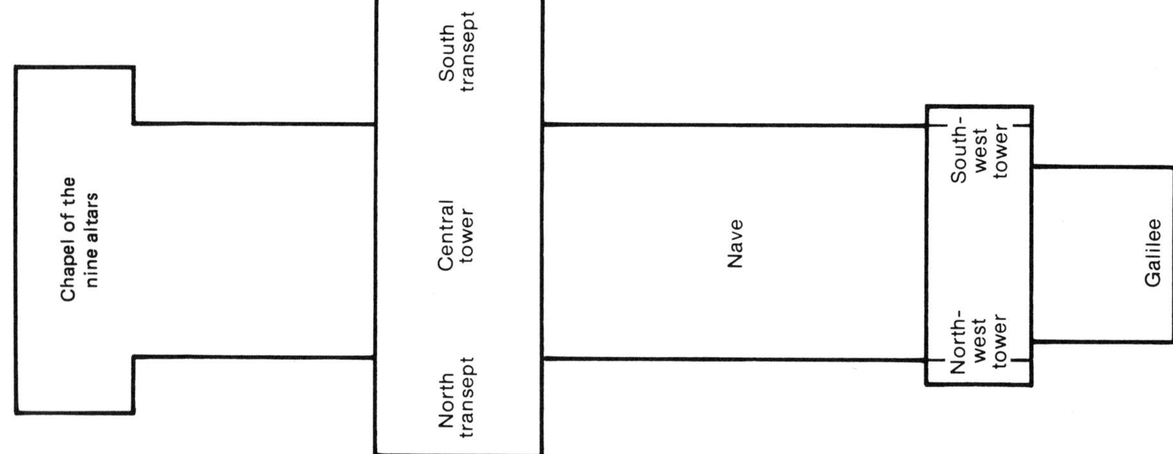

(a) Use the length to find the scale factor.

(b) Use the scale factor to find the width of the cathedral across the west towers, across the transepts and across the Chapel of the Nine Altars.

(c) Pace out 159 m in the playground to get an idea of the length of the building.

B Get an 'Esso' or other road map and use it to find the distances between the following cities (or use your atlas):

1 Birmingham and Glasgow.

2 Liverpool and London.

3 Cardiff and Stoke-on-Trent.

4 Bradford and Plymouth.

Make a note of the scale of the map.

C You will need a large-scale ordnance survey map of your town or city.

1 Find your school on the map.

2 Find your street on the map.

3 Estimate the direct distance home to school.

4 Measure the road distance home to school.

If you use the largest scale of survey map you will be able to find your own house or flat marked.

Unit M9 Symmetry

9·1 Line symmetry

If you can divide a figure into matching left-hand and right-hand halves the figure has **line symmetry**. The dividing line is called an **axis** of **symmetry**.

The points A and A′ are called images as they would come together if the shape were cut out and folded. The line joining AA′ is perpendicular to the axis of symmetry.

The axis of symmetry does not have to be vertical.

Both A and A′ are the same distance from the axis.

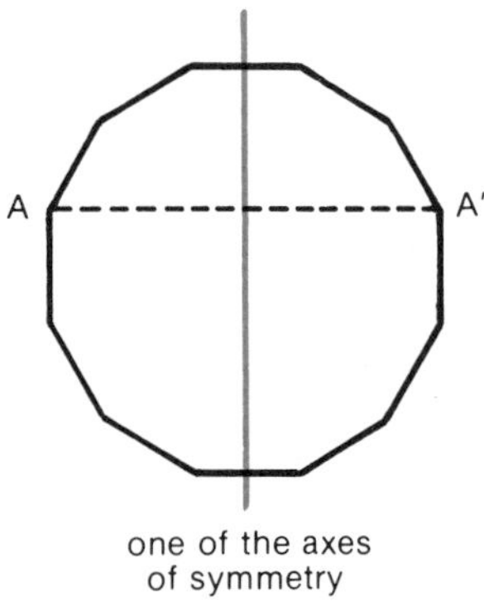

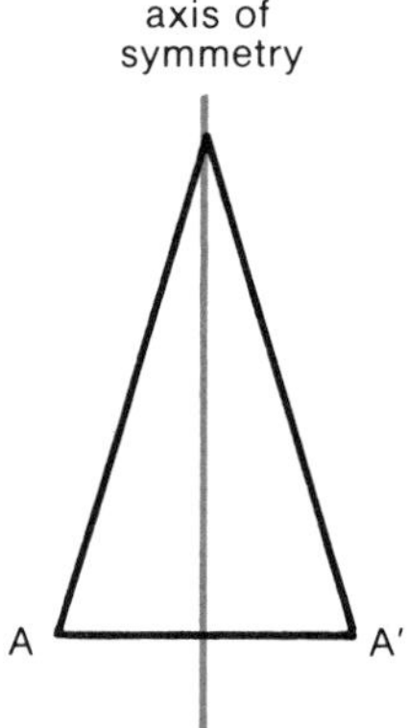

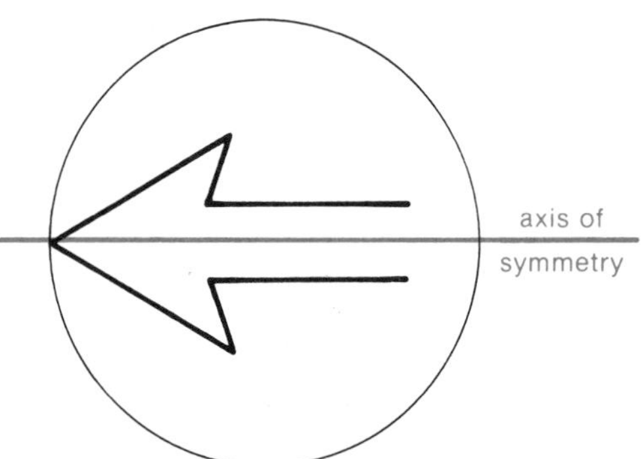

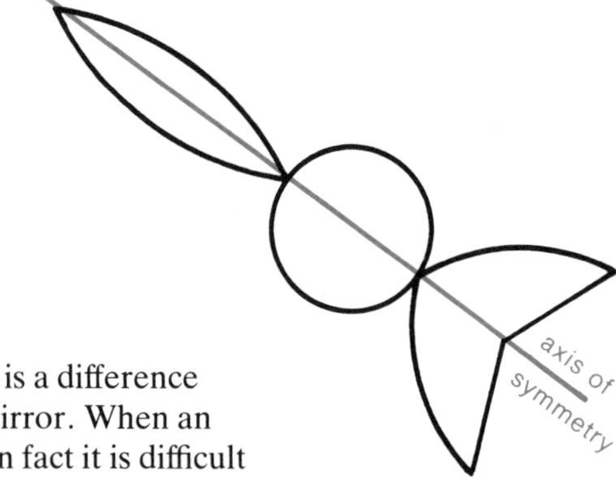

Although symmetry is often called reflection, there is a difference between mathematical reflection and reflection in a mirror. When an object is reflected in a mirror, the image is not solid. In fact it is difficult to say what the image consists of. Also no further reflection can bring the object back again. When a figure is reflected in an axis of symmetry however, the **reflection of the reflection** is the figure you started with.

Exercise 9·1

A Decide which lines are axes of symmetry in the following figures.

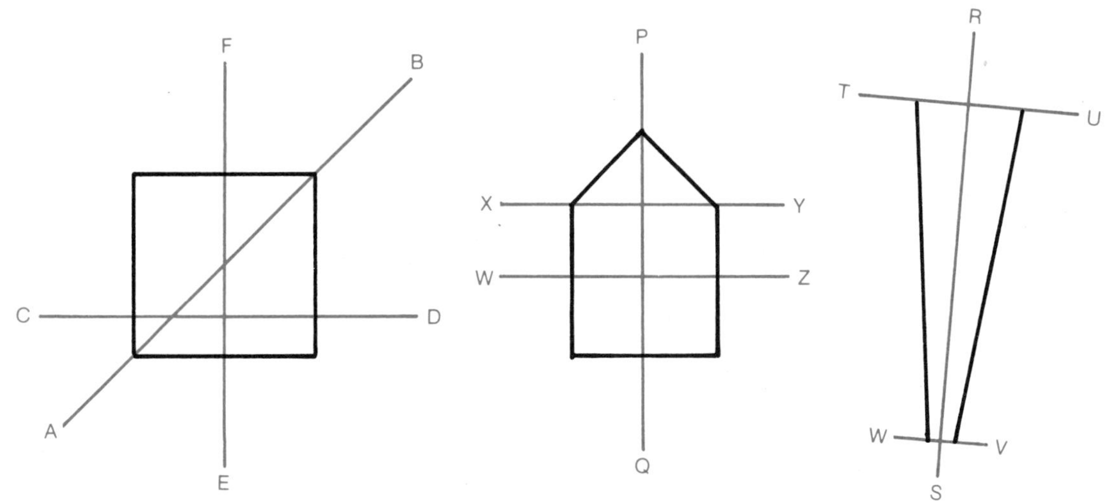

B **1** Copy these capital letters and mark in an axis of symmetry.

B D A H M X Y

Which letters have more than one axis of symmetry?

2 Sort out the capital letters into three groups:

(a) Those with one axis of symmetry.

(b) Those with more than one axis of symmetry.

(c) Those without symmetry.

3 Repeat question 2 for lower-case letters. (Use the small letters on this page.)

4 Copy the traffic signs below and mark axes of symmetry on them.

(a) No overtaking

(b) T junction

(c) road narrows

(d) Dual carriageway ends

(e) Maximum speed limit 70 mph (100 kmph)

C **1** In each of the figures below, one half of a symmetrical figure has been left out. Copy the figures and draw in the other half.

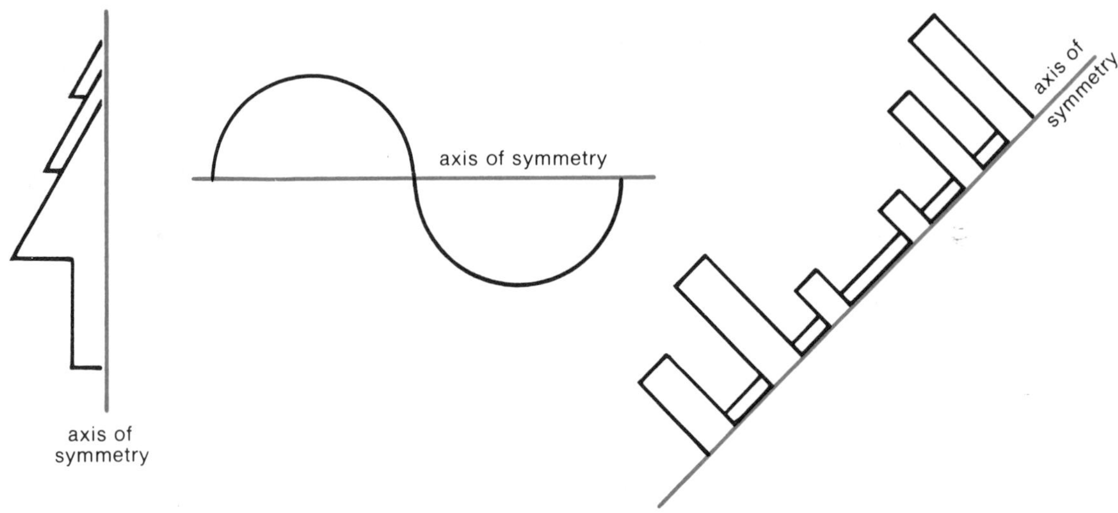

2 In the messages below, half of all symmetrical letters have been erased. Find the messages if you can.

(a) ᴨᴱLLᴖ

(b) ᴴᴖV ⁄ Rᴱ ⱽ Ↄᴸ

(c) ᴵ ᴗᴖN ᴦ Fᴸᴱ L VᴸLL

3 You may be surprised to find how much print can be omitted before a message is lost. Try covering a line of print so that only the top half is showing. Can you still read the words? Next cover the top half of the letters leaving the bottom half showing. Is this easier or harder to read than the top half? Can you read words when more than half the letters are covered?

9·2 Regular figures (polygons)

Straight-sided figures with all their sides and angles equal are called **regular**.

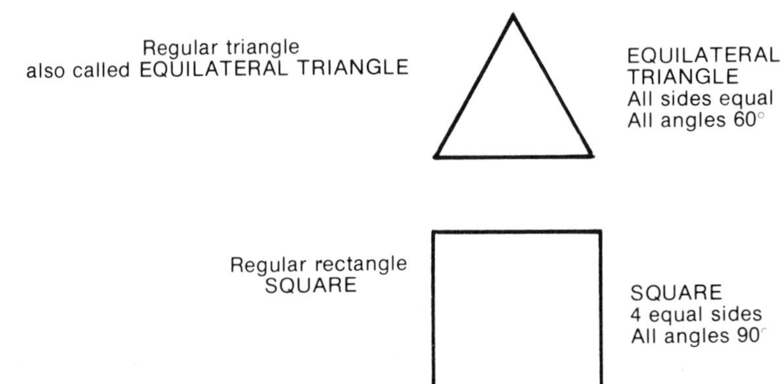

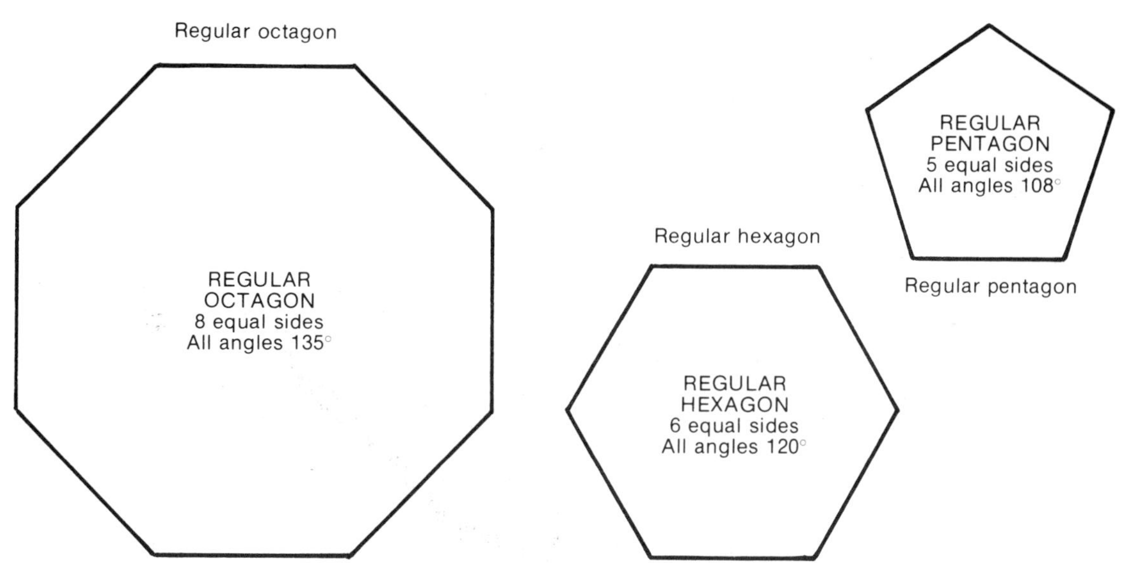

All regular polygons are symmetrical. They have the same number of axes of symmetry as they have sides.

Note that the angles can be found using the formula $180° - \dfrac{360°}{n}$

where n is the number of sides.

This follows from the fact that the *external* angles add up to 360°.

Example:

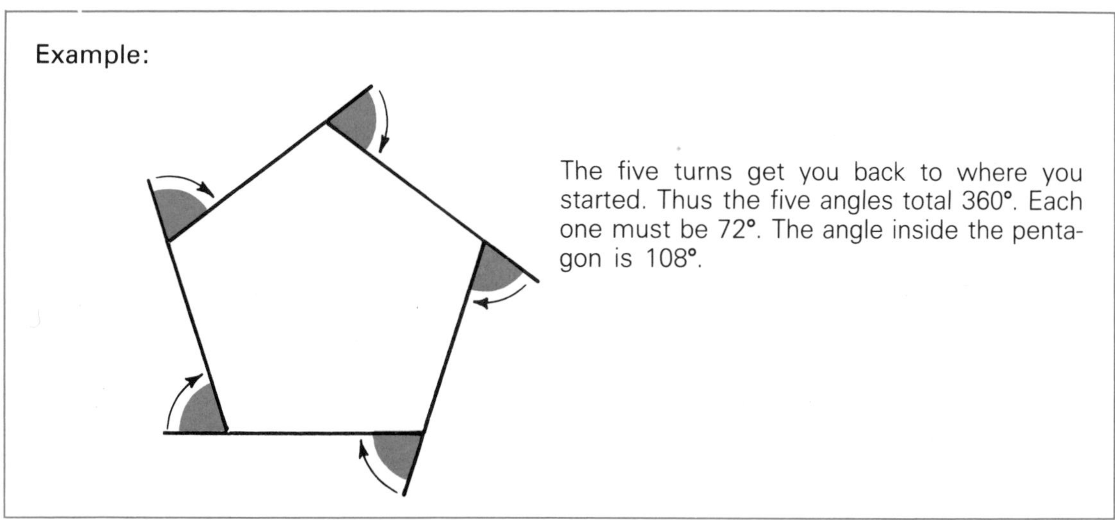

The five turns get you back to where you started. Thus the five angles total 360°. Each one must be 72°. The angle inside the pentagon is 108°.

Exercise 9·2

A **1** Make copies of all the regular polygons illustrated above. All you need to do is cover the printed picture with your paper and mark each vertex. The polygon is then formed by joining the marks.

2 On each polygon draw all the axes of symmetry. Do you agree that a regular polygon has the same number of sides, vertices and axes of symmetry?

3 Draw a regular pentagon.
   (a) Join every vertex to every other vertex.
   (b) Colour in the star you have formed.
4 Make six-pointed and eight-pointed stars from the regular hexagon and regular octagon.

B Each angle of a regular hexagon is 120°. This means that *all* the angles of a hexagon add up to 720° (6 × 120 = 720).

We could have shown this by dividing the hexagon into triangles.

The hexagon will divide into four triangles.
Each triangle has a total of 180°
Total angles for hexagon = 4 × 180° = 720°.

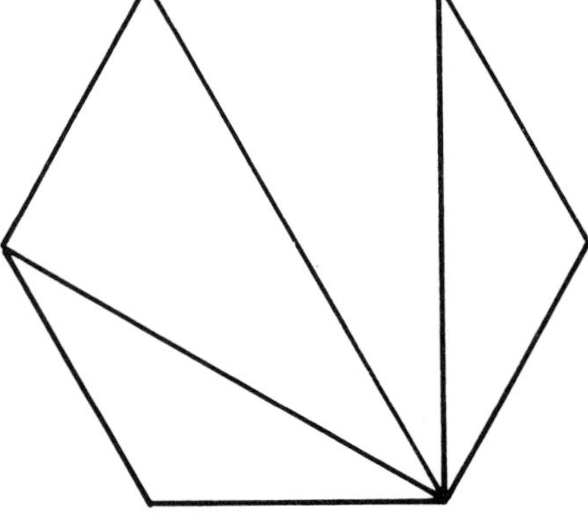

1 Use the triangle method to find the total angles in regular polygons with:
   (a) 8 sides (b) 12 sides (c) 20 sides (d) 25 sides.
2 These four hexagons are not regular, but their total angles can be found as in question 1.

   (a) Find the total angles in each hexagon.
   (b) Do you think that the angles of a hexagon add up to 720° whatever its shape?
3 How many triangles are formed when:
   (a) A hexagon is divided?
   (b) A pentagon is divided?
   (c) An octagon is divided?
   (d) A ten-sided polygon is divided?
   (e) A two hundred-sided polygon is divided?

4 The size of angle of a regular polygon can be found by the following program:

1Ø Count the sides of the polygon . . . n.
2Ø Divide the polygon into triangles and count them.
There will be n-2 triangles.
3Ø Multiply $(n-2) \times 180 \ldots m$.
4Ø Divide $m \div n \ldots$ this will give the size of each angle.

Show that the program gives correct answers for the size of angle for:

(a) An equilateral triangle (b) A square
(c) A regular pentagon (d) A regular dodecagon (12 sides)

9·3 Rotational symmetry

If an envelope is fixed with a pin and turned we say the envelope has been rotated about the pin.

Other things which rotate are: doors on hinges, door handles, wheels, helicopter blades, engine gears, etc.

If a shape can be turned into a new position which looks exactly the same as the first position we say the shape has **rotational symmetry**.

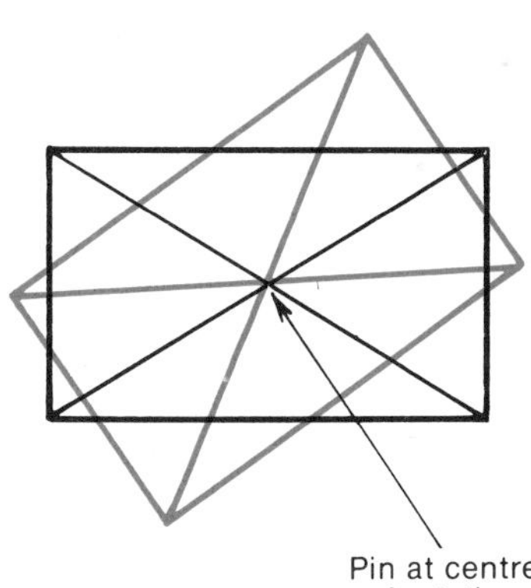
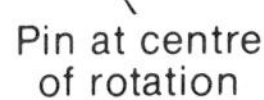

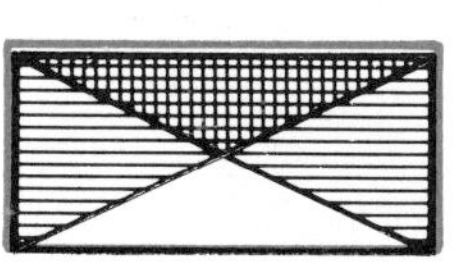
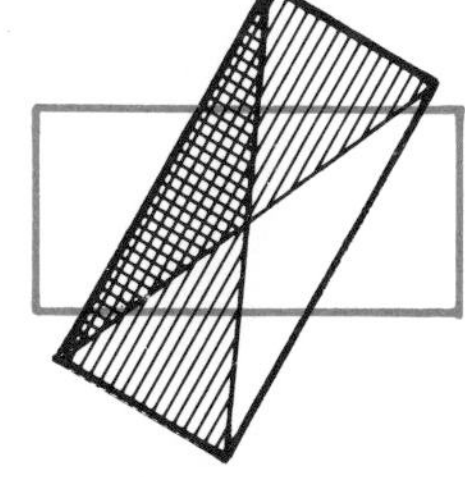
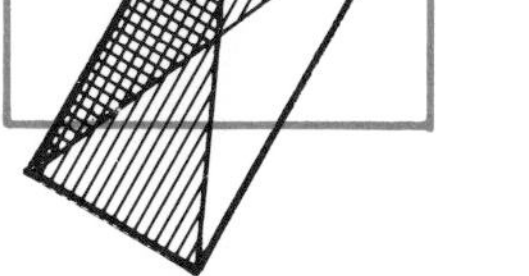

Rotated but *not* over original position

Rotated shape fits over original position

Exercise 9·3

A The letter A does not have rotational symmetry. You cannot turn the letter to a position over the original without turning it right round (through 360°).

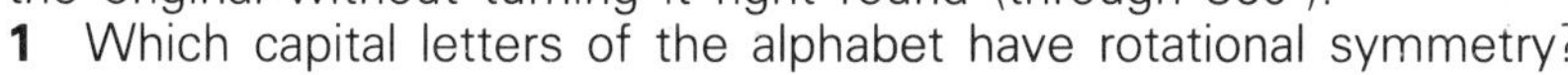

1 Which capital letters of the alphabet have rotational symmetry?
2 Which small letters have rotational symmetry, if any?
3 Which numerals have rotational symmetry?

B Copy the shapes below and mark the centre of symmetry.

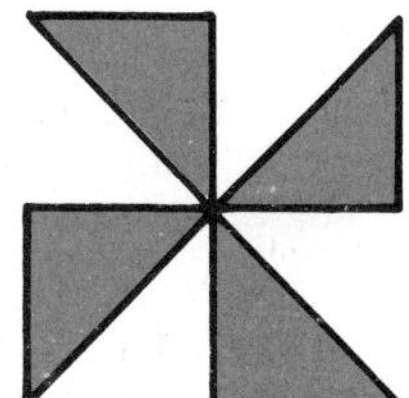

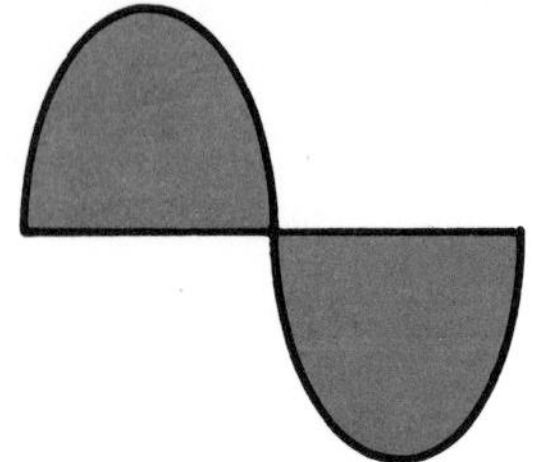

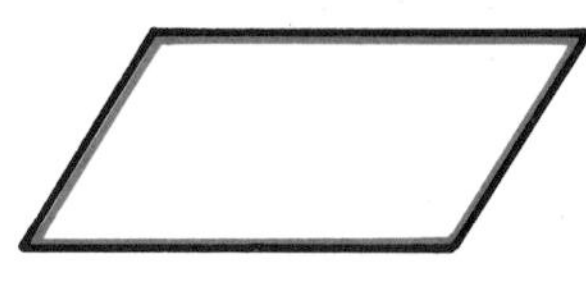

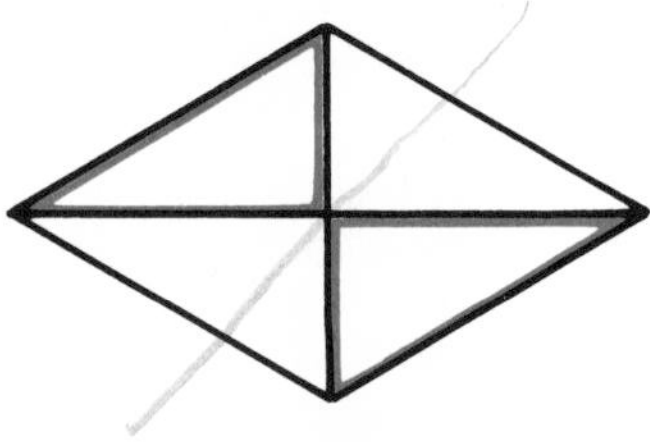

C **1** Which of the shapes in question B above have line symmetry as well as rotational symmetry?

2 Which of the following shapes have both rotational and line symmetry?

(a) Isosceles triangle
(b) Equilateral triangle
(c) Rectangle
(d) Rhombus
(e) *All* parallelograms
(f) *All* regular figures.

3 (a) The circle is sometimes called the perfect shape. Why do you think this is so?

(b) Describe what happens to the arc AB of the circle when the circle is rotated through 180°.

(c) These shapes inside the circle give the figure rotational symmetry. They are made by drawing two half-circles along the diameter.

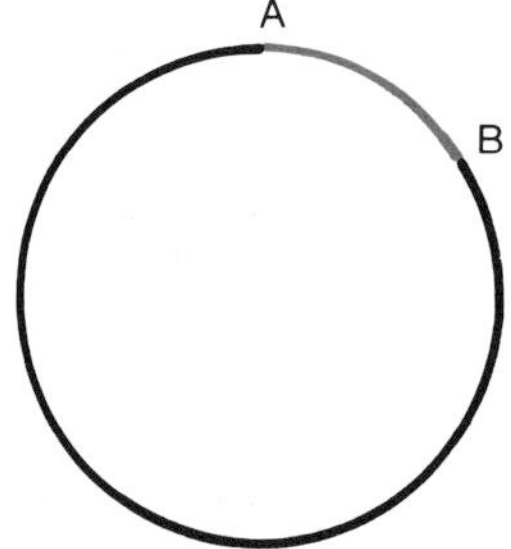

Make some similar designs with circles and half-circles that have rotational symmetry. Draw some shapes of this sort that have an axis of symmetry.

9·4 Applications of line and rotational symmetry

Many natural things have symmetry.

Butterfly

Flower

Snowflake

Artificial things also use symmetry to obtain pleasing designs, and because of the value of symmetry in machines.

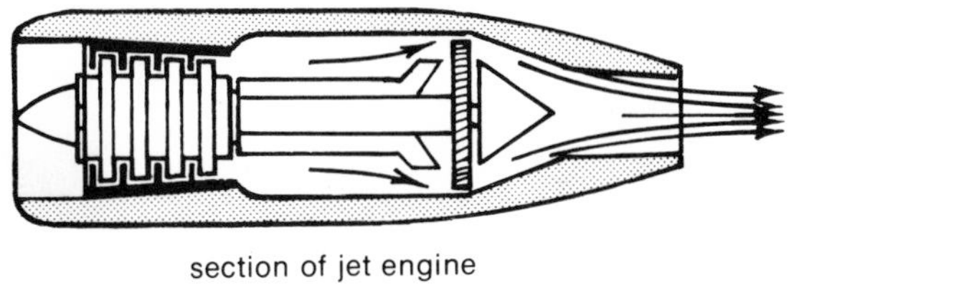

section of jet engine

ship's propeller

Exercise 9·4

1 Describe the symmetry of the objects in the pictures above.
2 Describe the symmetry in the buildings in the following plans of student flats.

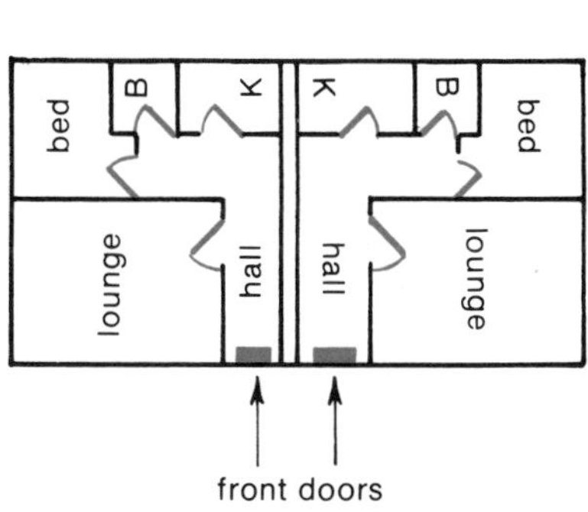

front doors

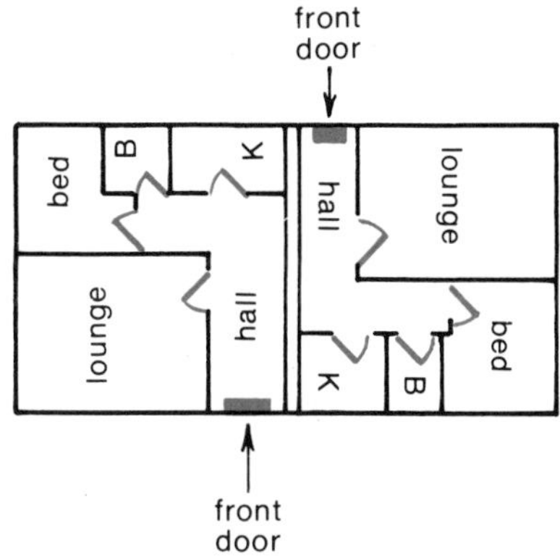

front door

front door

3 Where can you see symmetry used in the design of these buildings?

old church

large base skyscraper

4 Look at the buildings around you, school, church, home and shops to see where symmetry is to be found.

9·5 Construction with ruler and compasses

The symmetry of the rhombus enables us to bisect* lines and angles.

Because the rhombus can be folded over AB or over CD we can say that:

(a) AB bisects CD
(b) CD bisects AB
(c) The four angles at the centre are all right angles.
(d) AB bisects $\hat{A}$ and $\hat{B}$
(e) CD bisects $\hat{C}$ and $\hat{D}$.

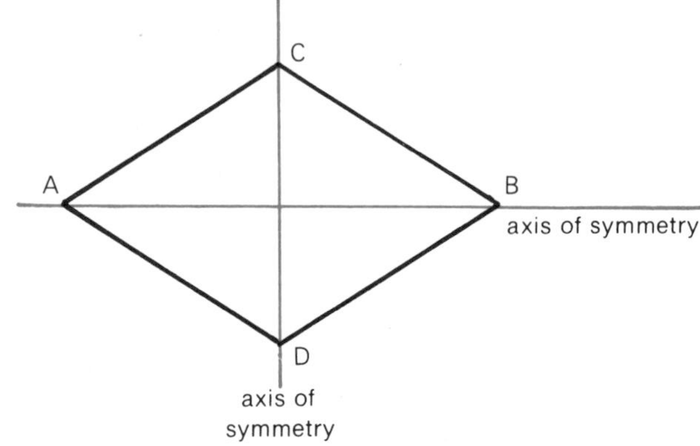

To draw the perpendicular bisector of a line segment

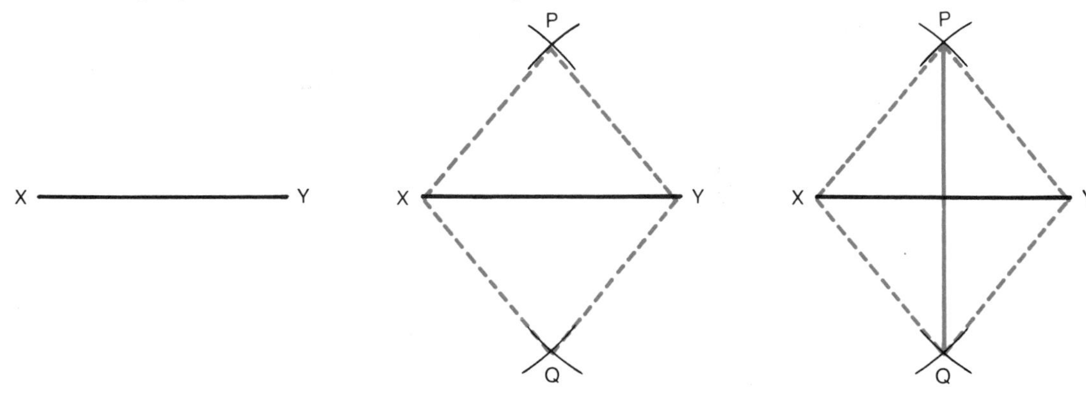

We want to construct the perpendicular bisector of XY

We draw a rhombus with XY as one diagonal

PQ is the required line, it is perpendicular to XY. It bisects XY.

This program summarises the method:
1∅ Choose a radius r. 2∅ Point at X, draw arcs (radius r) above and below XY. 3∅ Point at Y, draw arcs (radius r) above and below XY to meet those already drawn at P and Q. 4∅ Joint PQ.

* Divide into two equal parts.

To draw the bisector of an angle

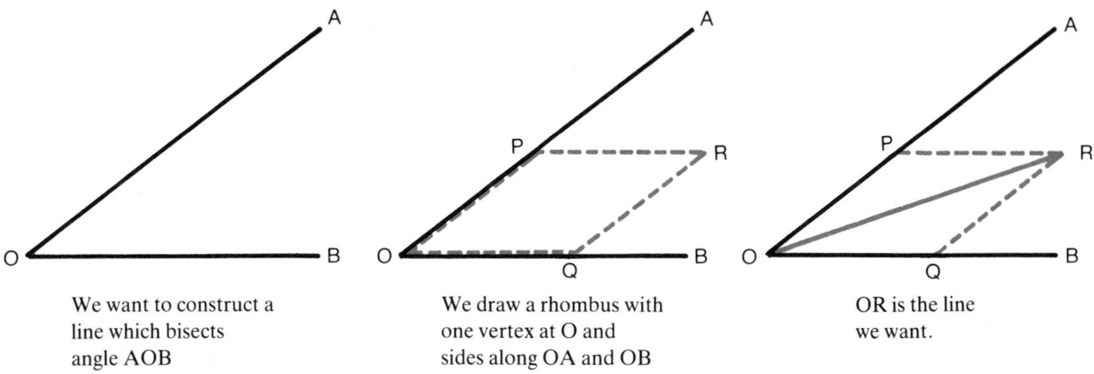

We want to construct a line which bisects angle AOB

We draw a rhombus with one vertex at O and sides along OA and OB

OR is the line we want.

Program summarising method of drawing bisector of angle AOB:
1Ø Choose a radius r. 2Ø Centre O, mark arcs (radius r) on OA and OB, P and Q. 3Ø Centre P draw an arc (radius r). 4Ø Centre Q draw an arc (radius r). 5Ø These arcs meet at R, draw OR.

Exercise 9·5 (work on 1 mm^2 graph paper if possible)

A **1** Draw three line segments and draw their perpendicular bisectors.

2 (a) Draw a triangle ABC, AB = 3 cm, BC = 4 cm and CA = 5 cm.
(b) Construct the perpendicular bisectors of AB and AC, and mark the point where they meet.

3 (a) Draw a triangle ABC, AB = 4 cm, BC = 6 cm with a right angle at B.
(b) Construct the perpendicular bisectors of AB and BC and mark the point where they meet.

4 Do you agree or disagree with this statement about all right-angled triangles?
'The perpendicular bisectors of the two shorter sides meet at the mid-point of the longest side.'

5 Draw any triangle ABC and construct the three perpendicular bisectors. Do they all pass through the same point?

6 Draw an obtuse-angled triangle.

(a) Where would you expect the perpendicular bisectors of the sides to meet?
(b) Draw the bisectors and check.
(c) If the bisectors of an acute-angled triangle meet inside the triangle while the bisectors of an obtuse-angled triangle meet outside, where would you expect the bisectors of a right-angled triangle to meet?

7 Two bisectors of the sides of $\triangle ABC$ meet at P. Show by copying the triangle and drawing that PA = PB = PC.

This means that a circle through A, B, C can be drawn with centre P. The circle is called the circumcircle of the triangle.

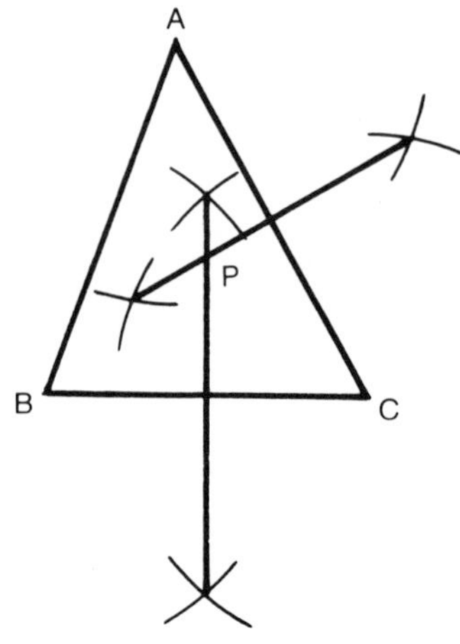

8 Draw bisectors and circumcircles for the following triangles:
(a) ABC where AB = 4 cm, BC = 5 cm and CA = 7 cm
(b) DEF where DE = 3 cm, EF = 4 cm, FD = 5 cm
(c) GHI where GH = 6 cm, HI = 6 cm, IG = 6 cm

B 1 (a) Draw three different angles AOB, where one is acute, one obtuse and one a right angle.
(b) Using compasses draw the bisector of each of the angles.

2 (a) Draw PQRS as shown.
(b) Draw XQ and YQ where XQ bisects PQR and YQ bisects PQS.
(c) Measure angle XQY.

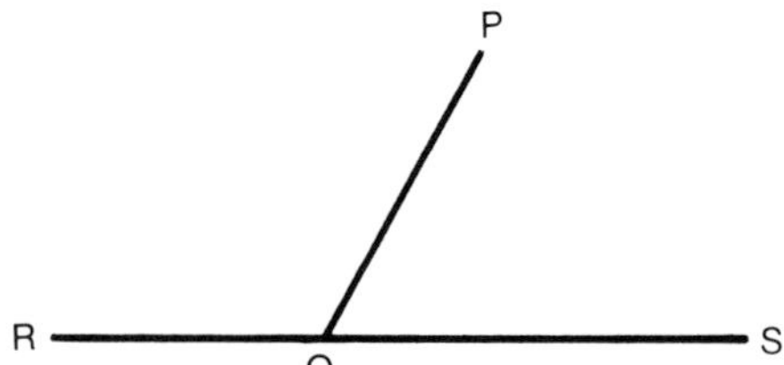

3 (a) Draw any triangle ABC and then draw the bisectors of each of the three angles.
(b) Do the three bisectors meet at a single point? Do you think that they should?
(c) Repeat (b) starting with an obtuse-angled triangle.

C 1 Find a compass and ruler method for drawing a perpendicular from a point to a line. (You could use a set-square, but it is interesting to try to find the exact perpendicular using compasses.)

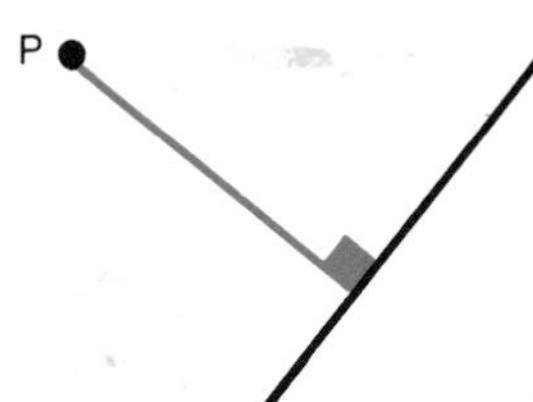

2 The perpendicular from a vertex to the opposite side of a triangle is called an altitude.

Draw a number of triangles and draw all three altitudes. Do you think that the altitudes of any triangle pass through a single point?

Unit M10 Averages

10·1 Average height and weight

The average height of five people can be found by adding their heights and dividing by five. For seven people you would add their heights and divide by seven.

Example:

Mr Green has two sons and a daughter. Their heights are 85 cm, 90 cm and 89 cm. What is the average height of Mr Green's children?

First add heights $85 + 90 + 89 = 264$
now divide by 3 $264 \div 3 = 88$
The average height is 88 cm

Note: (a) None of the children is 88 cm in height.
(b) Two are above the average and one is below the average.

Exercise 10·1

A **1** Find the average heights of these groups of boys and girls:
(a) John 91 cm, George 97 cm, Jack 95cm, Bob 92cm.
(b) Tim 62 ins, Trevor 64 ins, Derek 68 ins, Gary 70 ins, Colin 70 ins.
(c) Linda 95 cm, Sarah 84 cm, Tracy 90 cm, Nancy 88 cm, Anne 89 cm, Mandy 92 cm.

2 The heights of eight basketball players are given below. Find the average height for the group.
Smith 199 cm, Green 200 cm, Hill 197 cm, Walker 195 cm, Jones 197 cm, Brown 202 cm, Price 201 cm, Thomas 198 cm.

B **1** Mary has five aunts: Aunt May, Auntie Jill, Auntie Lucy, Auntie Lynne and Auntie Sara. Their weights are: 59 kg, 63.5 kg, 68 kg, 72.5 kg and 77 kg. What is their average weight?

2 Mrs Moore weighs herself every Saturday. Her weights over 6 weeks were: 59 kg, 61 kg, 62.3 kg, 61.5 kg, 61 kg, 61.4 kg.
What was the average weight for the six weeks?

3 Big Ben the weight lifter lifted 252 lb, 270 lb, 261 lb and 273 lb in four attempts. What was his average lift?

4 On 31 January 1982, twelve new babies were born at Fairview Maternity Hospital. Their weights were: 2.5, 2.7, 2.0, 2.25, 2.36, 3.2, 2.9, 2.8, 3.4, 3.6, 3.3 and 3.1 kg.
What was the average weight of the babies?

10·2 Other averages

Averages are often used to give an impression or 'feel' about information. Some examples are given below. Read the notes carefully.

(a) A cricketer scored 140 runs in 10 innings. His average is 14 runs per innings, but if he was only 'out' 8 times his batting average is $140 - 8 = 17.5$.

(b) A motorist travels 420 km in 3 hours. Then he has coffee and rests for 1 hour. He then travels a further 520 km in 4 hours. His average speed for the first part of the journey is

$420 \text{ km} \div 3 = 140$ km per hour.

His average speed for the second part of the journey is

$520 \text{ km} \div 4 = 130$ km per hour.

His average speed for the whole journey is

$940 \div 7 = 134$ km per hour

if you do not count the 'rest', or

$940 \div 8 = 117{\cdot}5$ km per hour

counting the 'rest' as travel time.

Exercise 10·2

1 Mary Jones was practising long jump. On Monday she jumped: 4·6 m, 4·9 m, 5·3 m, 5·1 m, 5·2 m, 4·8 m. On Tuesday she jumped: 5·2 m, 5·2 m, 4·7 m, 4·8 m, 4·8 m, 5·0 m. On which day did she have a better average?

2 Figures for rainfall over England and Wales are given below:

Month	Jan	Feb	Mar	Apr	May	June	July	Aug	Sep	Oct	Nov	Dec
mm	86	65	59	58	67	61	73	90	83	83	97	90

(a) What was the average rainfall per month for the first three months, the second three months, the third three months and the last three months?
(b) Which months had above average rainfall for the quarter?
(c) What was the average rainfall over the whole year?
(d) Which months had below average rainnfall in the year?

3 A driver wanted to work out the petrol consumption of her car. Each time she put petrol in the car she read the milometer. The readings are given below:

Milometer	Gallons of petrol put in tank
11 500	4
11 650	5
11 840	1
11 866	3
11 950	6

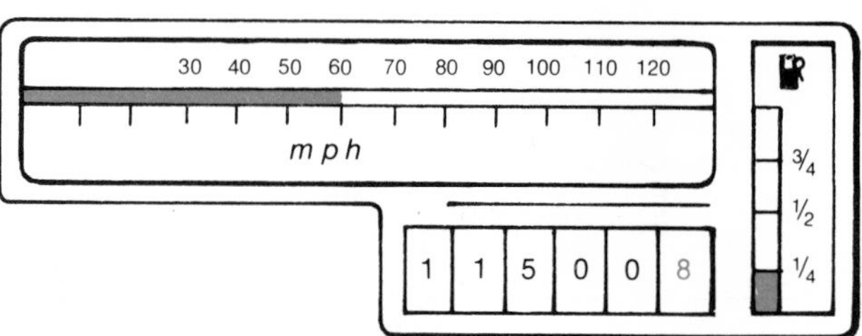

(a) How far did she travel on the first 4 gallons? What is the average petrol consumption at this point (in miles per gallon).
(b) How far did she travel on the first 9 gallons. What is the average petrol consumption now?
(c) Find the next two values for average consumption based on milometer readings 11866 and 11950.
(d) Why does the rate of consumption seem to change?

4 Tom thought he would like to be a bus driver, so he asked four young drivers how much they earned in a week. The figures were: £122, £134, £141 and £152. What was the average wage of the four drivers?

5 A batch of 24 light bulbs was tested to see how long they lasted. The results, in hours, are given below:

2245	2805	1925	2233	2624	1828
2168	2102	1873	2157	1961	2235
1735	2345	1944	2446	2020	2152
1844	1566	2426	3200	1466	2628

What was the average life of a bulb?

10·3 Average from a base line

53 mm
50 mm
59 mm
57 mm
54 mm

The average length of the five lines can be found by adding the lengths and dividing by 5.

$(53 + 50 + 59 + 57 + 54) \div 5 = 54{\cdot}6$ mm

This is the same as making one long line, by joining the five, and then dividing the long line into equal parts.

50 mm 3 mm
50 mm
50 mm 9 mm
50 mm 7 mm
50 mm 4 mm

We could take 50 mm as base line and find the average of the extra bits.

$(3 + 0 + 9 + 7 + 4) \div 5 = 4{\cdot}6$

this is the average *extra*

Average length = base + 4·6 = 54·6 mm as before.

Exercise 10·3

A Find the averages of the following sets of measurements using a base line.

1. 72 mm, 71 mm, 74 mm, 77 mm, 75 mm ... Wing spans of butterflies.
2. 1 hr 3 min, 1 hr 2 min, 1 hr 5 min, 1 hr 12 min, 1 hr 3 min, 1 hr 6 min, 1 hr, 1 hr 4 min ... Times for a railway journey which should take 1 hr 5 min.
3. £4·22, £4·15, £4·06, £4·19, £4·16, £4·08 ... Cost of TV for 1 week from 6 different shops.
4. 54·86 kg, 54·74 kg, 54·61 kg, 54·36 kg, 54·77 kg, 54·29 kg, 54·55 kg, 54·50 kg ... Weights of a boxer in training.
5. 26·4 litres, 25·3 litres, 25·8 litres, 26·1 litres, 25·2 litres, 26·5 litres ... Milk yields of a cow.

B Find the average of each of the sets of measurements in part A above without using a base line (we call this working with **raw data**). Check that you get the same result for the average as before.

10·4 The average

In everyday language we speak of the 'average person' when we mean 'most people'.

The average person thinks nuclear power should be developed.
The average man likes his beer cold.
The average woman prefers going out to work to working at home.

This average is called the **mode** in mathematical language.

> **Examples:**
> Out of 100 people who were asked what colour of car they preferred 7 like red, 14 liked black, 37 liked white, 30 liked lemon and 22 liked green.
> The mode is lemon (preferred by the largest group of people).
> 150 girls were asked what they spent each month at the hairdresser's.
> The result were: under £5...28 girls, £5–£10...67 girls, £10–15...40 girls, and over £15...15 girls.
> The mode was £5–£10...spent by the largest group.

Exercise 10·4

A What is meant by these statements?

1 The average man reads the sports pages first in his newspaper.
2 The average girl prefers pop music to Jazz.
3 The average teenager spends more on clothes than the average adult.
4 The average child leaves school at 16.

B Which is the mode in each of these sets of data?

1 Class sizes in primary school.

No. of children in class	*Percentage of all classes*
1–15	1·3
16–20	3·9
21–25	12·7
26–30	31·7
31–35	37·3
36–40	11·9
41 and over	1·3

This table tells you the percentage of classes with a particular number of children. e.g. 3·9% of all classes have between 16 and 20 children.

2 Hours of paid work done by a sample of 1000 schoolchildren aged 14.

Hours worked	*Number*	*%*
none	460	46
up to 5	235	23·5
5–10	200	20
10–15	60	6
over 15	45	4·5

This table tells you how many children are in each group. The percentage each group is of the whole 1000 is also shown. For example, 200 out of the 1000 children work between 5 and 10 hours a week. This is 20% of the sample.

3 If you know the **mode** you can tell quite a lot about a set of data but there are some things you cannot tell.

The mode time of a London–New York flight was found to be between $4\frac{1}{2}$ and 5 hours. The 'time tabled' flight was 4 hours.

Which of these statements follow from the above?
(a) The **average** flight time was $4\frac{1}{2}$ hours.
(b) The **average** flight time was 5 hours.
(c) The plane was **always** late arriving in New York.
(d) The plane was more often late than on time.
(e) The flight never takes more than 5 hours.

4 Explain why a shoe-shop owner would be interested in the mode-size for shoes. What other information about shoe size would be important for his business?

10·5 The average family

Sometimes the word 'average' does not mean mode. If we say the average family has 2·3 children we do not mean that most families have 2·3 children. Here the average is obtained by adding up all the children and dividing by the number of families. A similar calculation is used to find things like average income of a family, average amount spent on food of a family and so on.

Example:

In a certain town the number of children in each family was counted. The results are shown in the table below:

	No. of children in family	*No. of families*	*Children*
	0	142	0
	1	67	67 (67 × 1)
	2	82	164 (82 × 2)
	3	56	168 (52 × 3)
22 families with →	4	22	88 (22 × 4)
4 children in each	5	11	55 (11 × 5)
means 88 children	6	8	48 (8 × 6)
in this group.	7	1	7 (1 × 7)
	8	5	40 (5 × 8)
	Totals	394 ↑ Families	637 ↑ Children

Note: To get the number in the 'children' column multiply 'no. of children in family' by 'no. of families'.

To find the average size of the family we divide 637 ÷ 394 = 1·6. This tells you how many children there would be in each family **if all the children could be divided up equally between all the families.**

Exercise 10·5

1 Find the average number of children per family from the data in the following tables:

(a)

No. of children in family	*No. of families*
1	24
2	27
3	16
4	30
5	12
6	3
Total	

(b)

No. of children in family	*No. of families*
0	46
1	18
2	23
3	44
4	19
5	7
6	2
7	0
8	1
Total	

2 Children in a school were asked how many pets their families kept. 184 had no pets, 279 had one pet, 132 had two pets, 104 had three pets and 2 children had six pets.
What was the average number of pets per family?

3 A group of people recorded the hours of TV they watched on a Saturday. The results were:

Hours watched	0	1	2	3	4	5	6	7
Number of people	6	26	45	127	103	72	12	4

This information is written horizontally instead of vertically to save space!
Calculate the average viewing time.

4 The table below gives the amount spent (per person) on holidays for a number of families. Calculate the average amount per family.

	Amount spent	*No. of families*
Call this £25 ←	0–£50	48
Call this £75 ←	£50⁺–£100	12
etc. ←	£100⁺–£150	19
etc. ←	£150⁺–£200	27
etc. ←	£200⁺–£250	16
etc. ←	£250⁺–£300	2

10·6 The arithmetic mean

The average which is obtained by adding up all the values and dividing by the number of them is called the **arithmetic mean**. The numbers can be added one at a time or grouped.

Example:
Two dice were thrown 45 times and the scores recorded. Find the arithmetic mean of the scores.

Scores 3 3 3 3 3 4 4 5 5 5 6 6 6 6 6 6 6 7 7 7 7 7 7 7 7 8 8 8 8 8 8 8 9 9 9 9 9 9 10 10 10 10 11 11 12

(a) Adding the numbers as they stand = 318

Mean score $318 \div 45 = 7{\cdot}067$

(b) Grouping the same numbers and collecting the information into a frequency table.

Score (x)	*Frequency* (f)	*Score of group*
2	2	4
3	3	9
4	2	8
5	3	15
6	7	42
7	8	56
8	7	56
9	6	54
10	4	40
11	2	22
12	1	12
Totals	45	318
	total frequency	*total score*

The mean is the $\dfrac{\text{total score}}{\text{total no. of throws}} = \dfrac{318}{45} = 7{\cdot}067$

We use the symbol $\bar{x}$ for the mean. So $\bar{x} = 7{\cdot}067$ in this example.

Note: Method (a) is slow and it is easy to make mistakes. It is usually better to make the frequency table.

Exercise 10·6

Make frequency tables and then calculate means for the following data:

1 Scores on 50 throws of 2 dice (as it happened):
8, 2, 3, 10, 5, 7, 8, 6, 9, 6, 5, 5, 7, 6, 8, 4, 11, 6, 7, 9, 8, 8, 7, 10, 9, 6, 5, 6, 7, 4, 7, 8, 9, 5, 6, 6, 5, 3, 7, 8, 10, 10, 6, 8, 8, 4, 6, 5, 7, 7.

2 Ages of students in a class (years and months):
14·0, 14·0, 14·0, 14·1, 14·1, 14·2, 14·2, 14·2, 14·3, 14·3, 14·3, 14·3, 14·4, 14·4, 14·5, 14·5, 14·5, 14·6, 14·6, 14·6, 14·7, 14·8, 14·8, 14·9, 14·9, 14·10, 14·10, 14·11, 14·11, 14·11.

3 In 25 matches our team scored goals as follows this year, and last year:
This year 3, 2, 0, 1, 5, 2, 1, 2, 3, 0, 0, 4, 2, 2, 3, 1, 0, 0, 2, 0, 1, 0, 3, 4, 2.
(goals)
Last year 2, 2, 1, 4, 0, 0, 3, 4, 2, 0, 2, 0, 3, 4, 3, 1, 1, 2, 1, 1, 3, 0, 2, 0, 3.
(goals)
In which year did the team have a better goal average?
Note: It is very hard to compare the years *without* finding the mean!

4 The number of hours of sunshine in one day (collected over a whole year):
42 days with no sunshine
27 days with 1 hr
38 days with 2 hr
77 days with 3 hr
41 days with 4 hr
16 days with 5 hr
12 days with 6 hr
29 days with 7 hr
20 days with 8 hr
41 days with 9 hr
22 days with 10 hr
Note: It is the number of days which is the *frequency* in this case.

Unit M11 Probability

11·1 Luck and chance

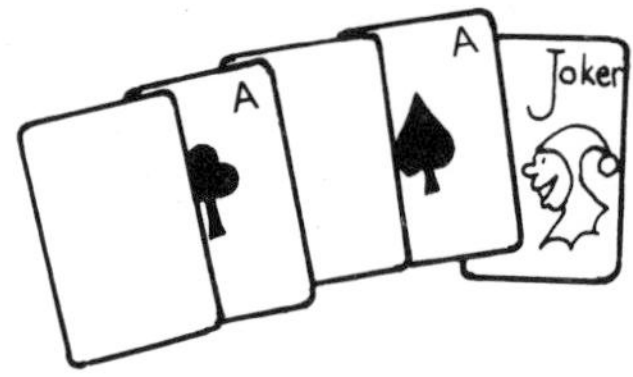

Some people seem to be lucky. They have more than their share of aces or less than their share of spots. Other people seem to be unlucky, but on the whole we expect things to even out in the long run.*

The study of the laws of luck and chance is called **probability**. Most people have some common-sense ideas about probability. These ideas have come from experience. Probability plays an important part in all our lives.

Exercise 11·1

A Say whether these people are lucky, unlucky or neither. Give reasons:

1 John throws a 6 every time with a die (dice).
2 Jack throws four sixes in 10 throws.
3 Tony throws one 6 in 10 throws.
4 Jean passes her driving test first time.
5 Paula is going on holiday.
6 Tina goes to the cinema three times a week.
7 Jerry has been selected for the school football team.
8 Jenny dropped an ear-ring down the drain.

B Explain how you would expect these events to even out:

1 Mrs Brown's first two children were girls.
2 Mary threw a die and scored 6 three times running.
3 Gary picked three apples. Two were perfect but one was bad.
4 Sara had her cycle stolen last week.
5 The first week in August was wet every day.
6 April, May and June were very dry in 1976.
7 This government is Conservative and so was the last.
8 The train was 5 minutes early arriving in London.

11·2 The raffle

There are many words to describe a raffle — lottery, sweep are two of them.

* This is one of the Rules of **probability**.

In a raffle there is a prize and a set of numbered tickets. When you buy a ticket you buy a chance to win the prize. The counterfoils of all the sold tickets are put into a hat and the winning number drawn out. If your counterfoil is drawn out you win the prize.
Your chance of winning depends on how many tickets you buy.

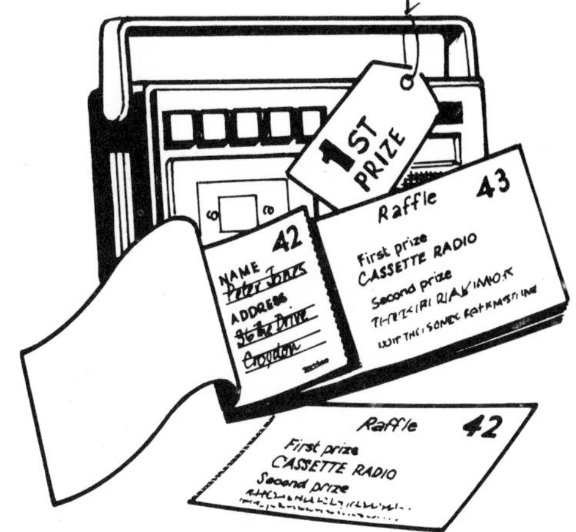

Examples:

(a) 100 tickets were sold in a raffle.
Marilyn bought 20 of them.
Marilyn's chance of winning is 20 ÷ 100 = 0·2

We say probability of Marilyn's winning is $\frac{2}{10}$ (20% or 0·2)

(b) 240 tickets were sold in a raffle.
Ken bought 8.

Probability of Ken's winning is $\frac{8}{240} = 0{\cdot}033\,33$.

You can improve your chance of winning by buying more tickets.

Exercise 11·2

A A raffle was held for a colour TV. There were 1000 tickets sold at 50p each. Mr Jones bought 200 tickets, Graham bought 40 tickets, Julie bought 15 tickets and Liz bought 5 tickets.

1 Who had the best chance (out of the four people) of winning the TV?
2 Who had the worst chance of winning the TV?
3 What is the probability that Mr Jones will win the prize?
4 What is the probability that Liz will win the prize?
5 Would Mr Jones be lucky if he won the prize?
6 Would Graham be lucky if he won the prize?

B A raffle was held for a holiday in Switzerland. There were 100 tickets altogether, each costing £5.

1 How could you be sure of winning the holiday?
2 How many tickets would you need to buy to have a 50% chance of winning the prize?
3 What chance (probability) would you have if you did not buy any tickets at all?
4 How many tickets would you buy to have a $\frac{1}{4}$ chance of winning?
5 Suppose you only had £50 and a holiday in Switzerland cost £200. Would it be a good idea to buy 10 tickets in the raffle? Give your reasons.

C A charity raffle was held for an old Rolls-Royce (worth £20 000).
There were 5000 tickets, each one costing £10.

1 If all the tickets were sold how much money would be given to charity?
2 Mr Rich wanted a 20% chance of winning. How many tickets should he buy?

3 Mr Poor bought one ticket and hoped for the best. What was the probability that he won the Rolls-Royce?

4 Four friends clubbed together and bought 1000 tickets. What was the probability that they won the car?

5 Jenny bought all the tickets with 9s on, because 9 was her lucky number. What was the probability that Jenny won? (Work out how many tickets she bought first.)

11·3 Probability values

You can see that the probability of winning a raffle changes from 0 (if you do not buy any tickets) to 1 (if you buy *all* the tickets). Other probabilities are fractions between 0 and 1.

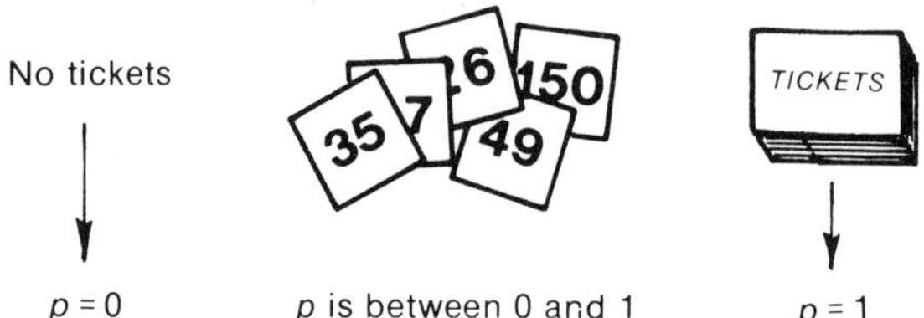

All events have probabilities between 0 and 1.

Examples:

(a) Four boys and a girl have a swimming race. If all the swimmers are equally good what is the probability that the girl will win?
This is like a raffle with 5 tickets. The probability that the girl will win is $\frac{1}{5} = 0{\cdot}2$.

(b) I throw a die. What is the chance that I score 5 or 6? This is like a raffle with 6 tickets numbered 1, 2, 3, 4, 5, 6. The score 5 or 6 is like ticket number 5 or ticket number 6 winning.
Probability of 5 or 6 is $\frac{2}{6} = 0{\cdot}3333$.

Exercise 11·3

A Find the probabilities of these events:

1 A coin comes down 'heads' when it is tossed.
2 A coin comes down 'tails' when it is tossed.
3 A dice shows 6 when it is thrown.*
4 A dice shows 3 when it is thrown.
5 An ace is drawn first go from a pack of cards.
6 A court card† is drawn first go from a pack of cards.
7 A red card is drawn first go from a pack of cards.
8 The Queen of Spades is drawn first go from a pack of cards.
9 The Queen of Spades is drawn when 10 cards are drawn from a pack of cards.
10 My choice of horse wins the Derby out of 22 horses (assuming that all horses have an equal chance).

B 1 Imagine a pack of cards numbered from 1 to 100. I choose one card. What is the probability that I choose:
(a) An even number?
(b) An odd number?
(c) A multiple of 10?
(d) A multiple of 5?

* This means that the 6 is uppermost.
† King, Queen or Jack.

(e) A square number? (f) A multiple of 7?
(g) An *even* multiple of 9? (h) An *odd* multiple of 15?

2 Imagine a pack of 26 cards with the capital letters of the alphabet printed on them. I choose

ABCDEFGHIJKLMNOPQRSTUVWXYZ

one card. What is the probability that:
(a) I choose a vowel?
(b) I choose a letter with an axis of symmetry?
(c) I choose a letter with a centre of symmetry?

3 Lynne applies for a job in a shop. What is the probability that she gets the job if:
(a) There is only one other person trying for the job?
(b) There are 10 other people trying for the job?
(c) There are 50 other people trying for the job?

4 Suppose you are told that a tennis player X has a probability of 0·7 of winning against tennis player Y.
(a) What does this mean?
(b) Would you expect X to win every game?
(c) How many games would you expect Y to win out of 50?

11·4 Some experiments

Ideas of probability come from experience.

In each of the experiments below try to guess what will happen before you count up the results.

Record your results in table form, and use 𝍸 for counting (5 strokes making a 'gate').

Example:

Toss a coin 50 times and record how many heads and tails you get.

Tossing coin							Totals
Heads	𝍸	𝍸	𝍸	𝍸	II		22
Tails	𝍸	𝍸	𝍸	𝍸	𝍸	III	28
	Total →						50

The probability of getting heads **from this data** is 22/50 = 0·44

Exercise 11·4

A **1** Toss a coin 100 times and record the number of times it falls 'heads' and ' tails'. Find the probability of 'heads' from your data.

2 Toss two coins 50 times and record:
(a) How many times you get both heads.
(b) How many times you get both tails.
(c) How many times you get one of each.

What is the probability that you get 2 heads with a single toss of two coins?

3 Toss a coin 50 times and record the changes. Count a 'change' when the result changes from H to T or from T to H. Count 'no change' when the result stays the same.

Example:

$$\text{H H T H H T T T H T H}$$

(arcs between adjacent letters labelled "change" above and "no change" below)

Would you expect more 'changes' or 'no changes'?

B **1** Throw an ordinary die 50 times and record the score each time. Put the results in a frequency table and find the average score. What would you have expected the average to be?

2 Throw a pair of dice 100 times and record the total score each time. (Scores from 2 to 12 will be possible.)
Which of the following agree with your results?
(a) Different scores have different probabilities.
(b) You are more likely to get a score between 5 and 9 than you are to get 2, 3, 4, 10, 11, or 12.
(c) You have less than 0·1 probability of scoring 12.
(d) You have the same probability of scoring 2 as you have of scoring 10.

3 Make a frequency table of your scores in question 2 and calculate the average score.

C You will need a box of drawing pins.

1 (a) Throw down ten drawing pins on to a level surface. Count how many fall with the point in the air.
(b) Repeat the experiment 50 times and make a frequency table of the results.
(c) Find the average number of pins with points up.
(d) Compare your average result with that obtained by another person.
(e) Would you expect the averages to be the same for two people?
(f) Repeat the experiment and find the average again. Is this new average close to the first one you found?
(g) Guess the probability that a single drawing pin will come down 'point up'?

Number with point in air (x)	*Number of throws* (f)	xf
0		
1		
2		
.		
.		
.		
10		
Totals	50	

2 (a) Count the number of letters in each word of one page of a book.
(b) Make a frequency table and find the average word length for the page.
(c) Compare the average word length for a book and a newspaper. (You will have to do some more counting!)

Number of letters in word (x)	*Number of words with letters* (f)	xf
1		
2		
3		
.		
.		
.		
Total		

11·5 Probability in life

Probability can give some guide to your life. Questions like, 'How long will I live?', 'Will I get married?', 'How many children will I have?' can be answered with better than a wild guess. You would have to find out the actual statistics which are published by the Government.

Example:

The table below gives expected length of life for males and females (as it was in 1976).

	Males		Females	
Age	*Number of survivors from 10 000 births*	*Expectation of life in years*	*Number of survivors from 10 000 births*	*Expectation of life in years*
0	10 000	69·4	10 000	75·6
5	9798	65·9	9842	71·8
10	9781	61·0	9830	66·9
15	9765	56·1	9820	62·0
20	9721	51·3	9802	57·1
25	9673	46·6	9787	52·2
30	9631	41·7	9758	47·3
35	9579	37·0	9724	42·5
40	9503	32·2	9669	37·7
45	9370	27·6	9575	33·0
50	9129	23·3	9415	28·6
55	8718	19·3	9166	24·3
60	8076	15·6	8807	20·2
65	7121	12·3	8263	16·3
70	5789	9·6	7466	12·8
75	4137	7·4	6282	9·7
80	2481	5·6	4664	7·1
85	1143	4·5	2478	5·3

Guesses Here are some of the guesses you can make using this table.

(a) If you are a 15-year-old boy now, the chance that you will die before 20 is $44 \div 9765 = 0{\cdot}0045$.

(b) The average 15-year-old girl can expect to live for a further 62 years.

(c) Your grandfather is now 75 years old. The probability that he will die before reaching 80 years is

$$(4137 - 2481) \div 4137 = 0{\cdot}4$$

So there is a probability of 0·6 that he will live to 80.

Exercise 11·5

A These questions refer to the life table above.

1 How long can these people expect to live:

(a) A boy aged 10? (b) A girl aged 15? (c) An infant girl aged 5?
(d) A man aged 40? (e) A woman aged 40? (f) A woman aged 70?
(g) A man aged 80? (h) A male new-born baby?

2 (a) How many men aged 40 will die before they reach 50 (out of 10 000 births)?
(b) What is the probability that a man aged 40 will live to 50?
(c) What is the probability that a man aged 40 will live to 60?
(d) What is the probability that a boy aged 15 will live to 65?

3 Repeat question 2 for women.

4 If you find this information interesting you might like to find out similar figures for other countries such as USA, Brazil, India and Nigeria. Your geography teacher will help you to find the data. (It is published by the World Health Organisation.)

B These questions refer to the table of age at marriage for Great Britain in 1977.

	Age at marriage	*frequency (thousands)*
Males	under 18	3
	18 but under 21	57
	21–24	137
	25–29	93
	30–34	42
	35–44	34
	45–54	19
	55 and over	20
Females	under 18	20
	18 but under 21	119
	21–24	120
	25–29	61
	30–34	29
	35–44	27
	45–54	15
	55 and over	13
	Total	404

1 (a) How many marriages were there altogether in 1977?
(b) How many boys under 18 were married?
(c) How many girls under 18 were married?
(d) What was the most popular age to get married for boys and for girls?
(e) Do you think that the man is generally older than the woman in a marriage? How is this shown in the figures?

2 A girl is now 15 years old.
(a) What is the chance that she will marry while under 21, assuming that she will marry?
(b) What is the chance that she will marry when over 30?
(c) A boy is 15 years old now. What is the chance that he will marry under 21, assuming that he gets married sometime?
(d) What is the chance that a man who marries is over 25 years old?

3 If you find this data interesting you can find a lot more information to study in the *Annual Survey of Statistics* published each year by HMSO. Your public library will certainly have a number of copies.

Unit M12 Angles

12·1 Angles at a point

If you face in one direction, then turn until you are back facing the same direction again, you will turn through 360°. This fact may be stated as:

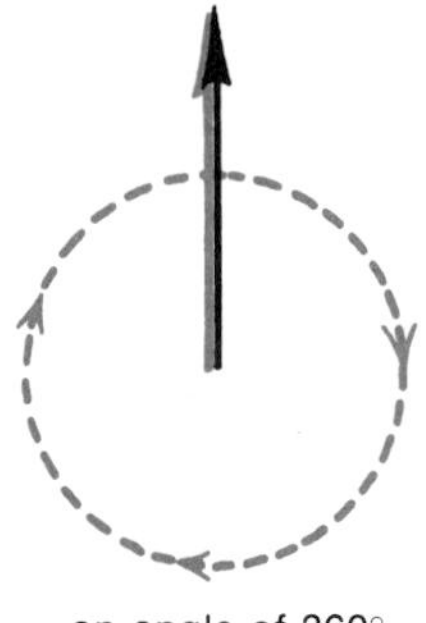
an angle of 360°

The angles at a point add up to 360°

It is possible to turn clockwise ↻, the same way as the hands of a clock, or anticlockwise ↺, opposite to the hands of a clock.*
It follows that:

1 The angle on a straight line is 180°

2 A right angle, made by dividing the complete turn into four equal parts, is 90°.

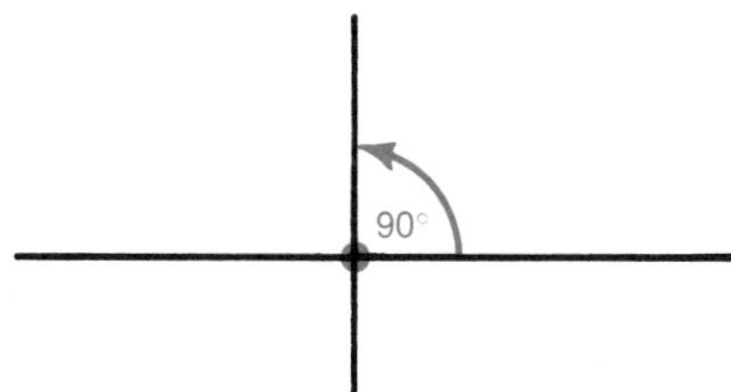

Exercise 12·1

A Find the angles marked $x°$.

1

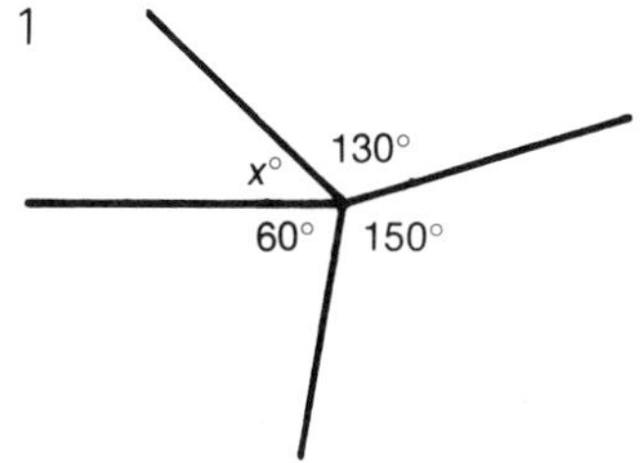

2

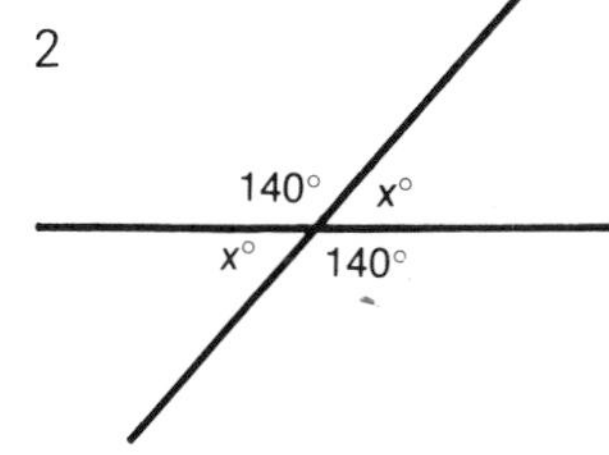

3

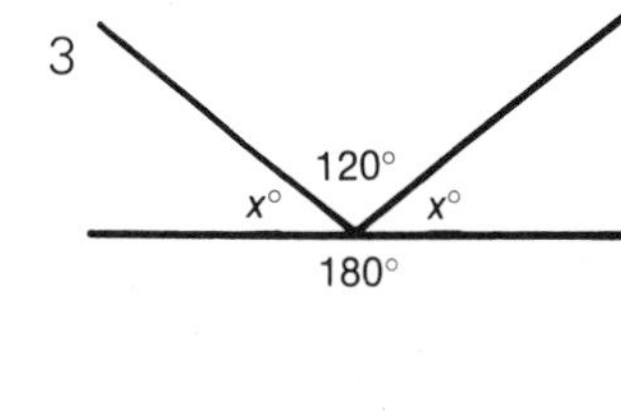

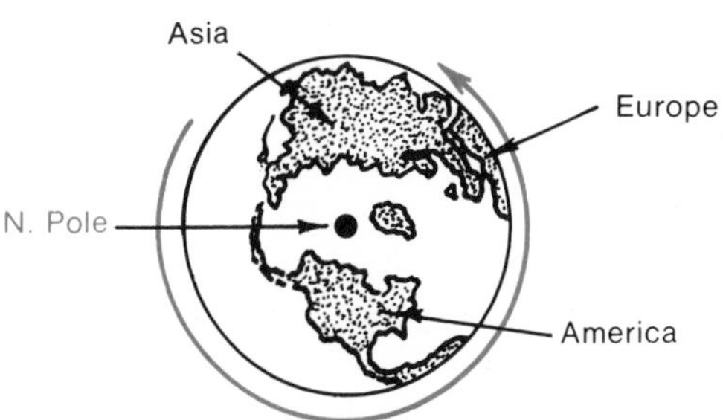

* If you were standing at the North Pole, the Earth would turn *anticlockwise* beneath your feet. What would happen at the South Pole?

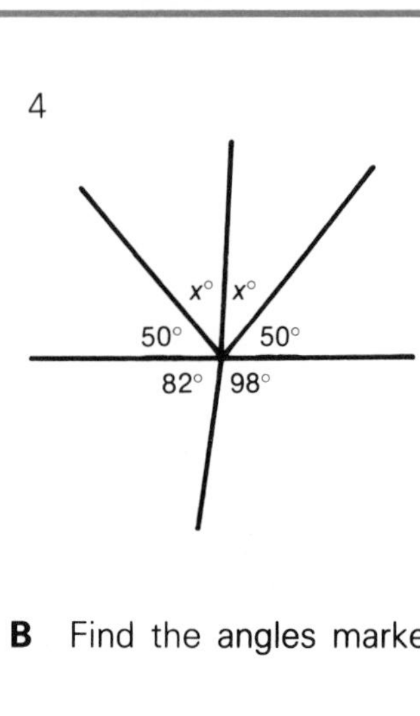

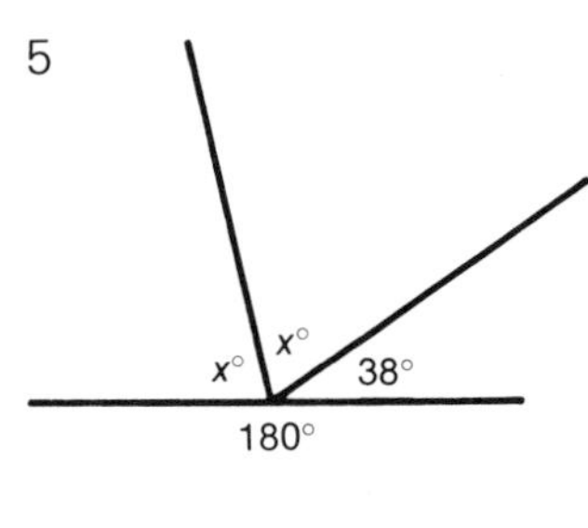

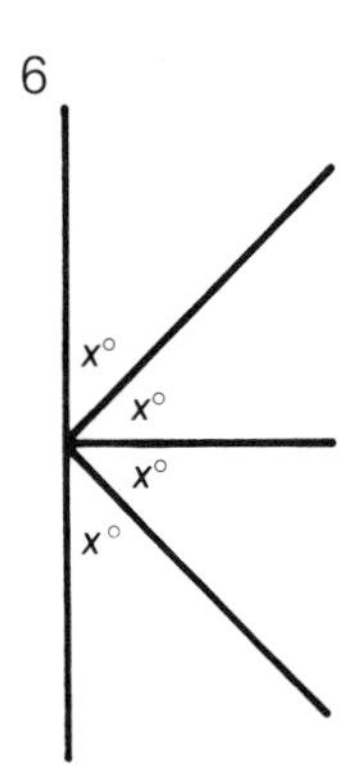

B Find the angles marked $x°$ in each diagram.

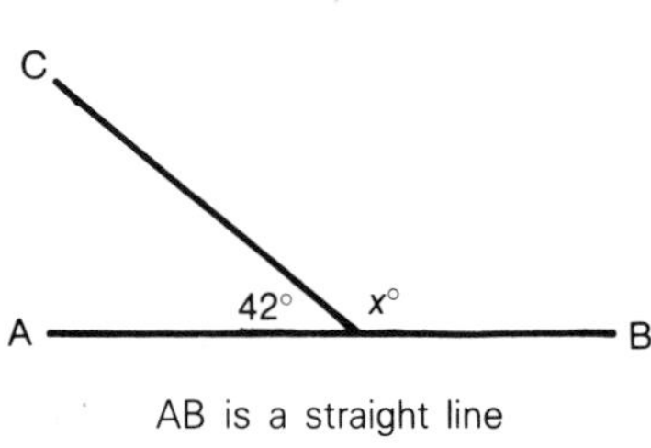

AB is a straight line

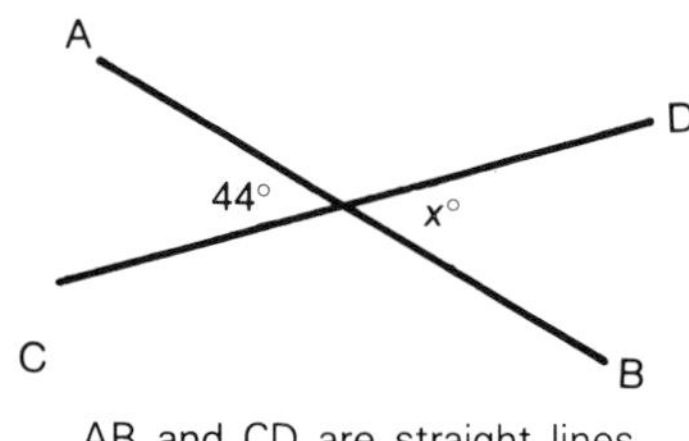

AB and CD are straight lines

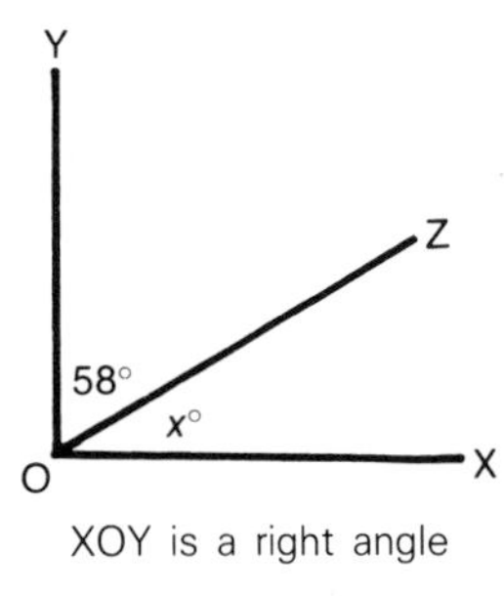

XOY is a right angle

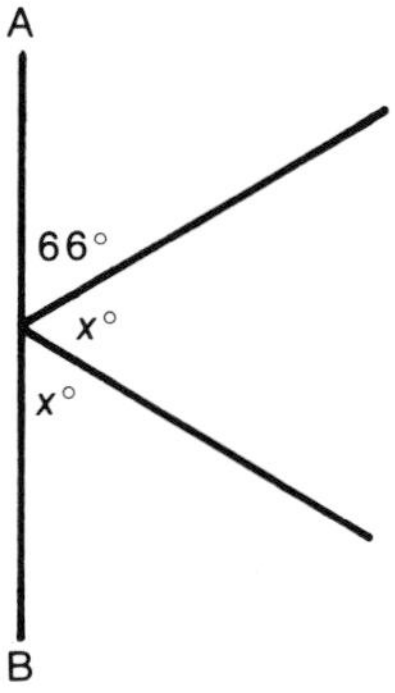

AB is a straight line

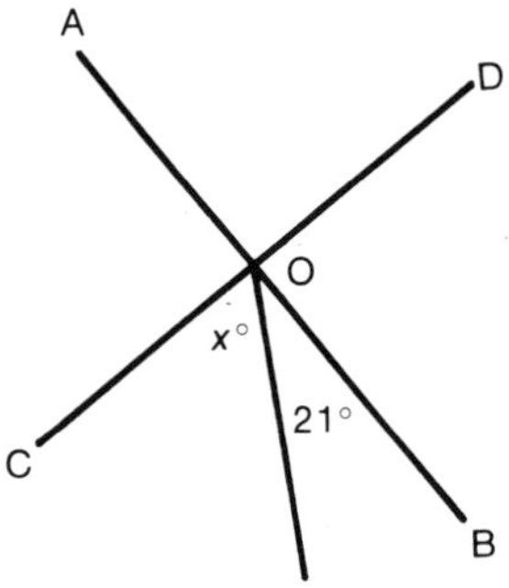

AB, CD are straight lines
AOD is a right angle

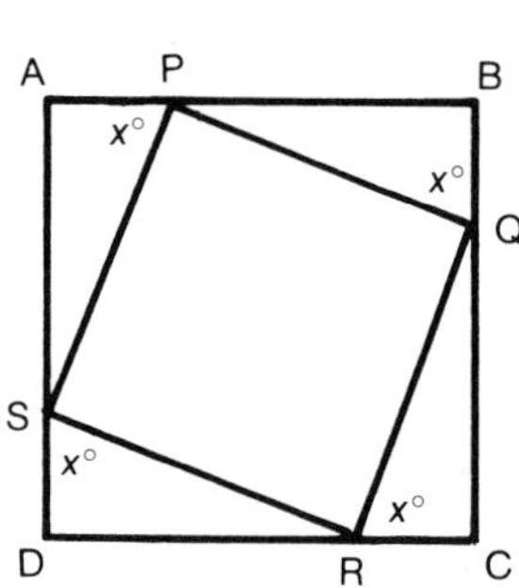

ABCD is a square
PQRS is a square

C These questions refer to the figure on the right.

1 Which of the lines AOD, FOC, BOE is a straight line? (One is slightly bent at O.)

2 Which line will I end up looking along if I start each time looking along OC and then:

(a) Turn clockwise through 44°?
(b) Turn anticlockwise through 180°?
(c) Turn clockwise through 180°?
(d) Turn anticlockwise through 135°?
(e) Turn clockwise through 143°?

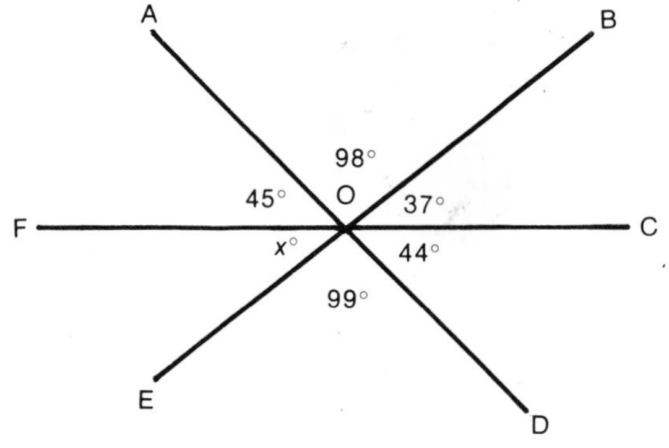

12·2 Vertically opposite angles and corresponding angles

When a pair of straight lines meet, two pairs of equal angles are formed. These pairs of equal angles are called **vertically opposite**.

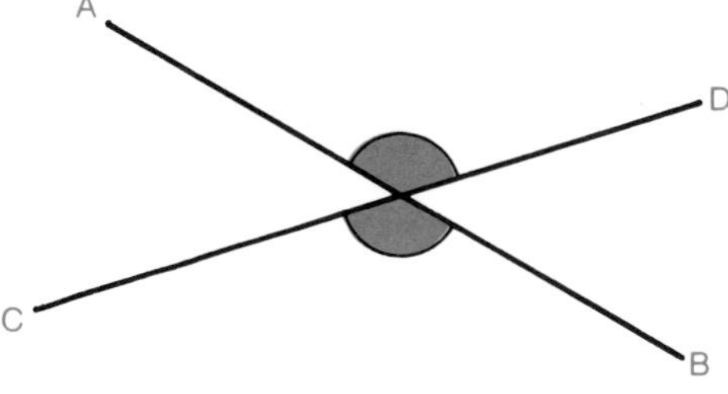

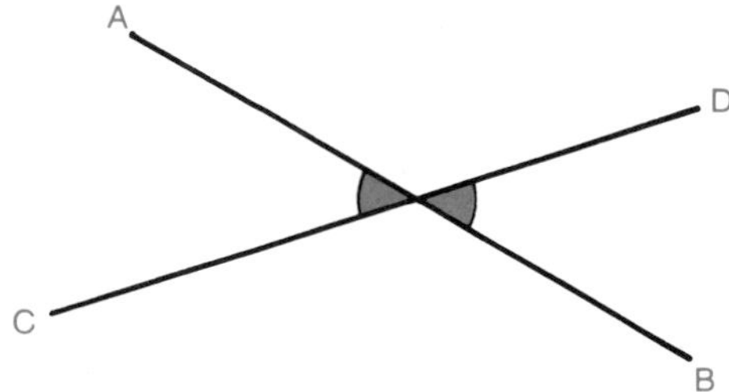

This is very easy to prove, as follows:

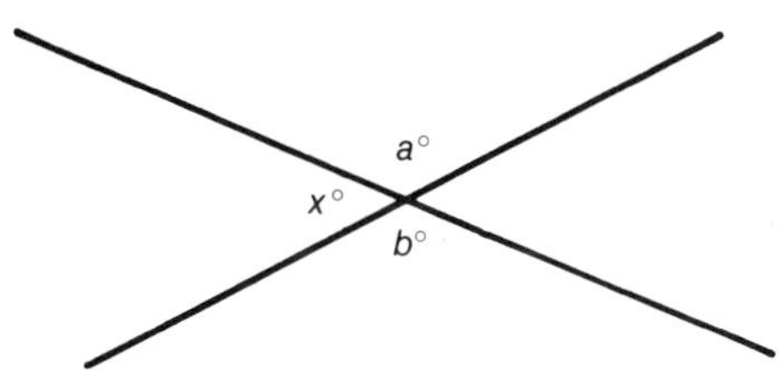

(a) $x° + a° = 180°$ (since CD is a straight line).
(b) $x° + b° = 180°$ (since AB is a straight line).
Therefore $a = b$

Note: The proof follows from the two statements about angles on a straight line and so we give details of the lines.

When a straight line cuts a pair of parallel lines, pairs of equal angles are formed.

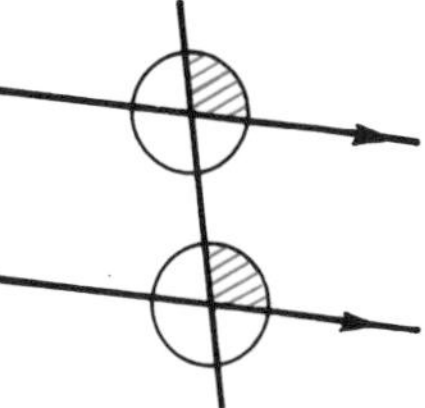

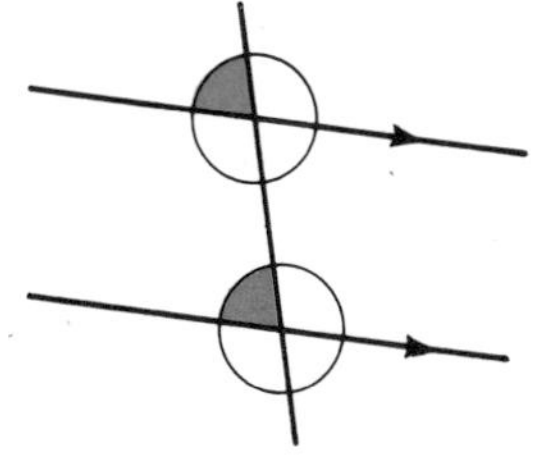

A pair of *corresponding* angles

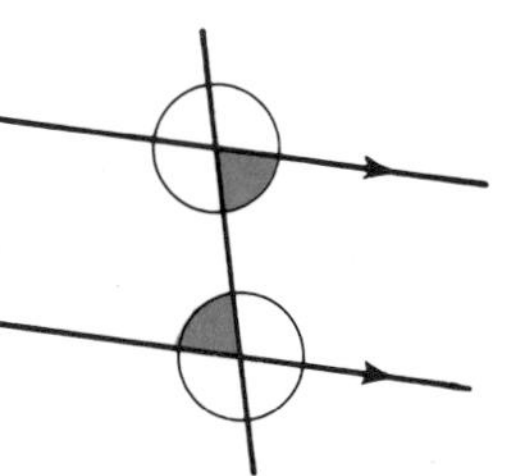

A pair of *alternate* angles

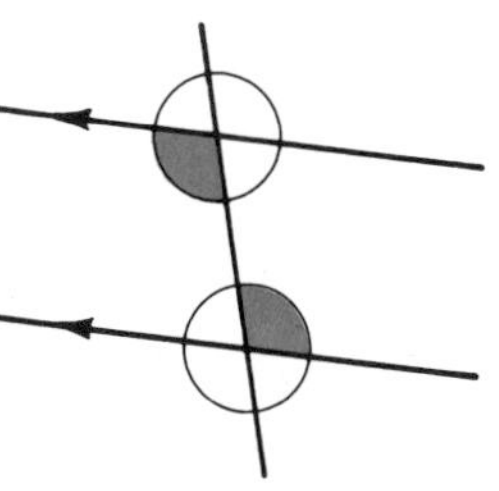

A pair of *alternate* angles

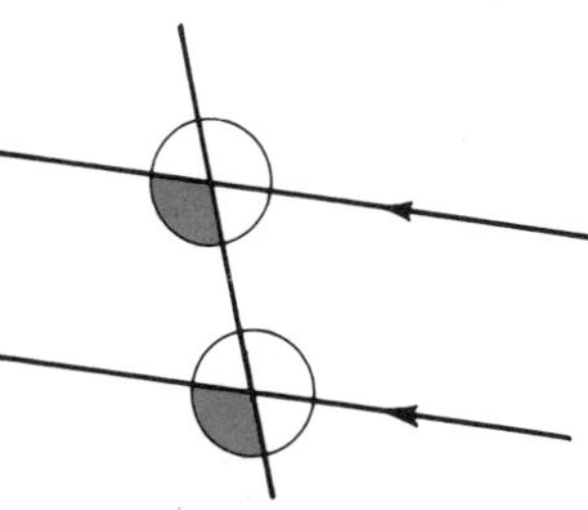

A pair of *corresponding* angles.

Exercise 12·2

A Find the angles marked $x°$. Give reasons.

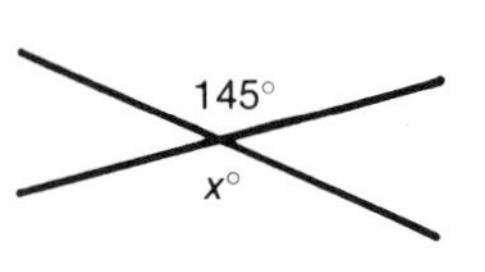

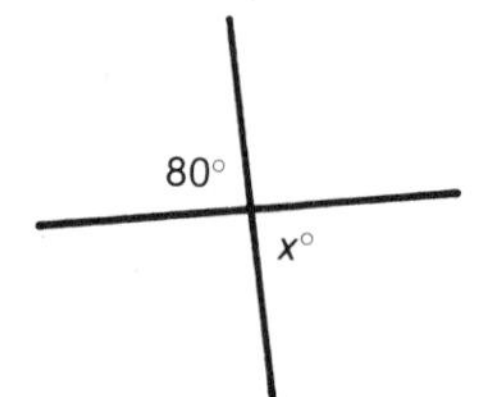

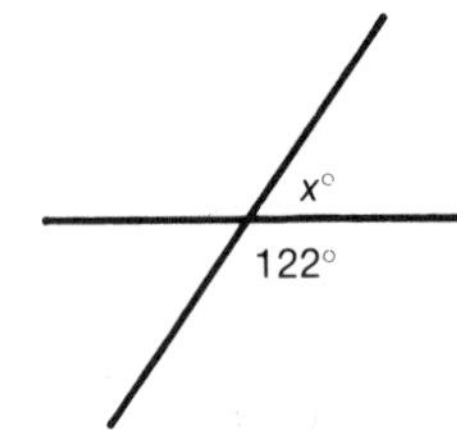

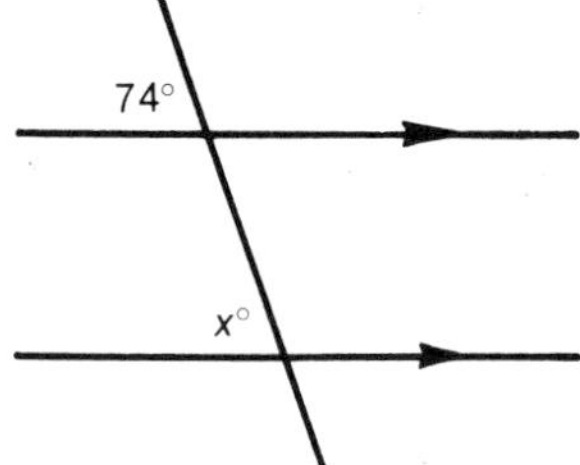

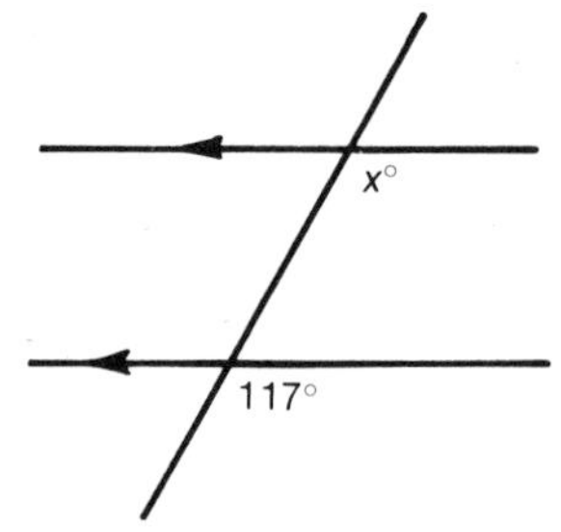

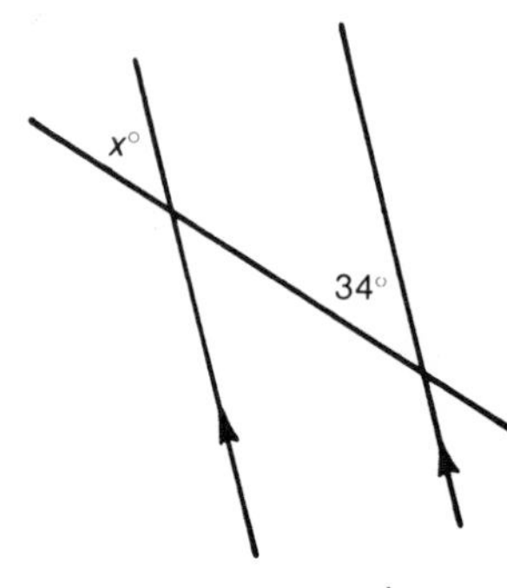

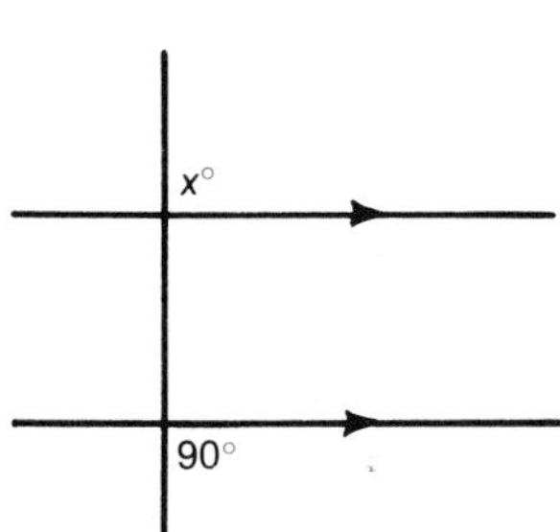

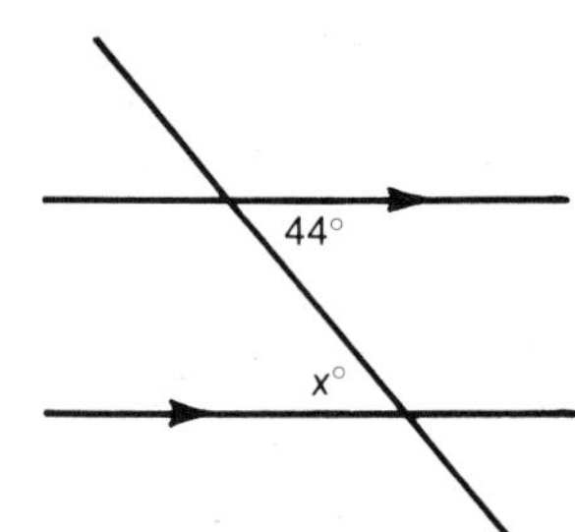

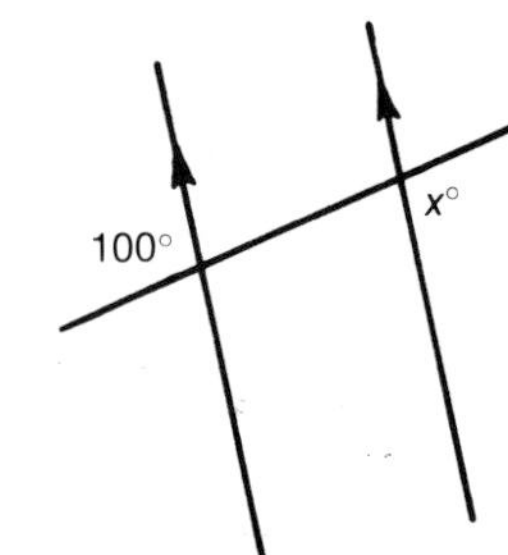

B PQRS is a *parallelogram*. $E\hat{P}A = 72°$.

1 Write down the values of:

(a) $Q\hat{P}S$ (b) $G\hat{S}A$
(c) $G\hat{S}B$ (d) $P\hat{S}Q$
(e) $H\hat{R}D$ (f) $E\hat{Q}D$
(g) $C\hat{Q}F$ (h) $F\hat{Q}R$

2 What do you notice about the *opposite angles* of the parallelogram?

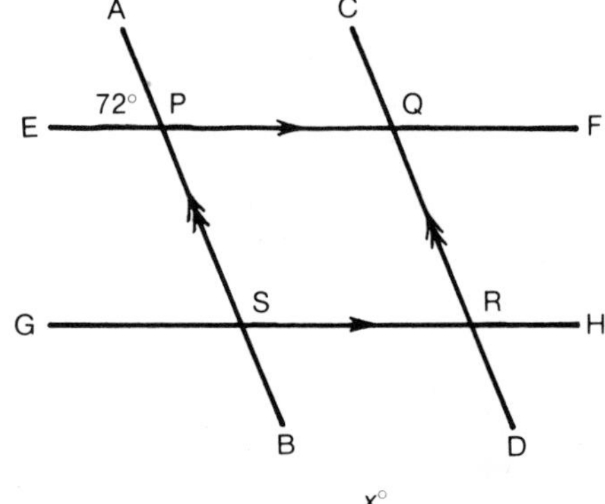

3 AB is parallel to CD.

(a) What is the value of x?
(b) What is the value of y?
(c) What is the size of $C\hat{X}D$?
(d) What is the sum of the three angles, $A\hat{X}C$, $C\hat{X}D$ and $B\hat{X}D$?
(e) What is the sum of the three angles, $C\hat{X}D$, $X\hat{D}C$ and $X\hat{C}D$?

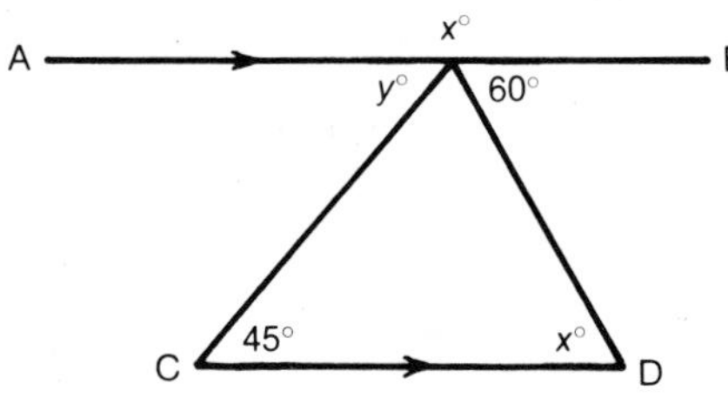

12·3 Angles in a triangle

To prove that the angles of a triangle add up to 180°:

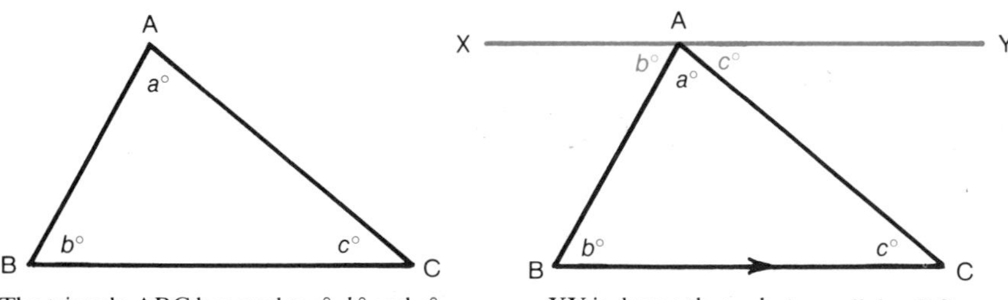

The triangle ABC has angles $a°$, $b°$ and $c°$. XY is drawn through A parallel to BC.

We can now see that $a + b + c = 180°$, because XY is a straight line. (We drew it!)

We did not say what a, b and c were, so the *result is true for all triangles*.

To prove that the exterior angle of a triangle equals the sum of the opposite interior angles.

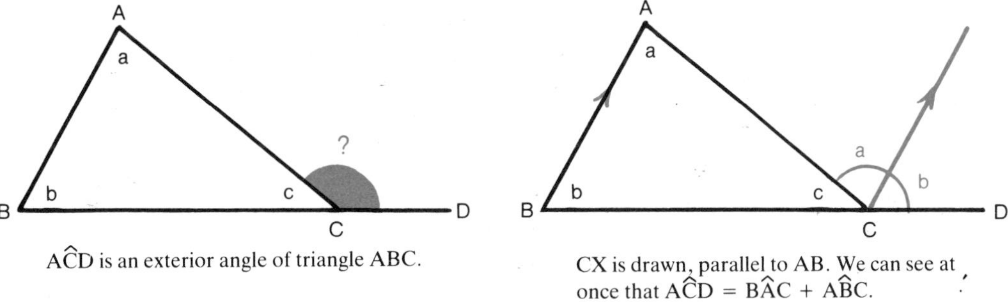

$A\hat{C}D$ is an exterior angle of triangle ABC.

CX is drawn, parallel to AB. We can see at once that $A\hat{C}D = B\hat{A}C + A\hat{B}C$.

We did not say what a, b and c were, so *the result is true for all triangles*.

Both of the above results show up clearly if you make a tessellation.

(a) Every triangle's angles add to 180° $(a + b + c)$.
(b) Every external angle of the triangle equals the sum of two opposite internal angles.
(c) The opposite angles of each parallelogram are the same.
(d) In a parallelogram, pairs of adjacent angles add up to 180° $(a + b + c)$.

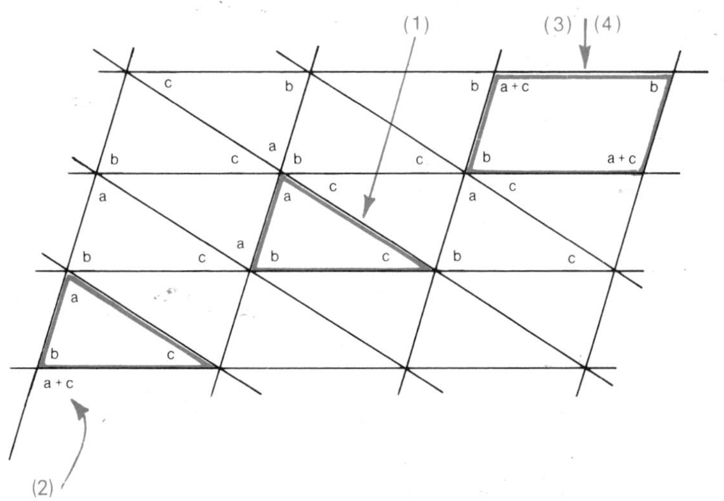

Exercise 12·3

A Calculate the values of the angles marked ? in these triangles.

1(a)

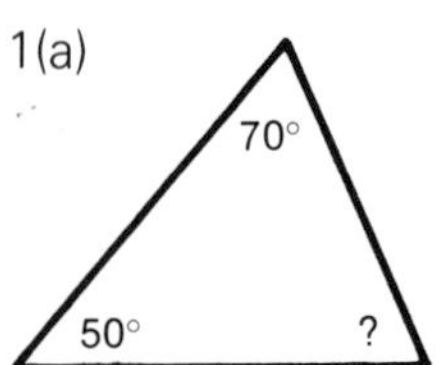

(b)

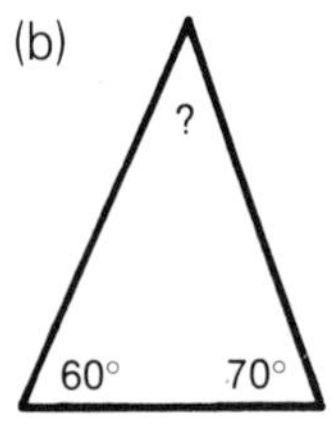

(c)

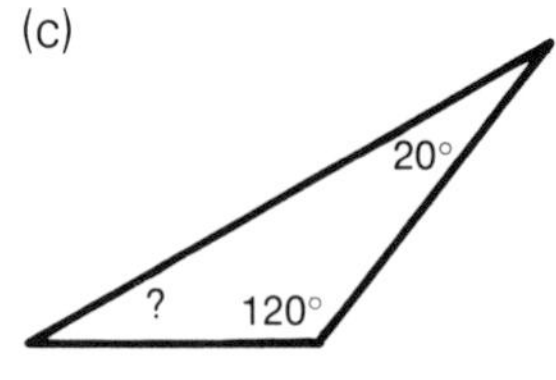

(d)

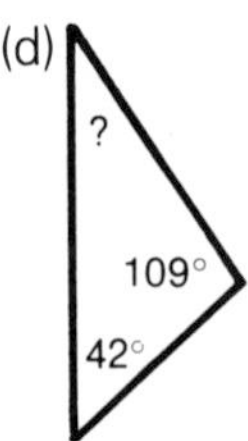

2(a)

(b)

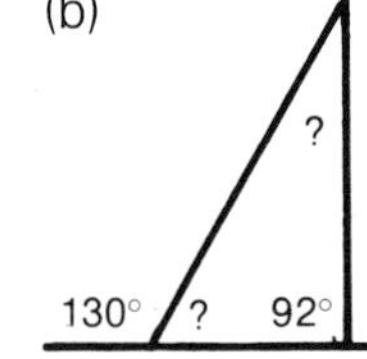

(c)

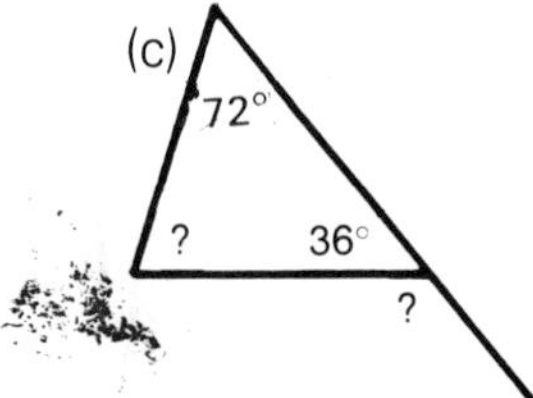

(d)

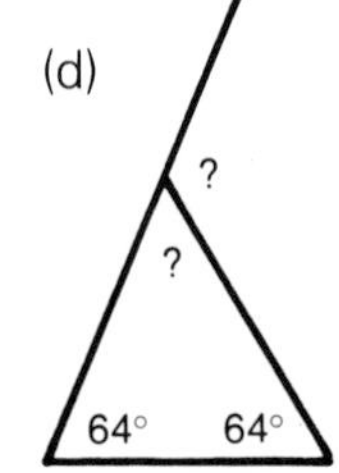

3(a)

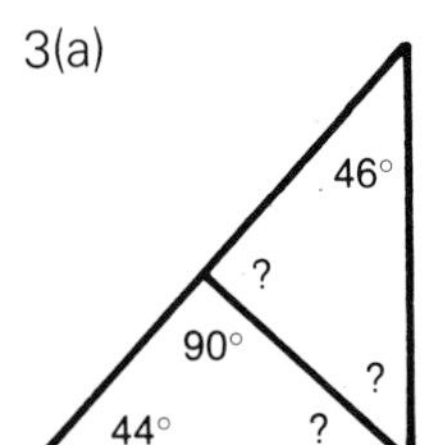

(b)

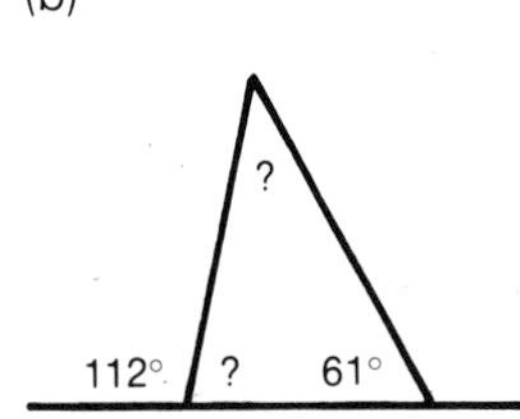

(c)

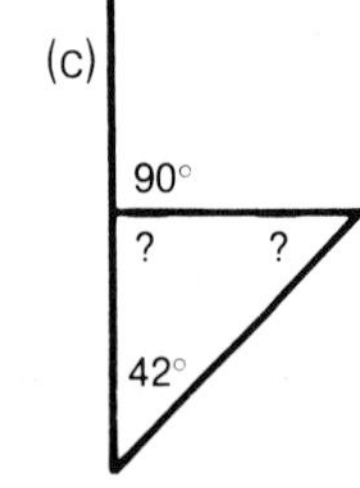

(d)

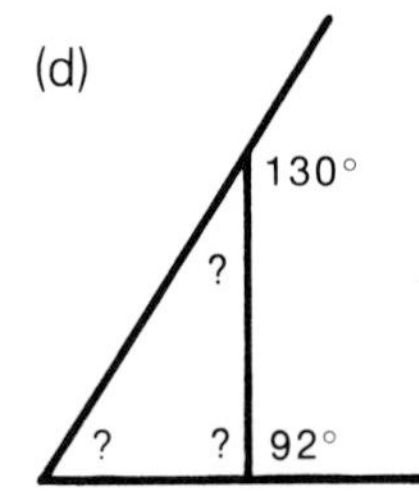

B **1** Copy this tessellation. (Draw the horizontal lines first.)

2 Mark all the angles with +, ✓, or ●.

3 Draw separately:

(a) All the **different** triangles you can see in the tessellation.

(b) All the different parallelograms you can see in the tessellation.

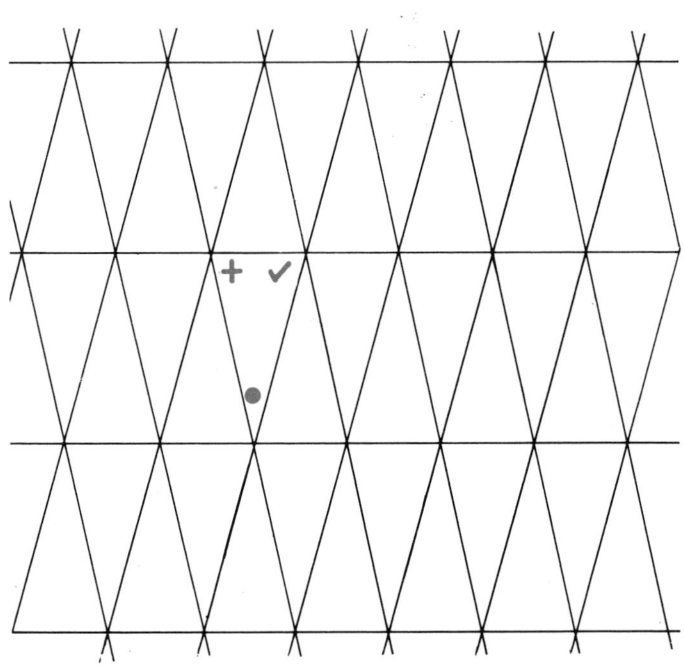

C 1 Calculate the values of the angles marked ? in these parallelograms.

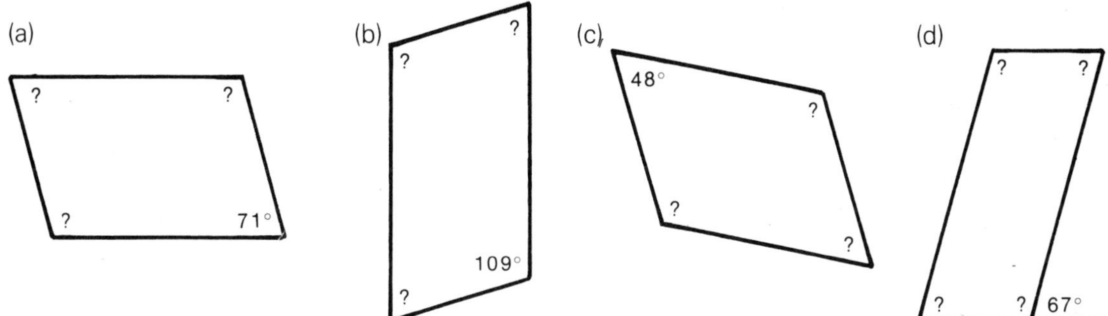

2 Which of the following quadrilaterals are parallelograms?
(Check the angles.)

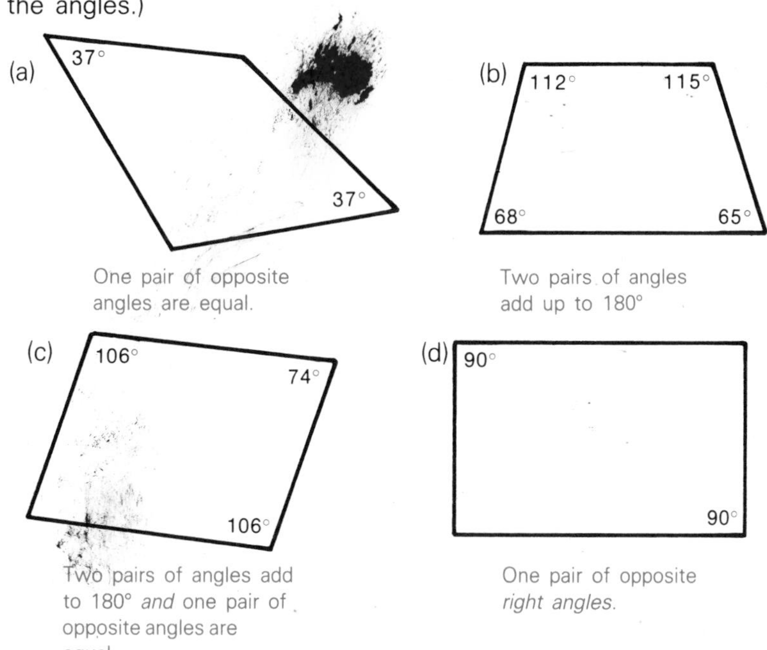

3 Calculate the values of the angles marked ? in the figure below given that: AD is parallel to EF, AE is parallel to BF and EC is parallel to FD.

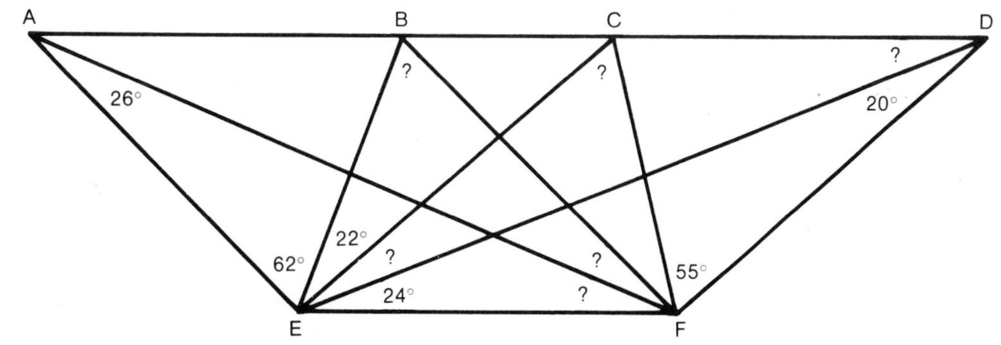

12·4 Angles in a quadrilateral

Every quadrilateral can be divided into two triangles. This means that the sum of the angles of any quadrilateral is 360°.

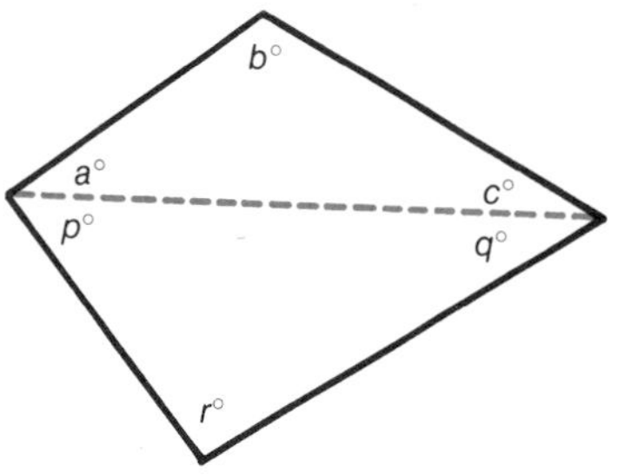

$$\begin{aligned} a + b + c &= 180^\circ \\ p + q + r &= 180^\circ \\ \hline a + b + c + p + q + r &= 360^\circ \end{aligned}$$

This method can be used to find the sum of the angles of any polygon. (A polygon is a closed figure with straight sides.)

A hexagon has six sides. It can be divided into four triangles. (Two less than the number of sides.)
Sum of the angles in a hexagon $= 4 \times 180^\circ = 720^\circ$

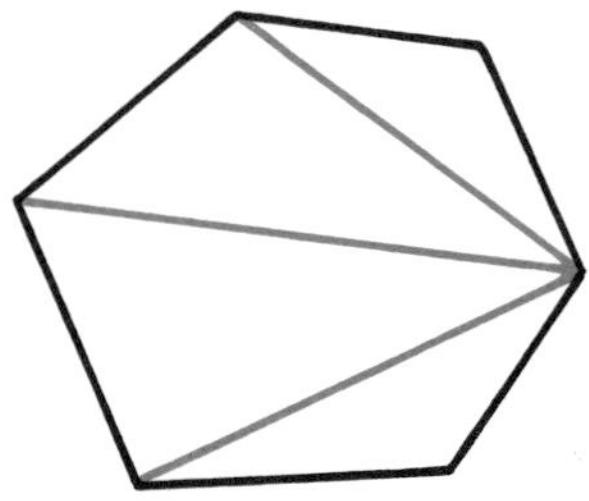

Exercise 12·4

A Use the fact that the angles of any quadrilateral add up to 360° to find the angle marked ? in the following quadrilaterals.

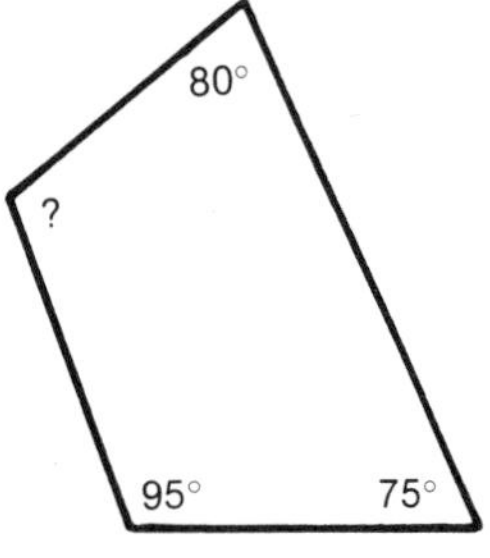

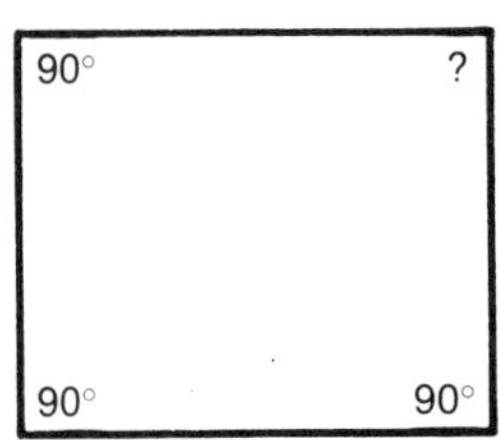

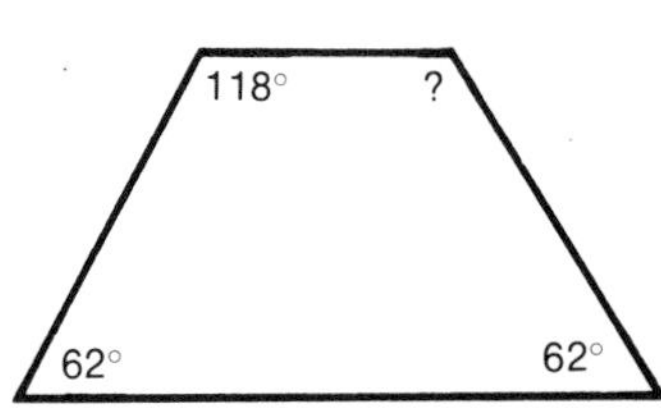

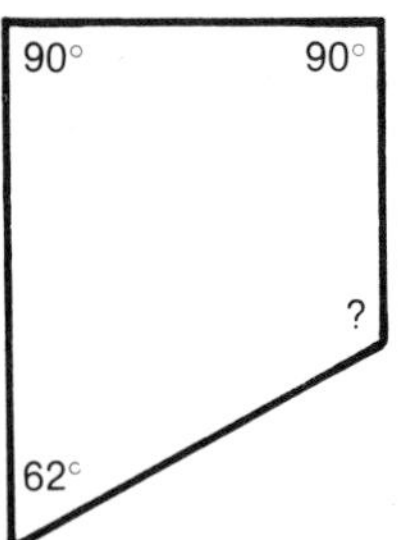

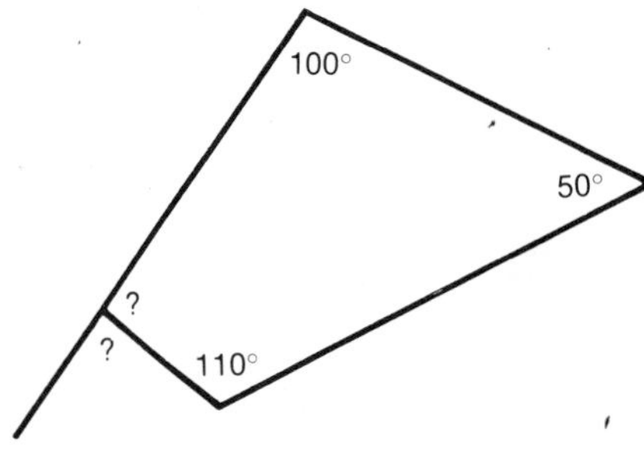

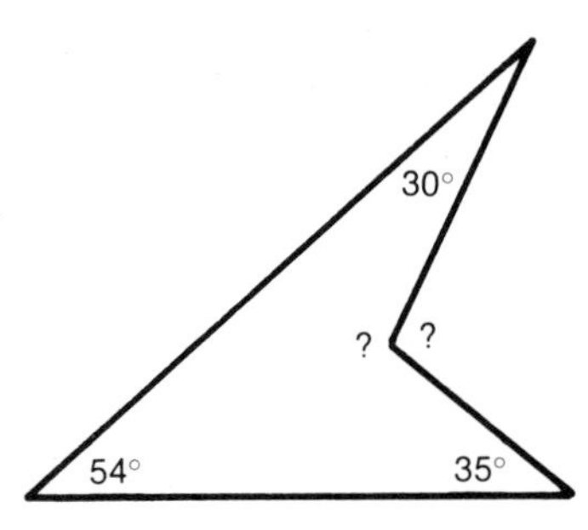

B Explain the following facts:

1. The angles of any pentagon add up to 540°... (equals 3 × 180°)
2. The angles of any hexagon add up to 720°... (equals 4 × 180°)
3. The angles of any octagon add up to 1080°... (equals 6 × 180°)
4. A regular octagon has eight equal angles. Therefore each angle must be 135°.

A regular octagon has eight equal angles and eight equal sides.

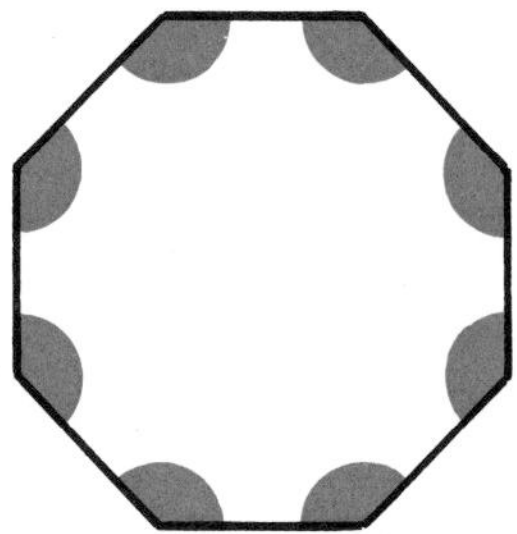

5. A figure whose sides are made of straight lines and whose angles add up to 360° can only have four sides.

C Find the value of the angles marked ? in the following figures. (Count the sides first!)

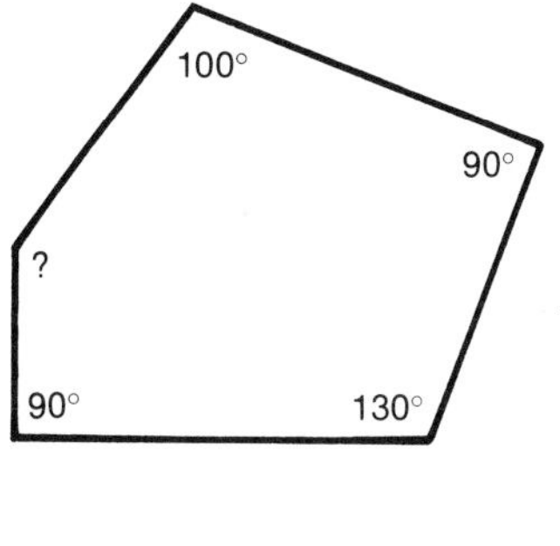

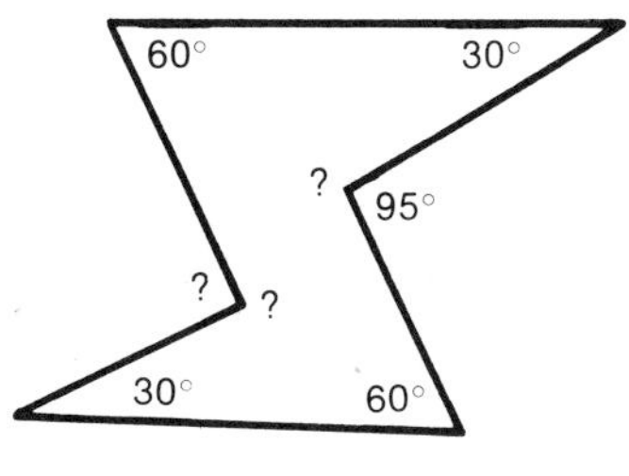

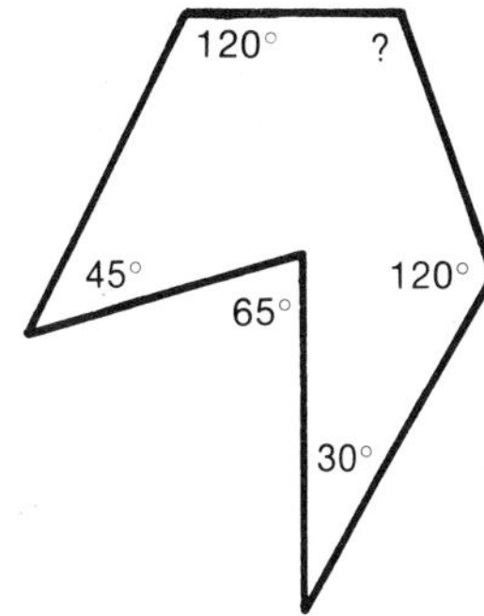

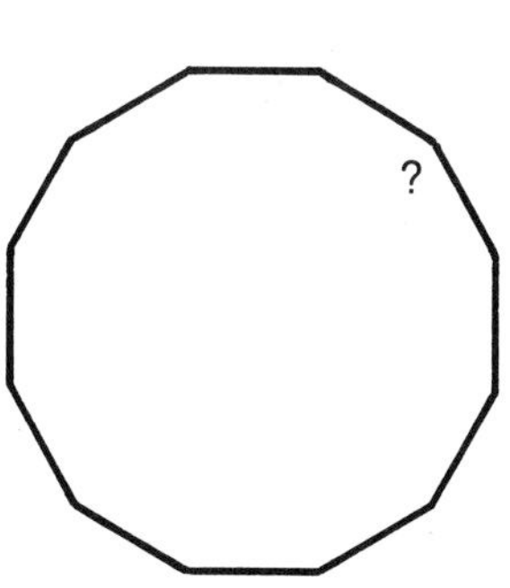

All angles equal

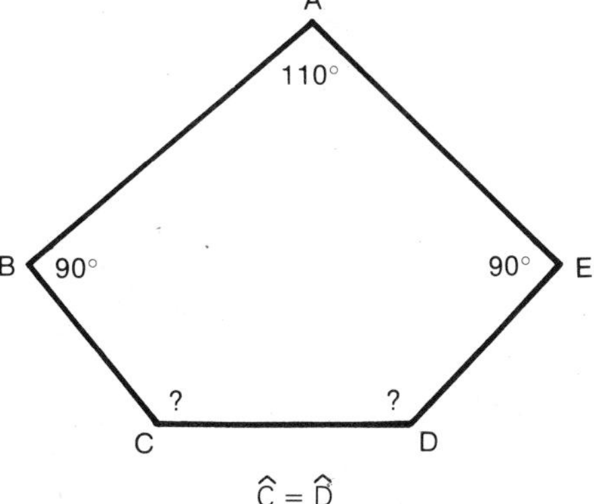

$\hat{C} = \hat{D}$

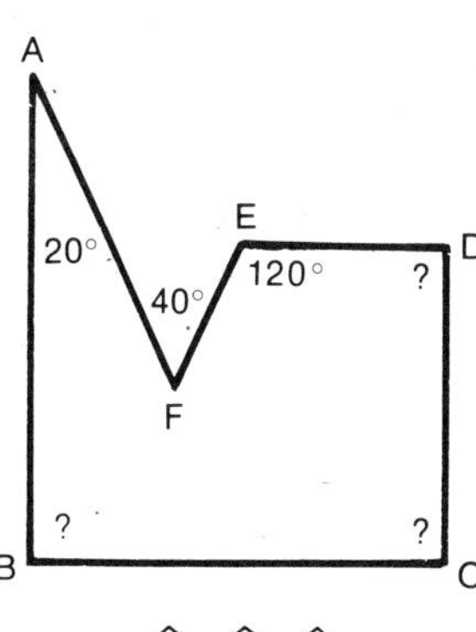

$\hat{B} = \hat{C} = \hat{D}$

12·5 Bearings

If you magnetise a needle and hang it so that it can move freely it will line itself up North/South. This is the basis of the magnetic compass

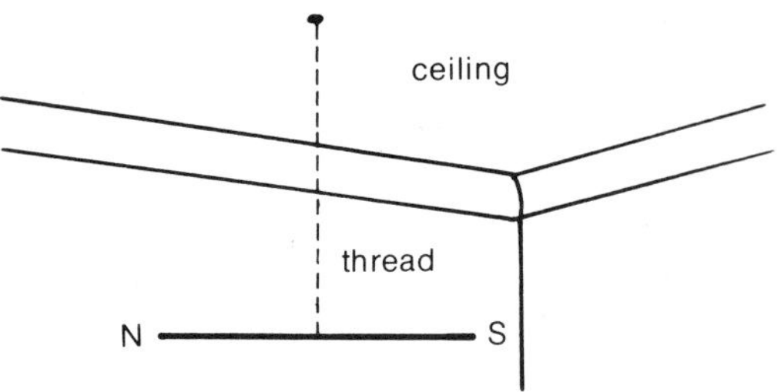

Ordinary compass: the needle is balanced on a pin.

Ships' compass: the needle is floating in oil.

Bearings are angles measured from North in a clockwise direction ↻
The angle is expressed in three figures to avoid mistakes.

Example:

The plan shows that the ship is on a bearing 040° from the lighthouse.

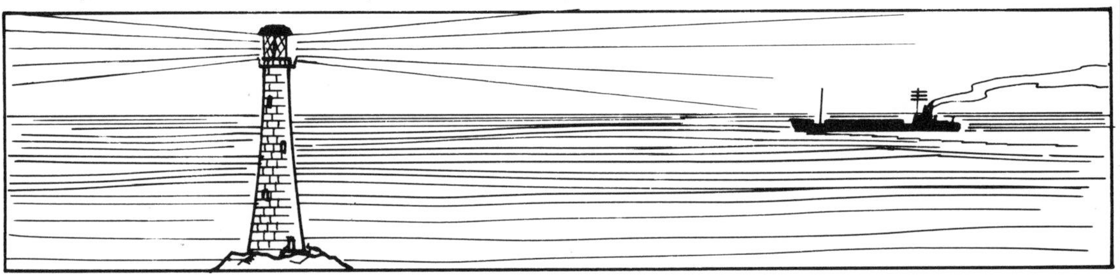

The angle between the direction of the ship and North is 40° measured **clockwise**. ↻ The ship is on a bearing of 040° from the lighthouse.

Note: The bearing depends on: (a) the position of the ship (b) where you are looking *from*.

N
W
E
S
40°
ship
lighthouse

Exercise 12·5

A Write down the bearing of B from A in the following diagrams:

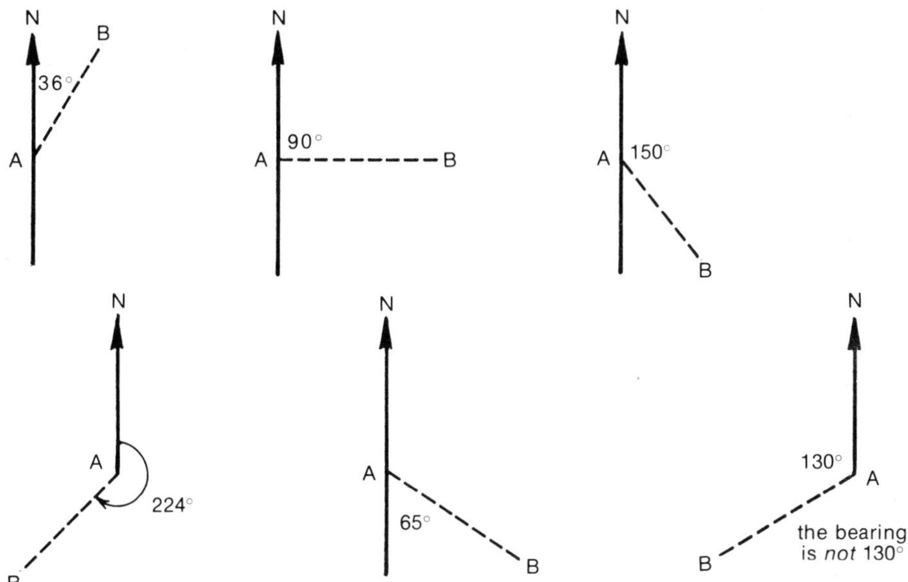

B Use a protractor* to find these bearings:

1 Lighthouse from church.
2 Pier from lighthouse.
3 Pier from sailing ship.
4 Island from sailing ship.
5 Steamer from lighthouse.
6 Steamer from sailing ship.

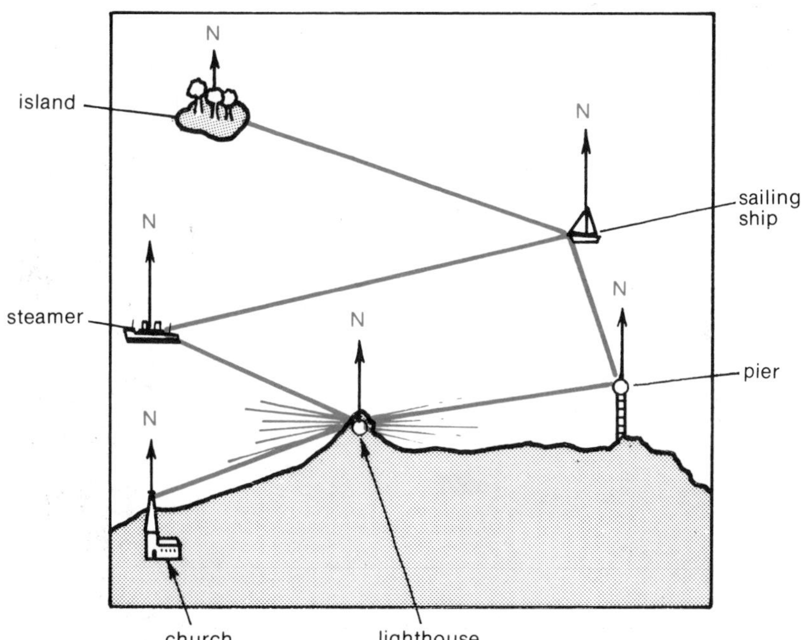

* When working with maps and bearings it is a good idea to use a 360° protractor, or to make one on a rectangle of card.

C The figure shows ships as they would appear on a radar screen. The rings correspond to distances of 10, 20, 30 and 40 km from the centre.

1. Which ship is at bearing 120° and distance 20 km?
2. What is the bearing and distance of A, B, D, E, and F from the centre?
3. Which ship is on bearing 270°?
4. If a ship on bearing 065° is 25 km from the centre, what is the nearest ship to it, out of A, B, C and D?
5. Copy the diagram and mark in ships: X at 155°, 32 km; Y at 282°, 15 km and Z at 340°, 35 km.

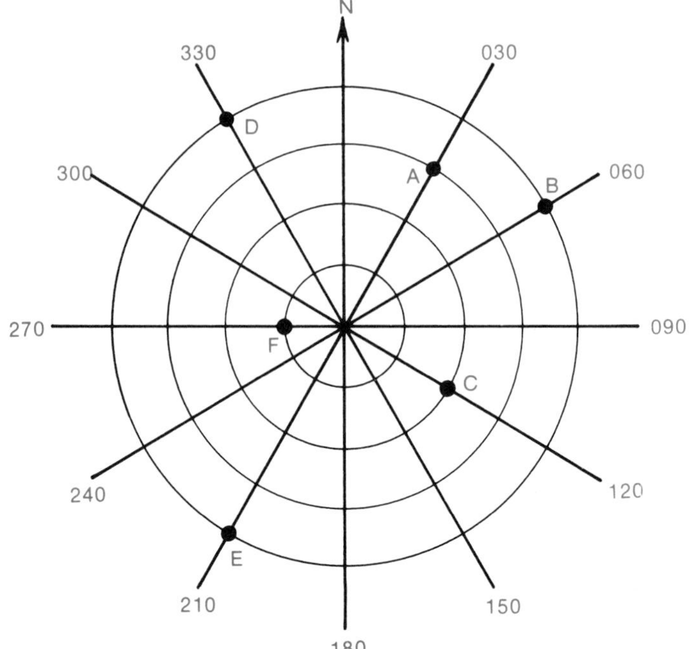

12·6 Back bearing and fixing position

If you know the bearing of B from A it is easy to find the bearing of A from B. This is called back bearing. Back bearings can then be used to fix position (i.e. find out where you are at sea when you can see landmarks such as lighthouses, church steeples or oil rigs.)

Example 1:

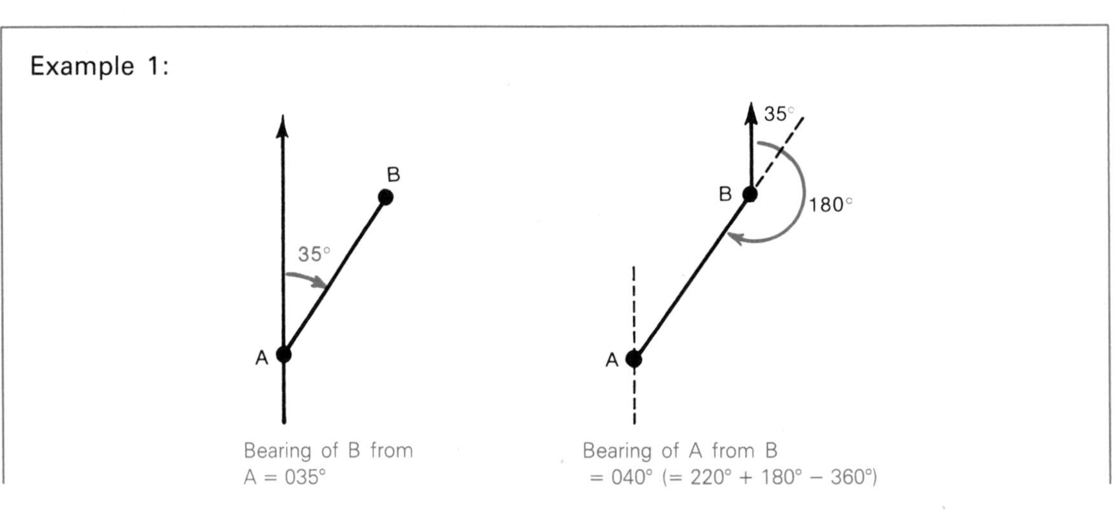

Bearing of B from A = 035°

Bearing of A from B = 040° (= 220° + 180° − 360°)

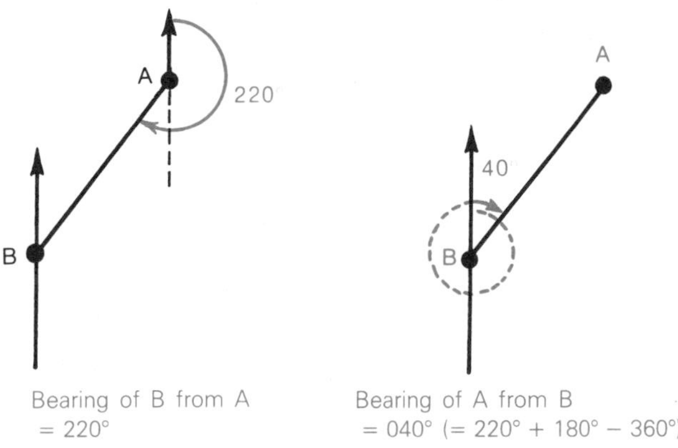

Bearing of B from A
= 220°

Bearing of A from B
= 040° (= 220° + 180° − 360°)

To find the back bearing, add 180° then subtract 360° if you can.
You should always look at the figure carefully when finding a back bearing. Make sure your answer agrees with common-sense.

Example 3:

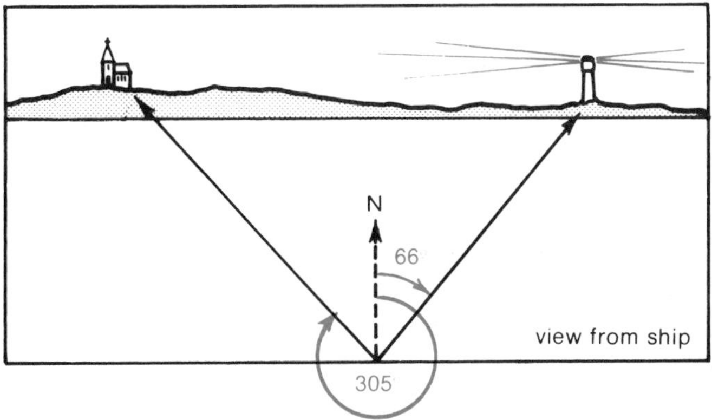

Question
The bearings to a church and lighthouse from a ship off the coast are 305° and 066°. Find the position of the ship.

1. Back bearings are:
   305° + 180° − 360° = 125°
   from the church and
   066° + 180° = 246°
   from the lighthouse.
2. Draw lines along the back bearings from church and lighthouse.
3. Position of ship is where the two back bearing lines meet.

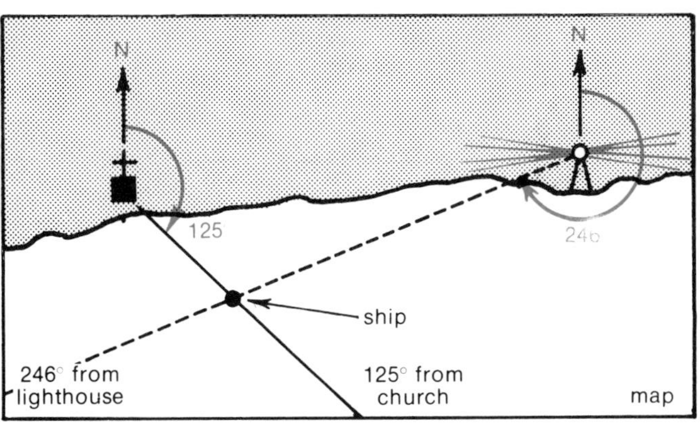

Exercise 12·6

A **1** An aircraft appears on bearing 120° from the control tower of an airport. What is the bearing of the control tower from the aircraft?

2 Find the back bearing if the bearing of B from A is:
(a) 040° (b) 130° (c) 170° (d) 226° (e) 345°
Make a sketch showing bearing and back bearing in each case.

B **1** An aircraft is being navigated using bearings to radio beacons X and Y (100 km apart and with Y due East of X). The navigator finds that the bearing of X is 330°, while the bearing of Y is 050°. Find, by careful drawing:
(a) the position of the aircraft
(b) the distance of the aircraft from X
(c) the distance of the aircraft from Y
(d) the distance of the aircraft from the base-line XY.

2 Describe my position (roughly) if:
(a) The bearing of Cambridge is 040° and the bearing of Oxford is 270°.
(b) The bearing of Brighton is 180° and the bearing of London is 000°.
(c) The bearing of Cambridge is 035° and the bearing of London is 050°.
(d) The bearing of Oxford is 290° and the bearing of Brighton is 200°.

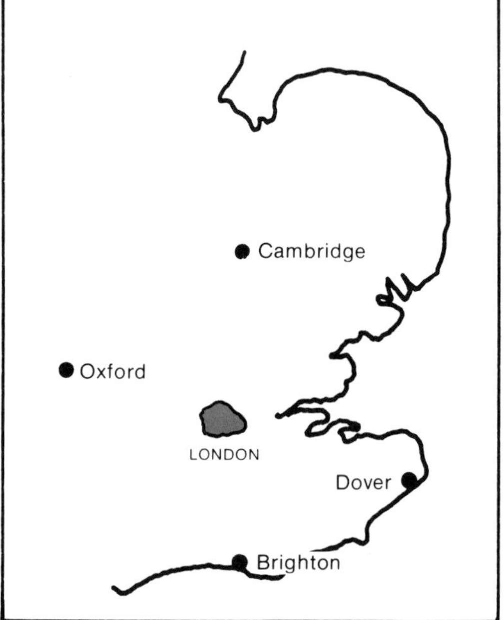

C Navigation of ships and aircraft usually depends on radio signals. Find out all you can about navigation from the school library, and write a report.

Unit M13 Similarity

13·1 Similar triangles

(a) Triangles which have the same shape are called **similar**. If they have the same size as well, they are called **congruent**.
(b) If △ABC is similar to △PQR, the angles of △ABC will be the same as the angles of △PQR.

Example:

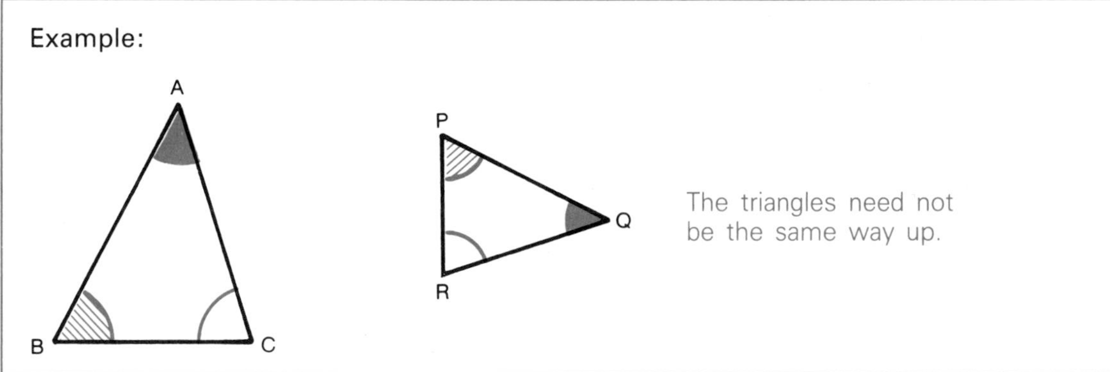

(c) In a pair of similar triangles one is an enlargement of the other.
(d) If two of the angles of $\triangle ABC$ equal two of the angles of $\triangle PQR$ then the triangles are similar. (The third angles, found by subtracting the sum of the others from 180°, will be equal.)

Example:

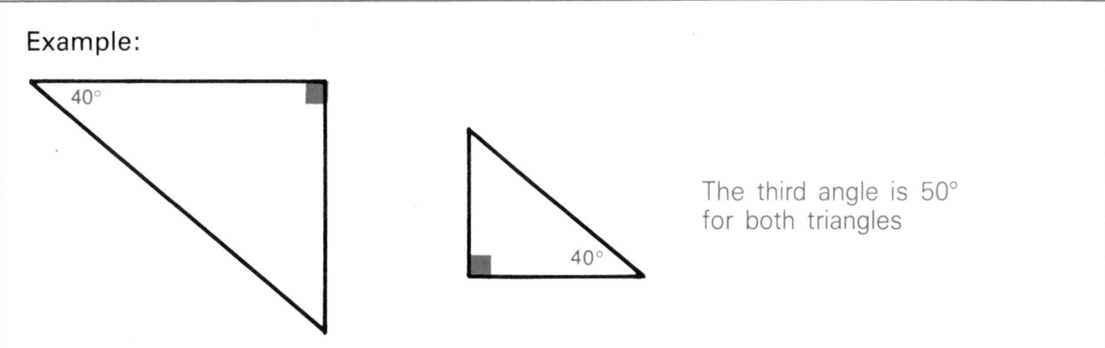

(e) Always calculate the third angles to check whether two triangles are similar.

Example:

$\triangle ABC$, $A = 35°$, $B = 70°$
$\triangle PQR$, $P = 75°$, $Q = 70°$

Subtracting from 180° shows that C = 75°, R = 35°. So the triangles are similar.

(f) If a triangle is cut by a line parallel to one of its sides, a similar triangle is produced.

Example:

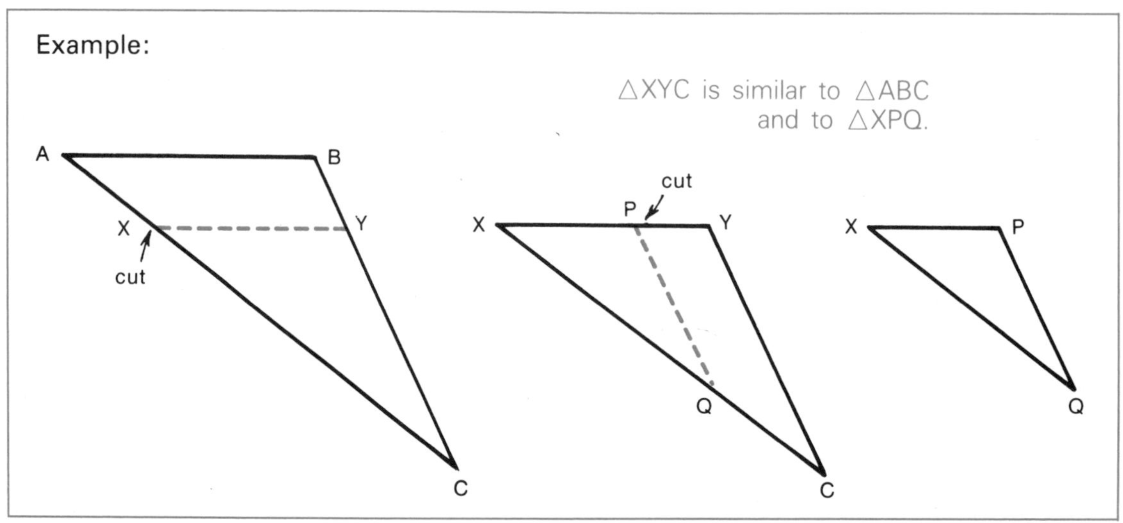

Exercise 13·1

A 1 Pick out five *pairs* of similar triangles from the twelve triangles below (∟ = 90°).

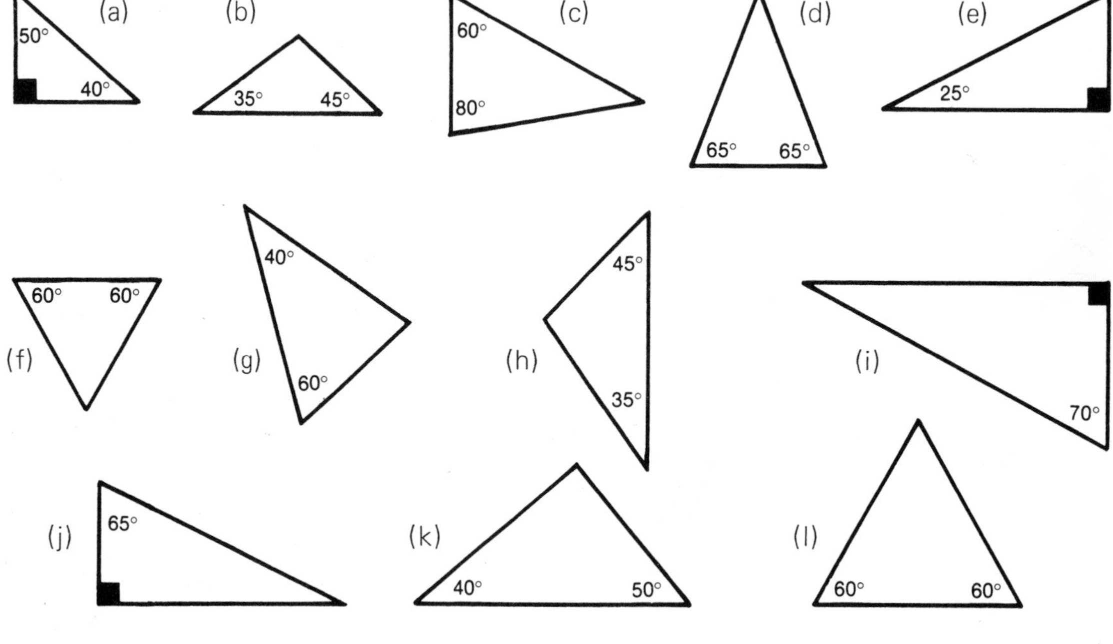

2 Calculate the angles marked ? in the figures below.

(a)

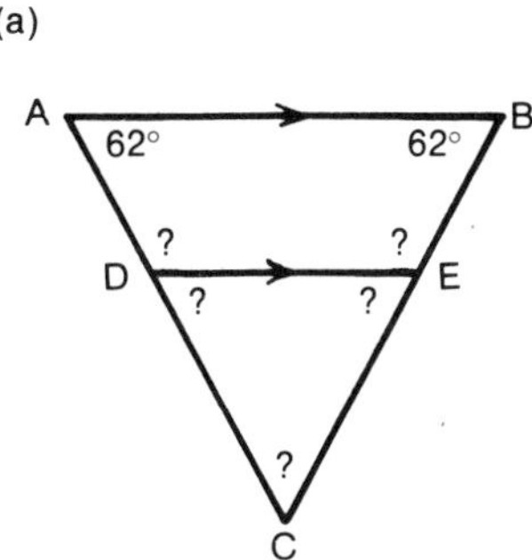

(b)

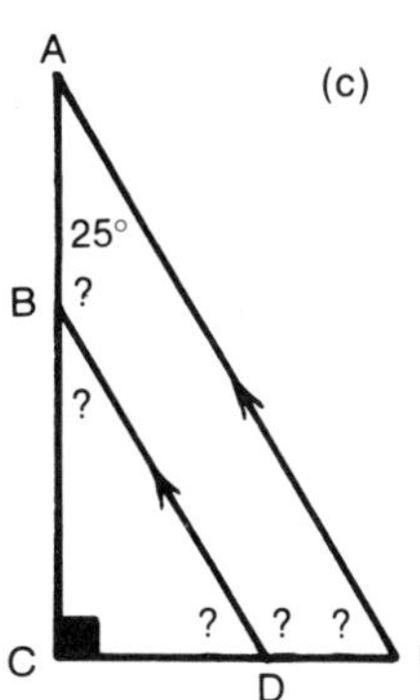

(c)

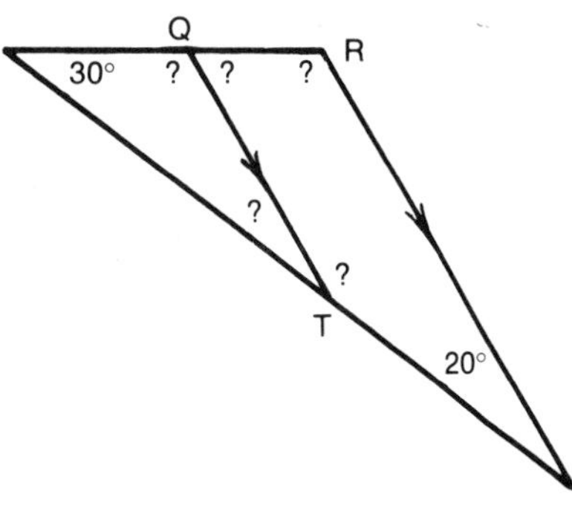

B 1 Calculate the angles marked ? in the right-angled triangles below.

(a)

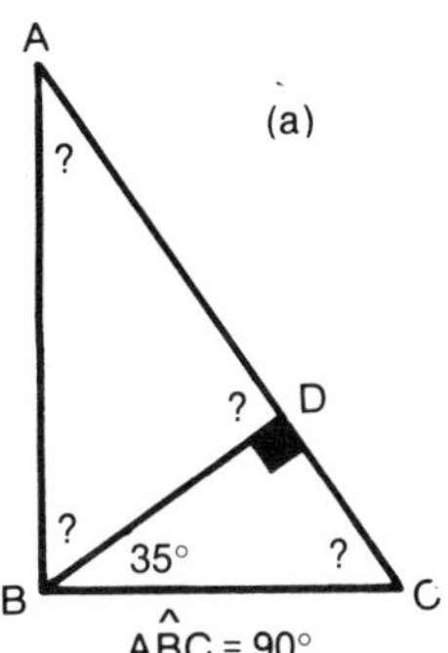

$A\hat{B}C = 90°$

(b)

$S\hat{P}Q = 90°$

(c)

$X\hat{Z}Y = 90°$

2 Make a diagram to illustrate the following fact:
In *any* right-angled triangle, when the perpendicular is drawn from the right angle to the opposite side, two right-angled triangles are formed. Both of these triangles are similar to the original triangle.

3 (a) Find $A\hat{B}D$, $D\hat{B}C$ and $B\hat{C}D$ in terms of a°
(b) Which of these statements is correct?
△ABD is similar to △ACB.
△BCD is similar to △ACB.
△ABD is similar to △BCD.

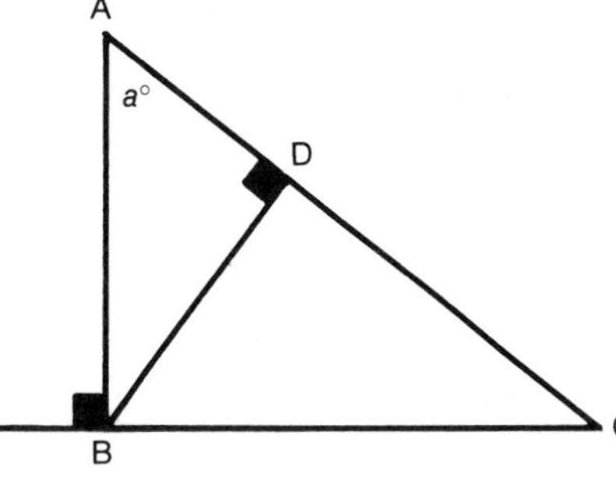

4 (a) Find all the triangles in the figure which are similar to △AXD.
(b) Find three pairs of congruent triangles in the figure.

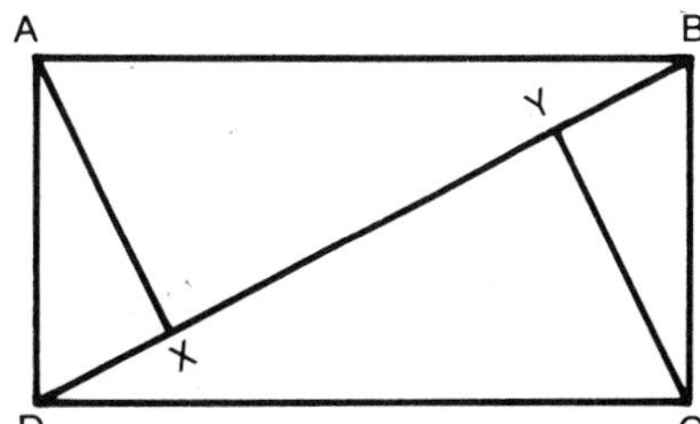

C The regular pentagon ABCDE has two different basic shapes of triangle.

1 What are the two shapes? (Give the angles.)

2 How many different sizes are there of each shape?

3 Name a triangle congruent to:

(a) △AFG (b) △AFE

(c) △BFA (d) △BGD

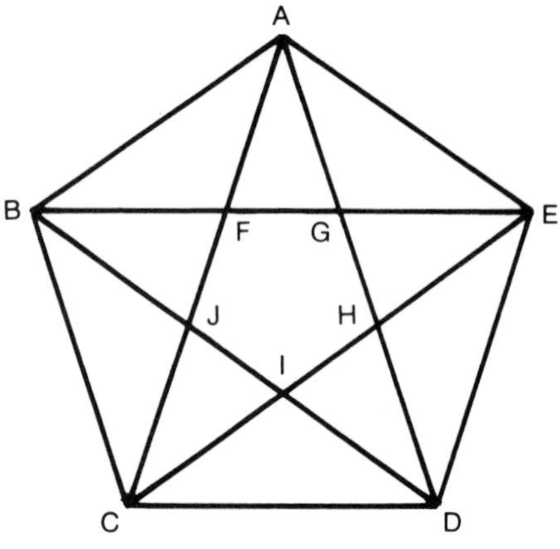

13·2 Ratios in similar triangles

When a figure is enlarged all lengths are increased in the same proportion. This can be seen by considering some examples.

Example 1:

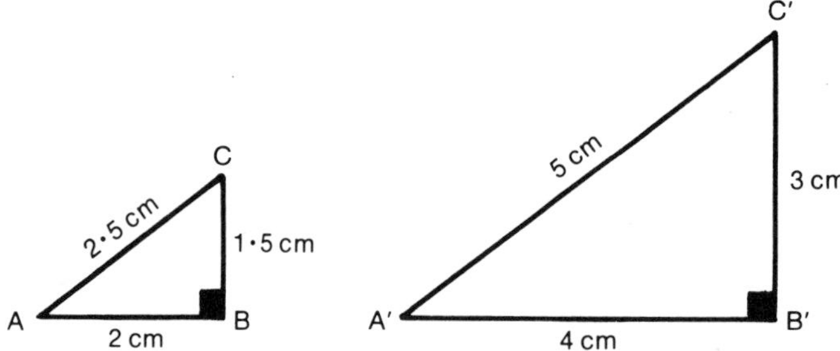

Each of the sides of △ABC is *doubled* in the enlargement.

The three ratios $\frac{A'B'}{AB}$ $\frac{A'C'}{AC}$ $\frac{B'C'}{BC}$ are the same, they all equal 2, so 2 is the scale factor of this enlargement.

Example 2:

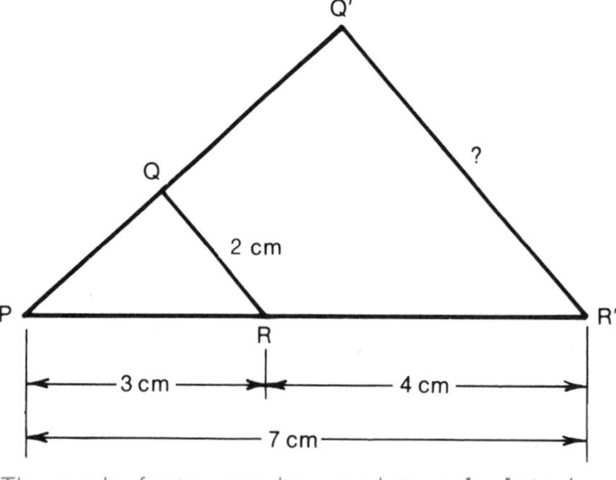

△PQR is enlarged to △PQ′R′.
PR is enlarged to PR′.
3 cm → 7 cm
The scale factor is 7/3 = 2·33

$$\frac{PQ'}{PQ} = \frac{Q'R'}{QR} = \frac{PR'}{PR} = 2{\cdot}33$$

Q′R′ = 2·33 × QR.
But QR = 2 cm from the figure
so Q′R′ = 2·33 × 2 = 4·66 cm.

The scale factor can be used to **calculate** lengths.

Exercise 13·2

A Calculate the scale factor for each of the pairs of triangles below. Calculate the length of the side marked ?.

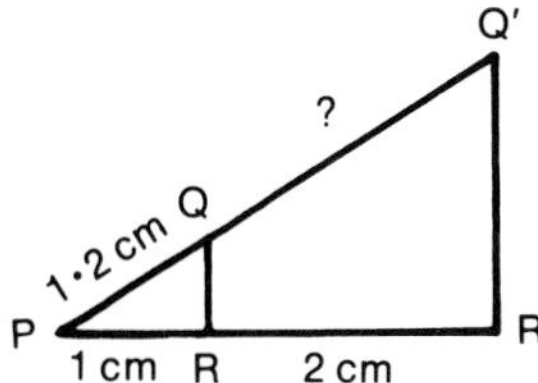

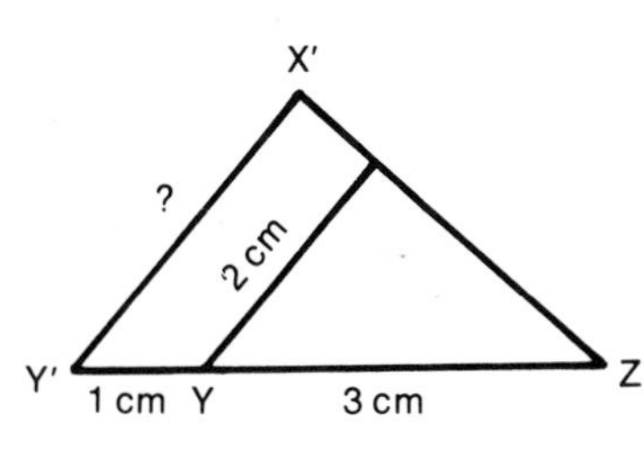

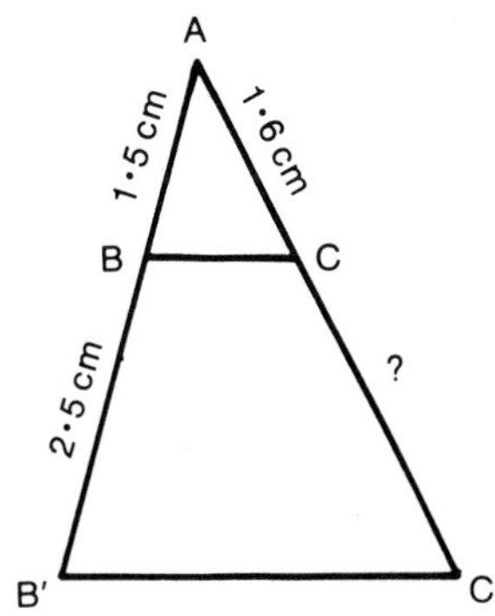

Check by measurement.

B **1** Measure the lengths AB, AC, BC, BD, AD and DC.

2 Calculate the ratios $\frac{BC}{AC}$, $\frac{AC}{DC}$ and $\frac{AB}{AD}$ from the measurements.

3 Explain your results calculated in question 2.

4 Find four other sides with equal ratios in the figure.

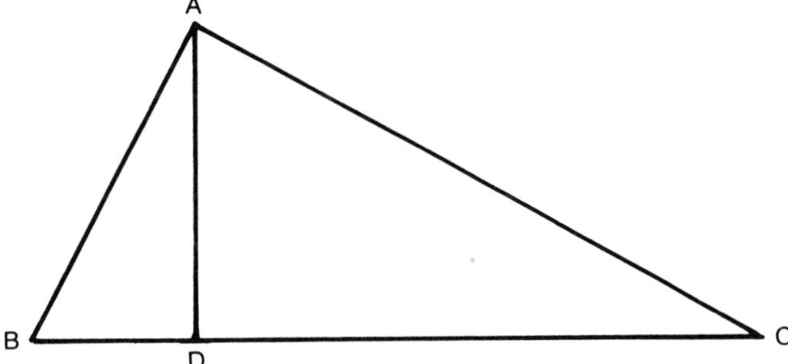

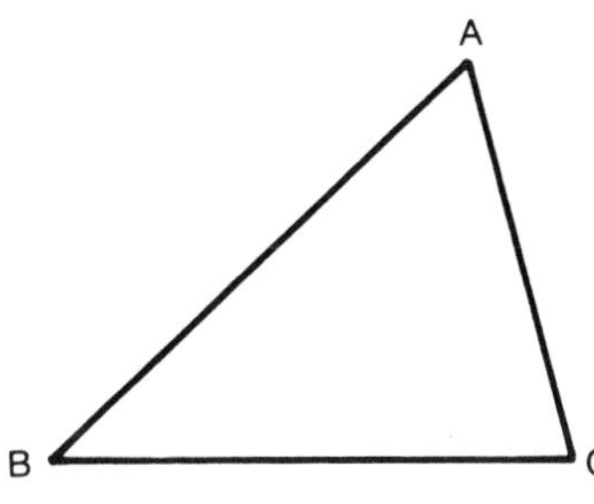

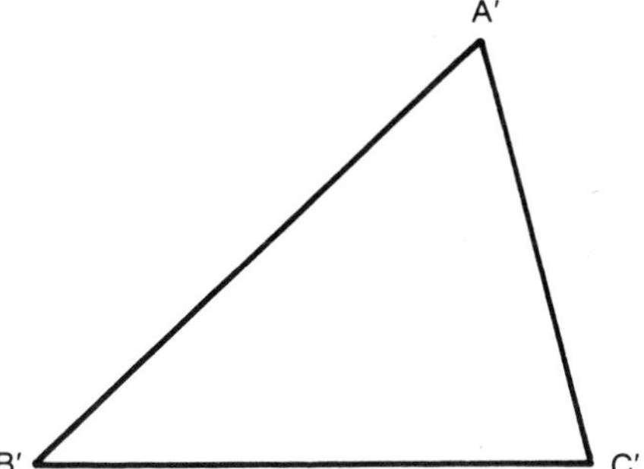

C $\triangle A'B'C'$ is similar to $\triangle ABC$.

1 Find, by measurement, the enlargement scale factor from $\triangle ABC$ to $\triangle A'B'C'$.

2 Measure AB, BC, CA and A'B', B'C', C'A' in millimetres.

3 Calculate these ratios:

(a) $\frac{AB}{AC}$ $\frac{A'B'}{A'C'}$ (b) $\frac{BC}{AC}$ $\frac{B'C'}{A'C'}$ (c) $\frac{AB}{BC}$ $\frac{A'B'}{B'C'}$

Comment on your results.

4 The three coloured triangles are all similar. Find the enlargement factor:

(a) From the small triangle to the middle sized triangle.

(b) From the middle-sized triangle to the large triangle.

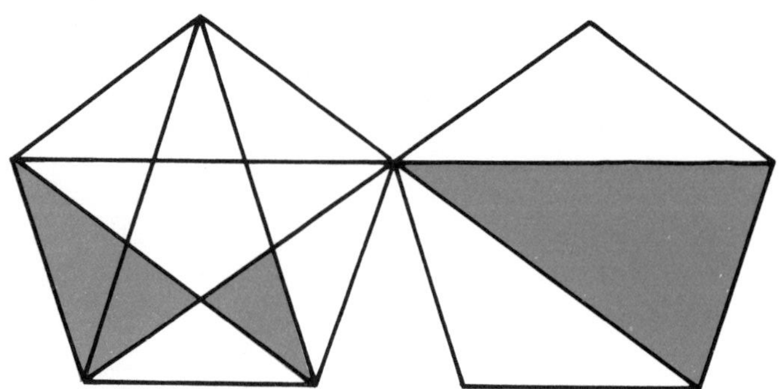

You will have to measure carefully first.

13·3 Applications

Solving problems using similar triangles

Many measuring problems can be simplified by drawing a similar triangle. Some examples are given below.

Example 1:

Finding the angle of elevation of the sun.

It is not safe to look at the sun.

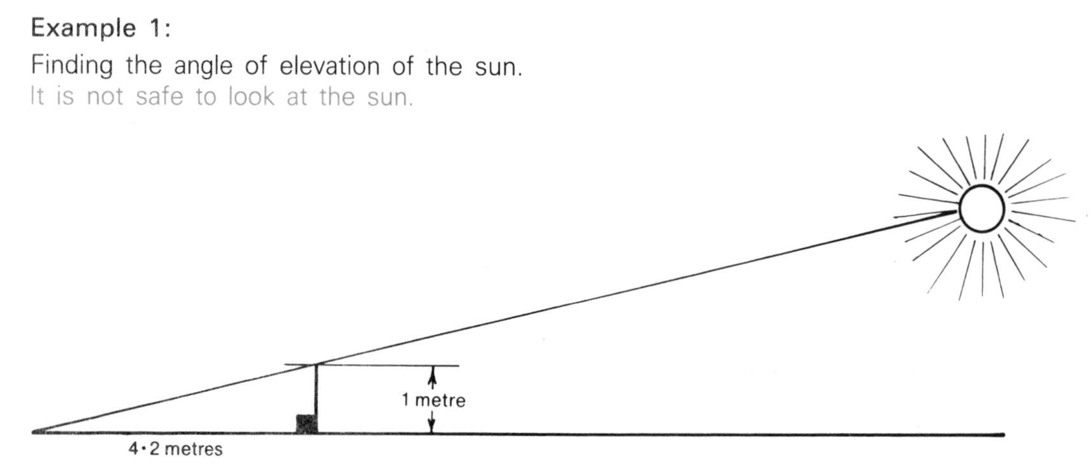

(a) Hold a 1 metre stick vertically and measure the shadow length.

(b) Now draw a similar triangle choosing a suitable scale (1 m = 2 cm).

(c) The angle can now be measured with a protractor.

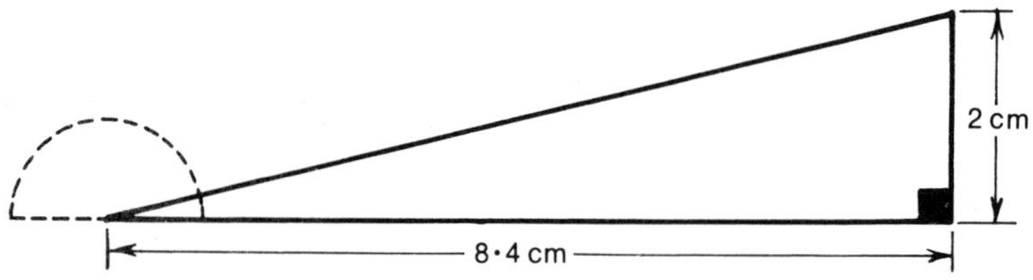

Finding the angle of elevation of the sun is important in navigation. Find out why.

Example 2:

Finding the height of a church spire.

(a) Fold a piece of paper into a 45° right-angled triangle. (This is very easy.)

(b) Hold the triangle with AB vertical and BC horizontal. (Ask a friend to judge whether BC is horizontal.)

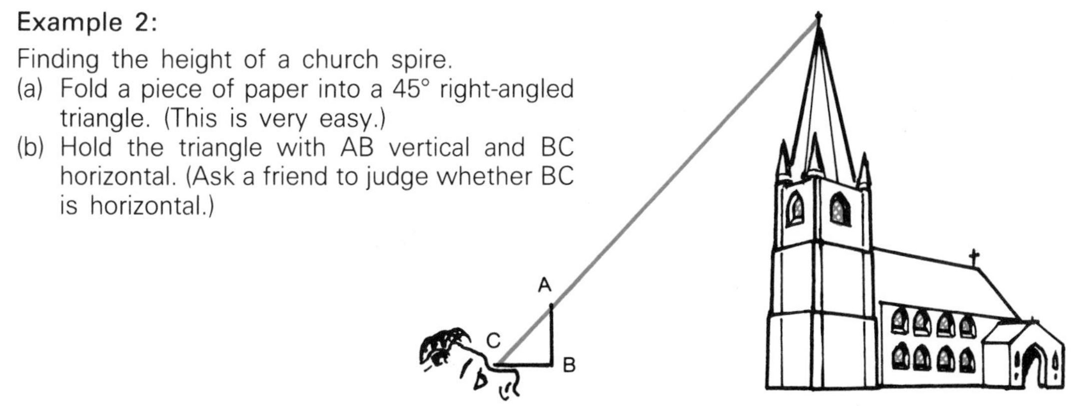

(c) Look along CA. Move towards the church till you just see the top of the spire.

(d) Measure your distance from the tower.

(e) The height of the spire equals your distance from the church *plus* the height of your eye above the ground.

Exercise 13·3

1 Use the methods described in the examples to find the angle of elevation of the sun on a sunny day. Note how the angle changes during the day. (Find out how this is used to tell the time by looking up **sundials**.) Write a report of your work.

2 Use the method described in the example to find the height of a tall building or tree near your home. Write a report of your work.

3 Three towns A, B and C are joined by straight roads, as shown.
Find the shortest distance across country from town A to the road joining B and C.
What are the similar triangles involved in this problem?

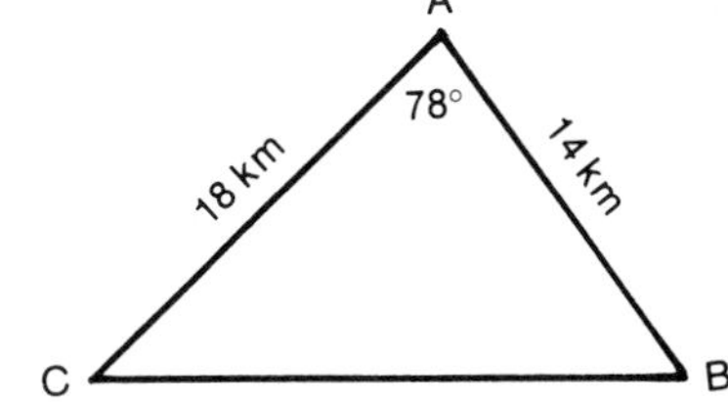

4 What similar triangles are involved in fixing position by back bearing? (See Unit 12.)

13·4 Ratios in the right-angle triangle: sine

Every right-angled triangle with angles 90° and 16° is similar to every other one.
In every such triangle the ratios of the sides are the same.
The ratio opposite/hypotenuse* is called the sine of 16° and written sin 16°

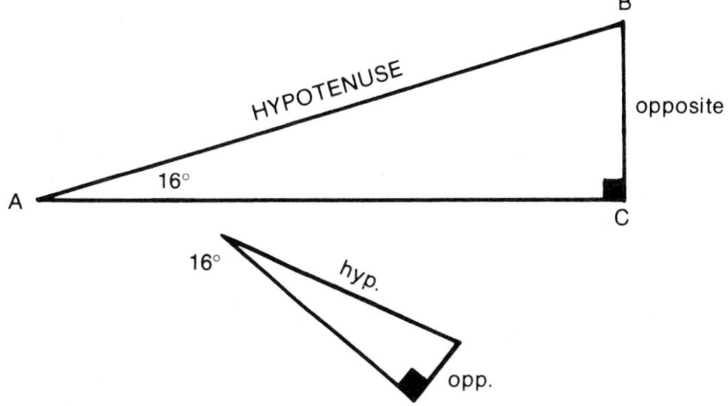

* The hypotenuse is the *longest side* in any right-angled triangle. It is the side *opposite* the 90° angle.

The value of this ratio can be found from the function tables in *Basic Maths Tables.*
Find 16 and read off the sine as 0·276, or if you have a scientific calculator, pressing [1] [6] [sin] will give 0·275 637 355.

The sine ratio can be used to solve problems.

Example 1:
In △ABC, $\hat{C} = 90°$, $\hat{A} = 16°$, AB = 7·5 cm . . . (See figure on page 105).
Calculate the length of BC using sine ratio.

$$\frac{BC}{AB} = \text{sine } 16° = 0{\cdot}276 \qquad BC = 7{\cdot}5 \times 0{\cdot}276 \text{ cm} = 2{\cdot}07 \text{ cm}$$

Example 2:
In △XYZ, $\hat{Y} = 90°$, YZ = 17 cm, $\hat{X} = 28°$
Calculate the length of XZ.

rough

$$\frac{YZ}{XZ} = \sin 28° = 0{\cdot}47 \qquad \frac{17}{XZ} = 0{\cdot}47$$

$$17 = 0{\cdot}47 \times XZ$$

$$XZ = 17 \div 0{\cdot}47 = 36{\cdot}17 \text{ cm}$$

Check by a scale drawing.

1. Draw a line and choose Y on it.
2. Draw a line, at Y, perpendicular to the first line. Mark Z, so that ZY = 1·7 cm.
3. Draw a line at 62° to YZ (because 28° = 90° − 62°).
4. Mark X where this line cuts the first line.

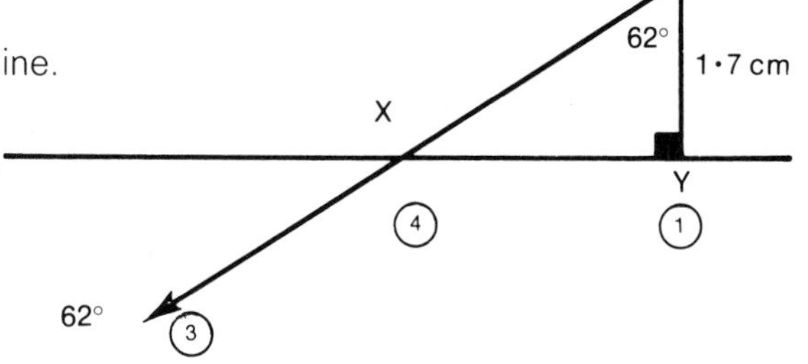

Measure XZ. It should be between 3·6 and 3·7 cm.

Example 3:
In △PQR, $\hat{Q} = 90°$, PR = 41 cm, $\hat{P} = 34°$
Calculate the length of RQ.

$$\frac{RQ}{PR} = \sin 34° \qquad RQ = 41 \times \sin 34° = 41 \times 0{\cdot}559 = 22{\cdot}9 \text{ cm}$$

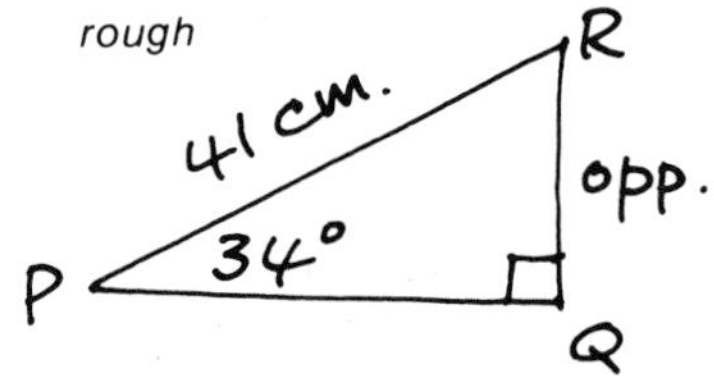

Check by scale drawing (1:10)

1 Draw a line PX.
2 Mark an angle of 34° at P, draw PY.
3 Mark off R, 4·1 cm from P, along PY.
4 Draw a perpendicular from R to PX to find Q.

On the drawing you would expect RQ to be 2·3 cm.

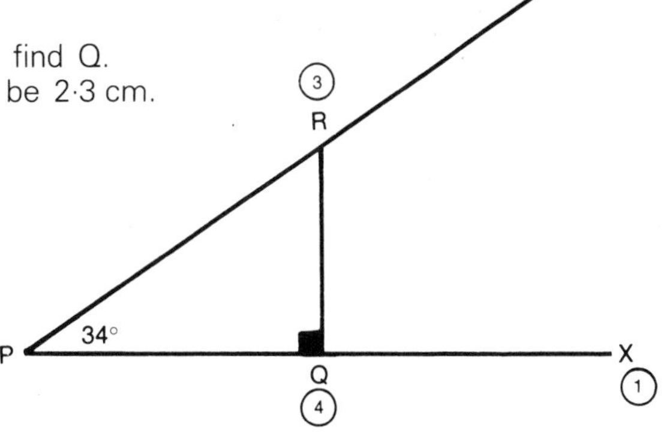

Exercise 13·4

A 1 Show, by careful measurement, that the following ratios are equal to sin 18° (found from tables).

$\frac{X_1Y_1}{OX_1}$ $\frac{X_2Y_2}{OX_2}$ $\frac{X_3Y_3}{OX_3}$ $\frac{X_4Y_4}{OX_4}$ $\frac{XY}{OX}$

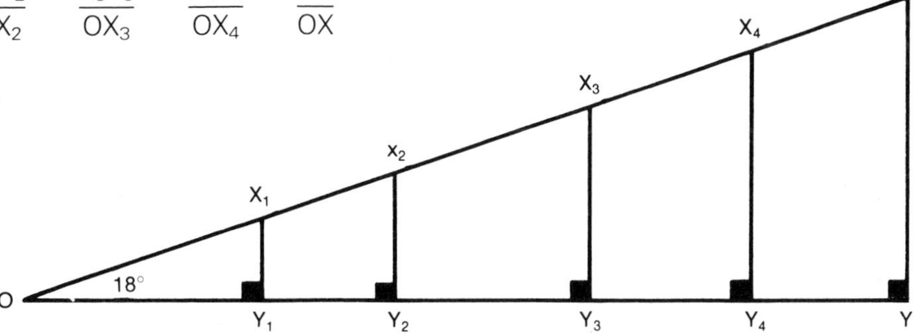

2 Find the ratio $\frac{BC}{AB}$ in each of the triangles below.
Check that in each case the ratio is equal to sin $\hat{A}$ (obtained from tables or calculator).

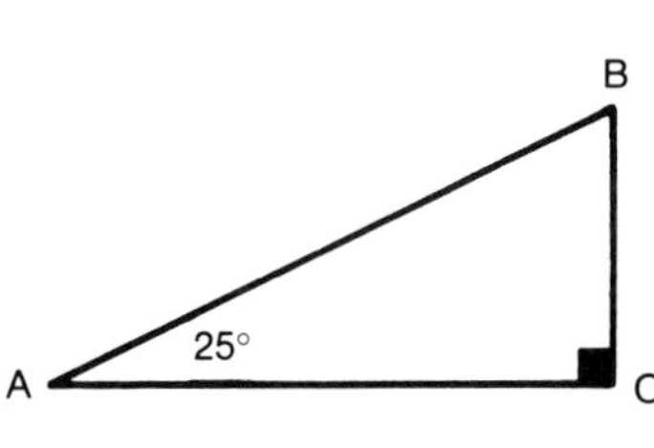

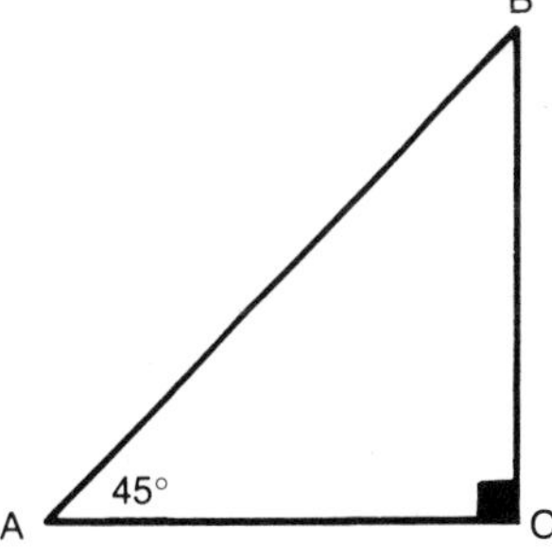

3 Find the sines of:
(a) 42° (b) 76·5° (c) 49·1° (d) 88° (e) 32·4° (f) 53·2°

4 Find the angles whose sines are:
(a) 0·177 (b) 0·509 (c) 0·60 (d) 0·95

B 1 Use sines to calculate the sides marked ? in the triangles below.

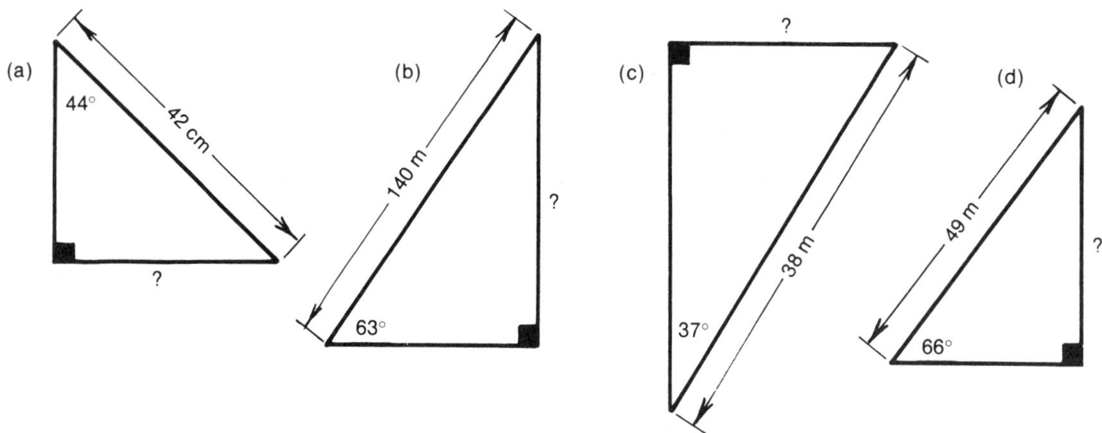

2 Use sines to calculate the sides marked ? in the triangles below. You may have to calculate the third angle of the triangle before you begin.

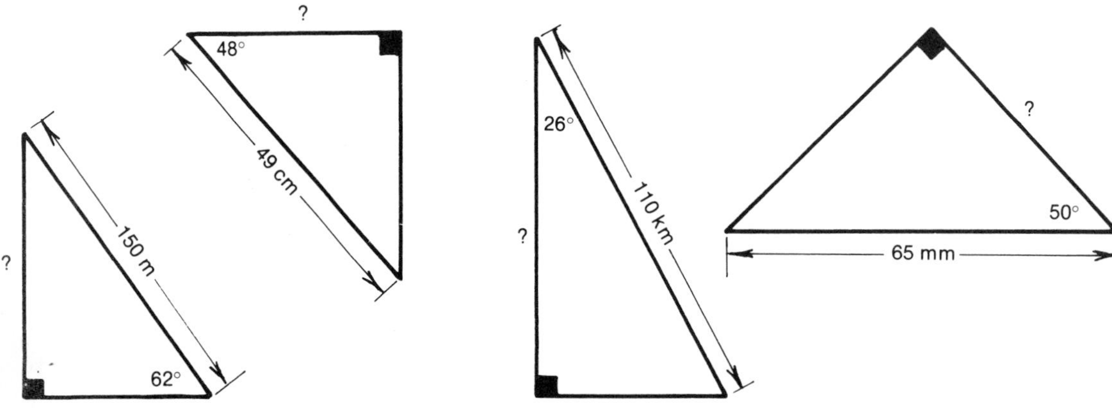

3 In each of the triangles below find the longest side. Remember you will have to divide by the sine when you are finding the longest side. (See example.) In each case make a scale drawing to check, using 1 mm^2 paper.

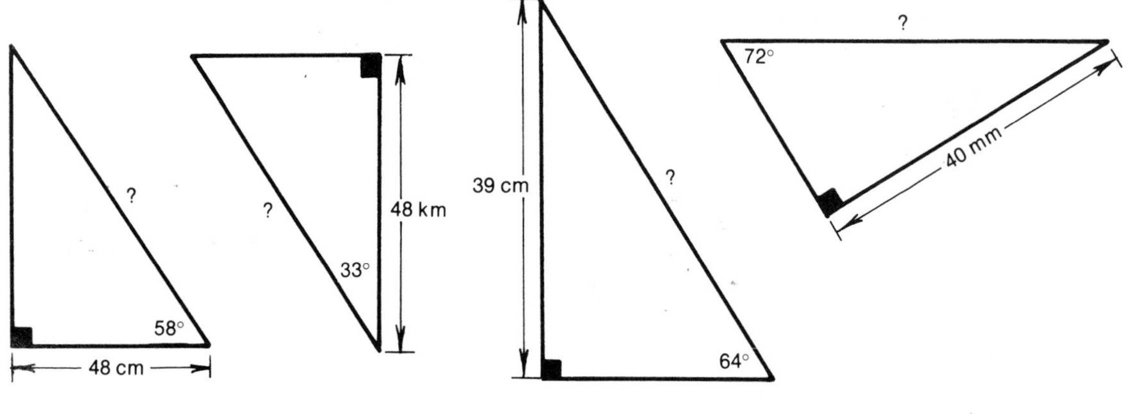

C 1 A roof slopes at 24° to the horizontal. The height of the roof above the walls is 2·6 m.

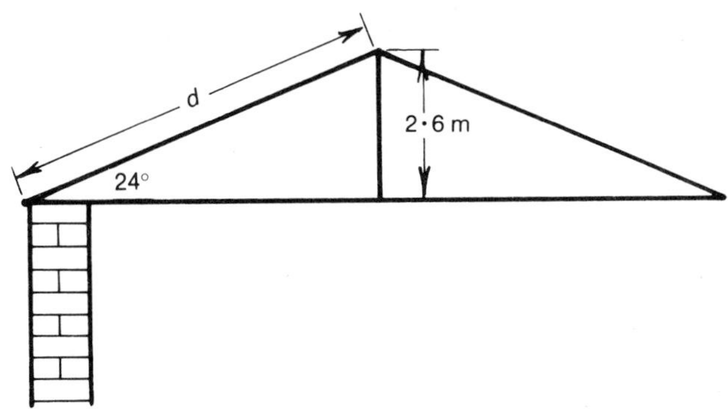

Calculate the sloping distance from the highest point to the wall (marked *d* on the figure).

2 An aircraft flies at 600 miles per hour in a direction N36°E (on bearing 036°).
(a) How far North does the aircraft fly in 1 hour (marked *n* on the figure)?
(b) How far East does the aircraft fly?

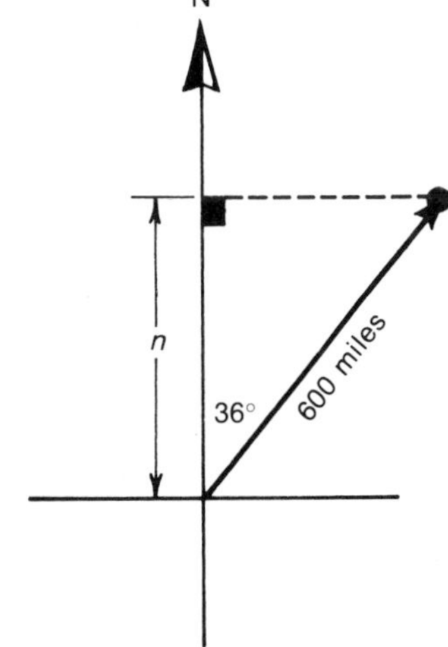

3 Study tables of sines to answer these questions. Is it true that:
(a) For any angle below 90°, sine of the angle is less than 1?
(b) Sine of an angle *increases* as the angle increases?
(c) Sine of an angle gets smaller as the angle increases?
(d) Sin 30° is exactly 0·5?
(e) Sines of small angles (below 10°) are between 0·000 and 0·100?
(f) Sines of angles over 70° are all more than 0·9?

Unit M14 The circle

14·1 Circumference

When you draw a circle with compasses the line you draw is the **circumference** of the circle.
The compass point is at the **centre** of the circle.

A line joining the centre to a point on the circumference is a **radius**.

A line joining two points on the circumference is a **chord**.

A chord which passes through the centre is a **diameter**.

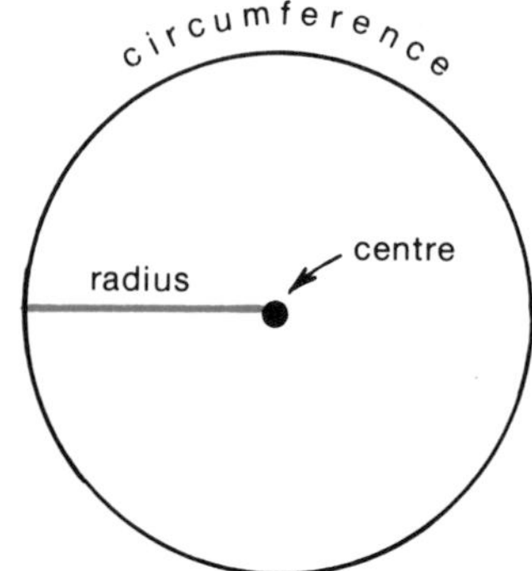

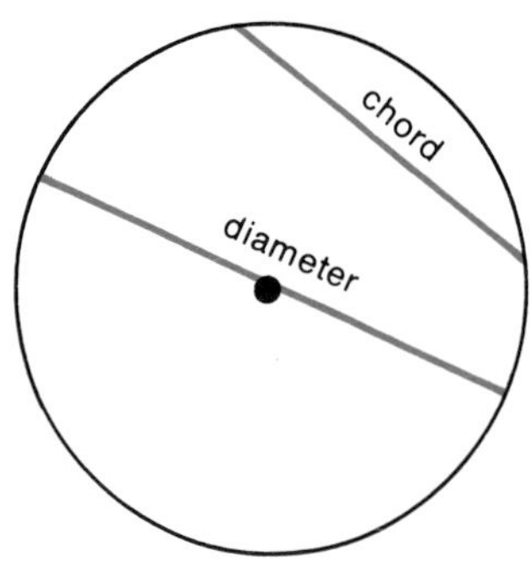

All circles are **similar**. Any circle can be formed by the enlargement of any smaller one.

The ratio $\frac{\textbf{circumference}}{\textbf{diameter}}$ is the same for all circles.
This ratio is given the sign π (pronounced 'pie'), a Greek letter.
The circumference of circles can be measured with a thin strip of 1 mm^2 paper. This paper may be curved around the circle.

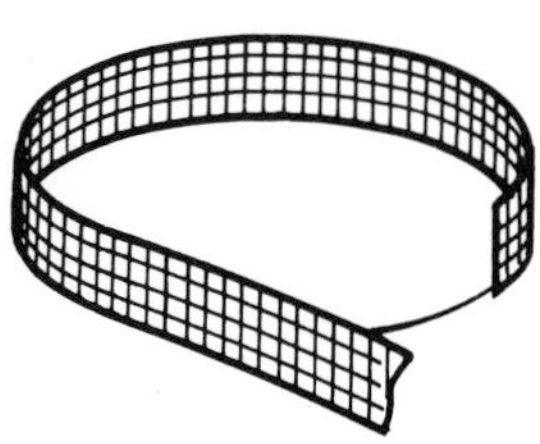

The value of π is roughly 3.
More accurate values are
3·1 . . . to 2 figures
3·14 to 3 figures
3·1416 to 5 figures
3·141 593 to 7 figures*

* π has been calculated to thousands of places, but it never gives any sign of a repeating pattern!

Calculations using π

Since we know the value of π for **all** circles, we can calculate the circumference of any circle if we know the diameter, and calculate the diameter if we know the circumference.

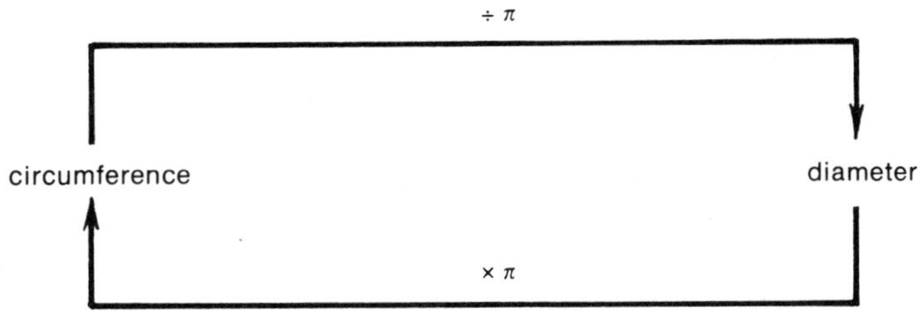

Examples:

(a) A circle has diameter 26 cm. What is its circumference?

Circumference = **Diameter** × π
= 26 × 3·14
= 81·64 cm

(b) A circle has circumference 104 m. What is its diameter?

Diameter = **Circumference** ÷ π
= 104 ÷ 3·14
= 33·1 m

Exercise 14·1

A **1** Measure the circumferences of these circles using a millimetre strip.

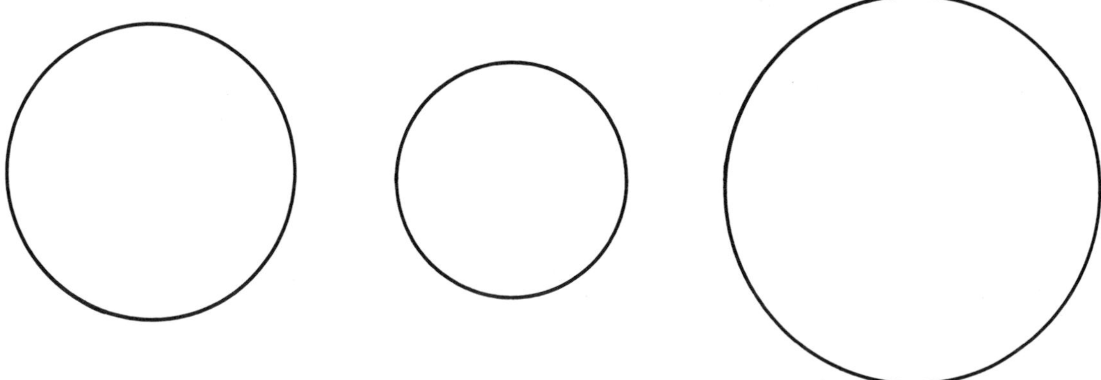

2 Measure the diameter of each circle and calculate the ratio $\frac{\text{circumference}}{\text{diameter}}$ for each circle.

3 Measure some circular or cylindrical objects such as dinner plates, bicycle wheels, jam-jars, etc. For each object calculate the ratio circumference/diameter. Do you find that all the ratios are near to π?

B Use the value $\pi = 3{\cdot}14$.

1 Find the circumference of the circle whose diameter is:
(a) 4 cm (b) 2·6 cm (c) 22 mm (d) 4·3 m (e) 12·8 km

2 Find the diameter of the circle whose circumference is:
(a) 8 cm (b) 3·9 m (c) 45 m (d) 72 mm (e) 4·5 km

3 Find the circumference of the circle whose **radius** is:
(a) 6 cm (b) 4·3 m (c) 55 mm (d) 10·6 km
Remember, double the radius to find the diameter.

C **1** A circular running track is 400 m long. What is the diameter of the running track?

2 The circumference of an oil drum is 2·4 m. What would be the length of a line of 20 such oil drums standing side by side?

3 Measure the circumference of your head and use the measurement to **estimate** the distance from ear to ear in a straight line.

4 The circumference of the Earth at the Equator is about 40 000 km. What is the diameter of the Earth, between two points on the Equator?

5 The Earth moves in a near-circle around the Sun. The distance from Earth to Sun is 152 million kilometres. How far does the Earth travel in a year?

14·2 Arcs

A part of the circumference of a circle is called an **arc**.

If it is more than half of the circumference it is called the **major arc**, otherwise it is a **minor arc**. Exactly half a circle is called a **semi-circle**, or **semicircular arc**.

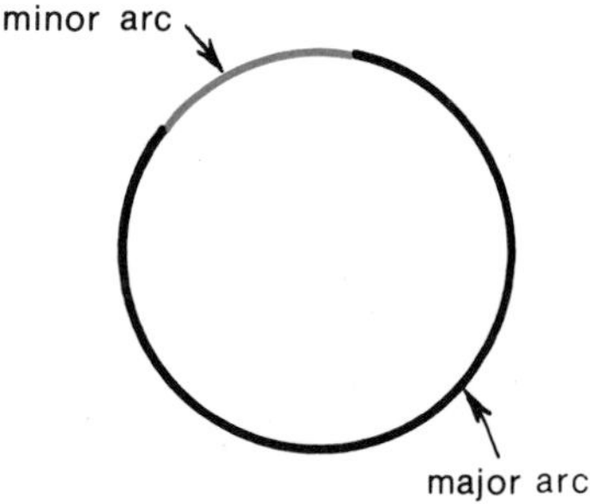

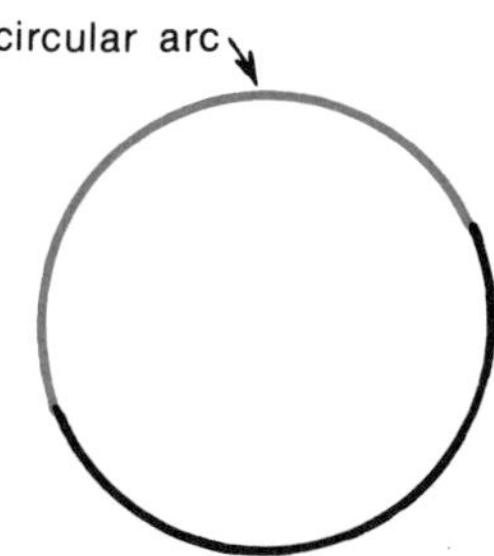

To find the length of an arc, we use the angle **subtended** by the arc, at the centre of the circle. This tells us the fraction of the whole circumference that is covered by the arc.

Examples:

(a) The arc is exactly half as long as the circumference

$$\frac{180}{360} = 0{\cdot}5 = \frac{1}{2}$$

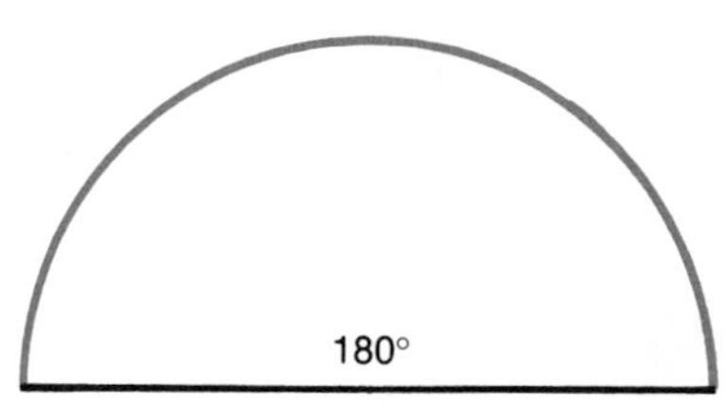

The arc subtends 180° at the centre.

(b) This arc is one third of the circumference

$$\frac{120}{360} = \frac{1}{3} = 0{\cdot}333$$

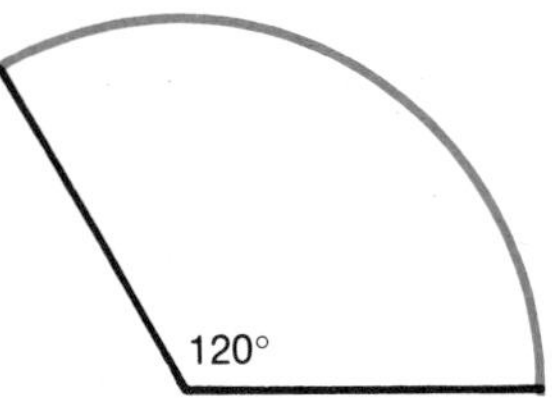

The arc subtends 120° at the centre.

(c) Find the length of an arc of a circle radius 5 cm, that subtends 40° at the centre.

$$\frac{40}{360} = \frac{1}{9} = 0{\cdot}111$$

The whole circumference is $\pi \times 10 = 3{\cdot}14 \times 10 = 31{\cdot}4$ cm
The length of the arc is $31{\cdot}4 \times 0{\cdot}111 = 3{\cdot}49$ cm

(d) The length of an arc of a circle, radius 10 cm, is exactly 10 cm. Find the angle this arc subtends at the centre.

The whole circumference is $(10 \times 2) \times 3{\cdot}14$ cm

$$\frac{\text{the arc}}{\text{the whole circumference}} = \frac{\text{the angle}}{360}$$

Thus the angle $= \dfrac{360 \times 10}{10 \times 2 \times 3{\cdot}14} = \dfrac{3600}{62{\cdot}8} =$ about $57{\cdot}3$*

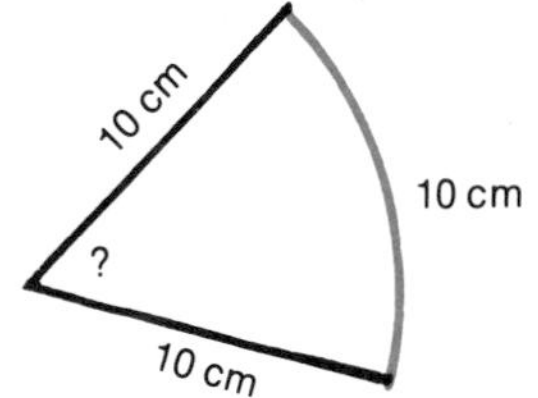

* This angle is used as a Standard measure, called 1 radian.

Exercise 14·2

A Calculate the length of each of the arcs in the figures below.

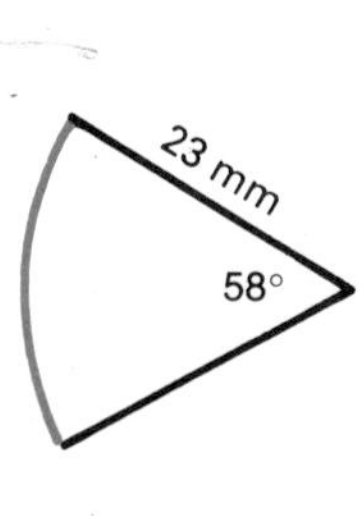

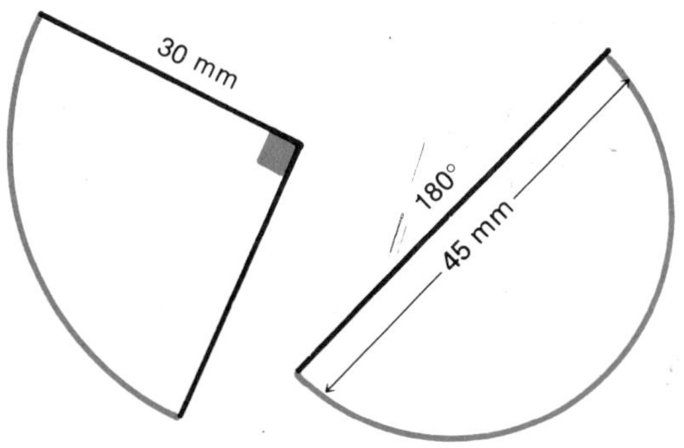

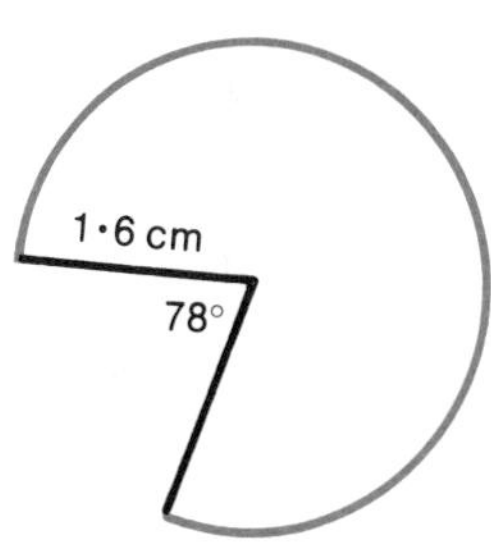

Calculate the circumference of the whole circle first.
Check by measuring with a 1 mm^2 strip.

B Calculate the angle subtended by each of the arcs below.

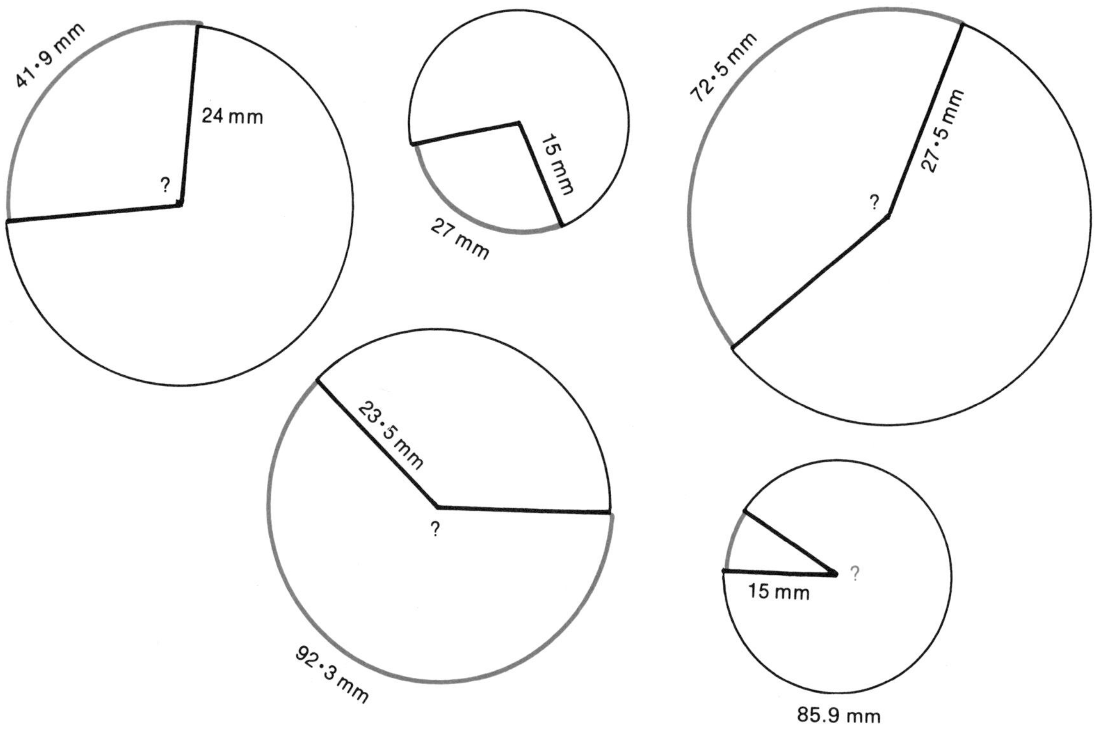

Check by measurement with a protractor.

C 1 Calculate the radius of each of the arcs below. You will need to calculate the whole circumference first. Divide by π to find the diameter and then halve to find the radius.

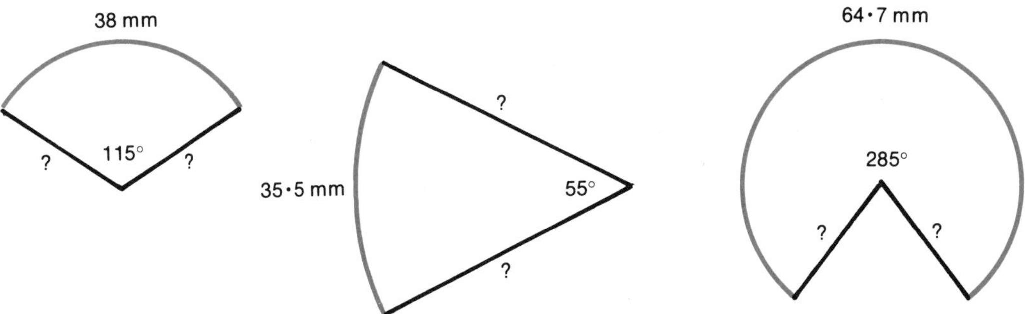

2 The centre span of a bridge is suspended from a steel structure whose shape is an arc of a circle. Calculate the length of the structure if the radius of the circle is 2000 m and the angle at the centre is 20°.

3 A skirt is made from two pieces of material cut as shown. Calculate the length of the waist **and** the hem.

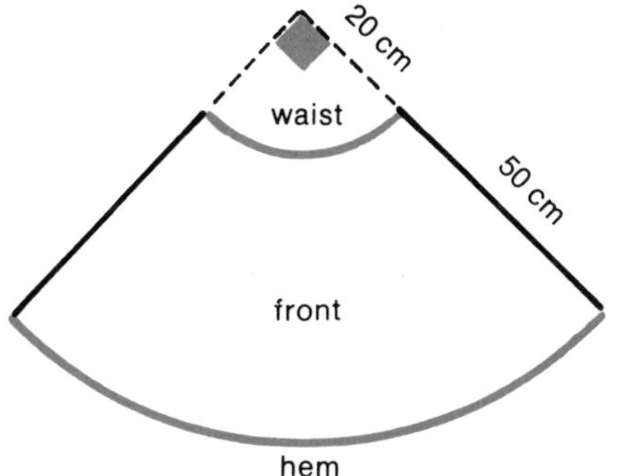

Remember the skirt is made from two pieces.

4 *A puzzle*
A belt was put round the Earth and pulled tight. 'It's too tight,' said the Earth, so an extra 6 metres was added to the length of the belt. How far away from the Earth would the lengthened belt stand? 'One metre away from the Earth at every point,' said Pat. 'That's ridiculous,' said Mike, 'It can't be as much as that! There were only 6 metres to share with the whole 40 *million* metres of the Earth's circumference.' Pat was right! Can you see why?

14·3 Areas of circles

The area of the circle is between $2r^2$ and $4r^2$. This suggests roughly $3r^2$. The exact area is πr^2, where $\pi = 3{\cdot}1416\ldots$ (as before).

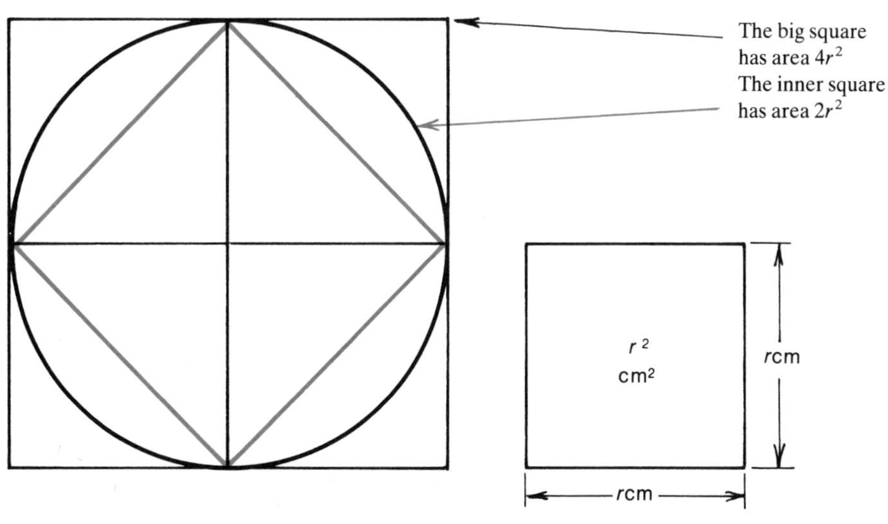

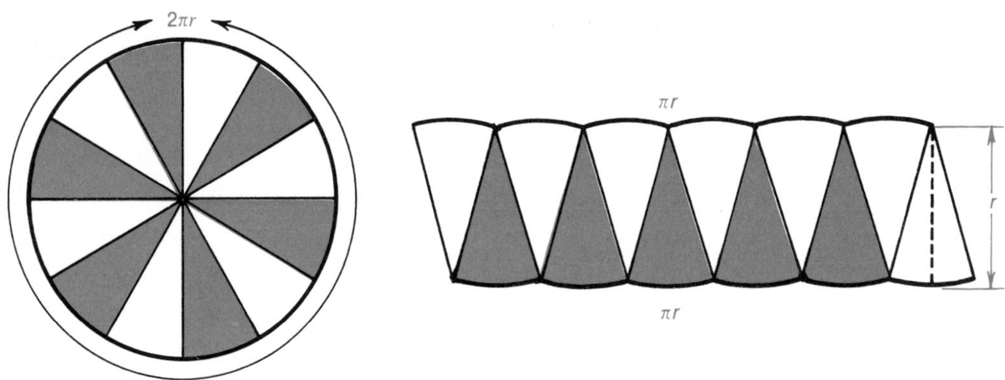

This circle is divided into 12 equal **sectors** which are then arranged as a near-rectangle, πr long and r wide. Thus the area of a circle is seen to be $\pi r \times r = \pi r^2$

Calculating the area of a circle

Examples:

(a) Find the area of a circle whose radius = 42 mm.

Area = πr^2 Area of circle = $3{\cdot}14 \times 42 \times 42$
$= 5538 \text{ mm}^2$

(b) A circle has area 600 cm^2. What is its radius?

Area = πr^2 $3{\cdot}14 \times r^2 = 600$
$r^2 = 600 \div 3{\cdot}14$
$= 191{\cdot}08$
$r = \underline{13{\cdot}82}$ (Use Square Root Tables or [√].)

Exercise 14·3

A **1** Calculate the area of circles with radius:
(a) 12 cm (b) 42 mm (c) 6 m (d) 4·3 km (e) 85 m (f) 7·3 cm

2 Calculate the area of circles with diameter:
(a) 10 cm (b) 28 mm (c) 4·9 m (d) 0·45 km (e) 66 m (f) 18·5 cm
Calculate the radius first.

3 (a) A roundabout has a diameter 140 m. What is the area of the roundabout?
(b) The road around the roundabout is 20 m wide. Find the area covered by the road and the roundabout together.

4 What is the area of a 10p coin? How many 10p coins could you lay side by side in a square box of side 1 m? How much space would not be covered by the coins? (The 10p coin has a diameter of 28 mm.)

B **1** Calculate the radii of the circles whose areas are:
(a) 100 cm^2 (b) 500 cm^2 (c) 1 m^2 (d) 250 m^2 (e) 0·65 m^2 (f) 11·2 cm^2
Remember: Calculate r^2 by dividing the area by π.
Then find the square root using tables or [√].

2 A circle fits exactly in a square 7 cm by 7 cm. What is the area of the circle? What would be the area of the circle which passes through the four corners of the square? (You will have to find the diameter first!)

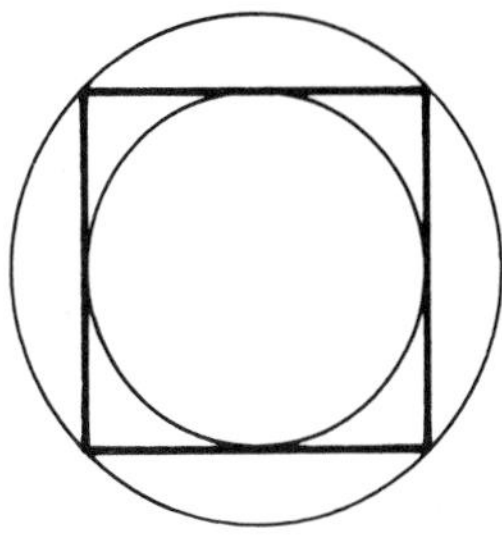

3 A farmer has 500 m of wire fencing. What is the area he can enclose with his wire if he arranges it in a circle?

Compare this area with the area he could enclose with a square-shape or rectangle.

4 A water tank 2 m high holds 200 m^3 of water when it is full. This means that the area of its base must be 100 m^2. What is the circumference of the tank? (The tank is a cylinder in shape, so its base is circular.)

5 Circular metal badges 5 cm in diameter are cut from a sheet of metal 1 m long and 50 cm wide. How many badges can be cut? What area of metal is wasted?

14·4 Sectors

When a circle is cut up by a pair of radii, the pieces are called **sectors**. The area of the sector depends on the size of the angle at the centre.

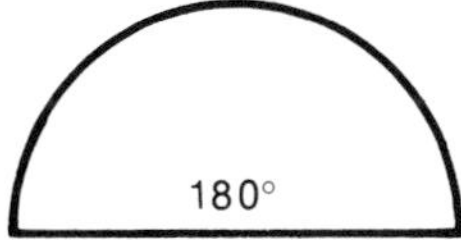

180° sector is a semicircle. The area is half of the whole circle

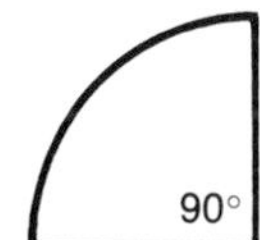

90° sector is a quarter circle. The area is one quarter of the whole circle.

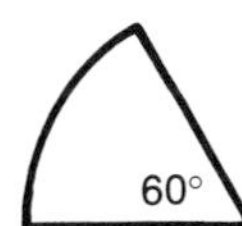

60° sector. The area is one sixth of the whole circle. $\left(=\frac{60}{360}\right)$

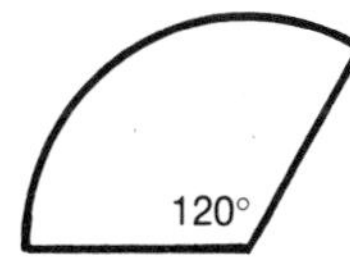

120° sector. The area is one third of the whole circle. $\left(=\frac{120}{360}\right)$

Examples:

(a) Calculate the area of a sector of a circle with radius 8 cm whose angle at the centre is 48°.

Area of whole circle $= \pi \times 8 \times 8 = 201 \text{ cm}^2$

Area of 48° sector $= \frac{48}{360} \times 201 \text{ cm}^2$

$= 26{\cdot}8 \text{ cm}^2$

(b) A 60° sector of material is cut from a rectangle 1 m × 2 m. The radius of the sector is 75 cm. How much material is left?

Area of whole circle (radius 75 cm) is $\pi \times 75 \times 75 = 17\,671{\cdot}5 \text{ cm}^2$

Area of 60° sector is $\frac{60}{360} \times 17\,671{\cdot}5 = 2945 \text{ cm}^2$

Area of rectangle 1 m × 2 m $= 2 \text{ m}^2 = 20\,000 \text{ cm}^2$

Material left $= 20\,000 - 2945 = 17\,055 \text{ cm}^2$

Exercise 14·4

A Calculate the areas of the following sectors:

1 Radius 10 cm, angle at centre 90°.
2 Radius 12 cm, angle at centre 40°.
3 Radius 50 mm, angle at centre 66°.
4 Radius 75 mm, angle at centre 120°.
5 Radius 5 km, angle at centre 200°.
6 Radius 100 m, angle at centre 310°.

B Calculate the angle of the following sectors. Calculate the area of the whole circle first. Then find the proportion

$$p = \frac{\text{area of sector}}{\text{area of whole circle}}$$

The angles will be in the same proportion, i.e.

$$\left(\frac{\text{angle of sector}}{360°} = p\right) \Rightarrow \text{angle} = 360 \times p$$

1 Area 30 cm^2, radius 4 cm.
2 Area 10 m^2, radius 0·16 m.
3 Area 450 m^2, radius 7 m.
4 Area 5 km^2, radius 416 m.

C **1** A lighthouse beam is 15° wide and 5 km in range. It is used to guide ships in a safe channel between rocks. What is the area of sea lit by the lighthouse?

2 A sector of a circle has an area exactly 10 cm^2 and a radius of 8 cm. What is the angle of the sector?

* One calculator sequence is: [r] [×] [=] [×] [π] [÷] [A] [÷] [3][6][0] [1/x] You might find a simpler one.
(r × = × π: *Area of whole circle*; A: *Area of sector*)

3 The pie-chart shows what is happening to all 18-year-olds. The whole circle represents 100%. Calculate the angles for each sector.

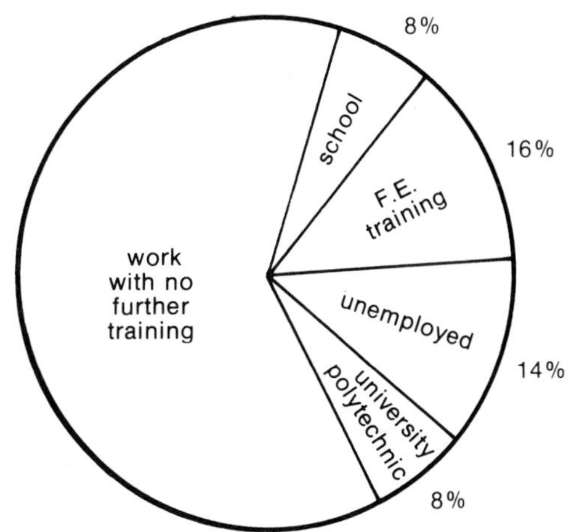

4 Draw pie-charts to compare the information for United Kingdom and France given below.
In the UK
3% of the workers work in agriculture
41% of the workers work in industry
56% of the workers work in services (transport, civil service, local government).
In France
12% of the workers work in agriculture
40% of the workers work in industry
48% of the workers work in services

Unit M15 Relations

15·1 Related numbers

John and his sister Jean have been left £100 to share by an uncle. The money is in £10 notes.

The table shows all the possible sharings, without changing any £10 notes. The relationship between the pairs of numbers is written:

$$x + y = 100$$

↑ *John* ↑ *Jean*

	John (x)	Jean (y)	
Jean has	0	100	← *Jean has all*
more than	10	90	
John	20	80	← *Jean has 4 times*
	30	70	*as much as John*
	40	60	
Both have the same	50	50	
	60	40	
	70	30	
John has	80	20	
more than	90	10	
Jean	100	0	← *John has all*

The relationship enables you to find a value for y if you know a value for x (or find a value for x if you know a value for y).
It is sometimes called an *equation in two unknowns*.

Example 1:

The school council is a committee of 12 boys and girls.
The relationship can be written: $x + y = 12$

(x: no. of boys on the committee; y: no. of girls on the committee)

(a) If we also know that the number of boys must equal the number of girls, we can find x and y.

$$\left.\begin{aligned} x + y &= 12 \\ x &= y \end{aligned}\right\} \Rightarrow \quad x = 6 \text{ and } y = 6.$$

(b) If the rule is that there must be at least 3 of each sex on the committee, we can find some possible values for x and y.

x	y
3	9
4	8
5	7
6	6
7	5
8	4
9	3

$x = 2$ and $y = 10$ are not allowed because there would be less than 3 boys etc.

Example 2

Given $2x + 3y = 14$, find y if:
(a) $x = 2$ (b) $x = 5$

(a) $x = 2 \Rightarrow 2x = 4$
$\Rightarrow 4 + 3y = 14$
$\Rightarrow 3y = 10$
$\Rightarrow y = 10 \div 3 = 3{\cdot}333$

These steps can be followed on a calculator especially using memory.

Put value in for $x \rightarrow$ [x] [×] [2] [=] [Min] [1] [4] [−] [MR] [÷] [3] [=]

(b) $x = 5 \Rightarrow 2x = 10$
$\Rightarrow 10 + 3y = 14$
$\Rightarrow 3y = 4$
$\Rightarrow y = 1{\cdot}333$

If you make a table of values for x and y, you will find patterns.

x	y
0	4·666
1	4·000
2	3·333
3	2·666
4	2·000
5	1·333

Each value of y is 0·666 less than the previous one.

Exercise 15·1

A **1** Given that $x + y = 20$, calculate y if:
(a) $x = 3$ (b) $x = 7$ (c) $x = 8{\cdot}5$ (d) $x = 0$ (e) $x = 2{\cdot}6$

2 Given that $x + 2y = 14$, calculate y if:
(a) $x = 0$ (b) $x = 4$ (c) $x = 10$ (d) $x = 3{\cdot}7$ (e) $x = 4{\cdot}9$

3 Given that $3x + 2y = 24$, calculate y if:
(a) $x = 0$ (b) $x = 1$ (c) $x = 5$ (d) $x = 7$ (e) $x = 4{\cdot}4$
(f) $x = 8{\cdot}25$ (g) $x = 1{\cdot}06$ (h) $x = 142$

4 Given that $4x - y = 18$, calculate x if:
(a) $y = 2$ (b) $y = 4$ (c) $y = 10$ (d) $y = 1{\cdot}5$ (e) $y = 3{\cdot}6$ (f) $y = 10{\cdot}7$

B **1** Make a table of values from $x = 0$ to $x = 10$, for the relation $2x + 3y = 25$

2 Make a table of values from $x = 0$ to $x = 10$, for the relation $2{\cdot}3x + 1{\cdot}7y = 14{\cdot}8$... (Use calculator routine.)

3 Make a table of values from $x = 0$ to $x = 10$, for the relation $2x - y = 15$. Note that y will have negative values for x less than 7·5.
(For example, $x = 1 \Rightarrow 2x = 2$
$\Rightarrow 2 - y = 15$
$\Rightarrow y = -13$ since $2 - {}^{-}13 = 15$)

4 Make a table of values from $x = 0$ to $x = 10$, for the relation $2x - 3y = 12$. For which of these values is:
(a) $x > y$?
(b) $y < 0$? (negative)

C **1** A home for animals has cages for cats (two cats in each cage) and for dogs (one dog in each cage). Altogether the home can keep 20 animals. How many cats and dogs could there be when the home is full?

2 Peter and Paul are left £400 by their auntie. How much do they get if:
(a) Peter has twice as much as Paul? (b) Peter has four times as much as Paul?
(c) Peter has £250 more than Paul? (d) Paul has £60 more than Peter?

3 Mary buys some packets of crisps (20 p a packet) and some bottles of fizz (40 p a bottle). She writes the total cost as

$$20x + 40y$$

x = the number of packets of crisps, and y = the number of bottles of fizz.
(a) Work out the value of $20x + 40y$ if:
$x = 10,\ y = 10$
$x = 5,\ y = 10$
$x = 3,\ y = 4$
$x = 0,\ y = 0$
(b) The total cost comes to £20. How many packets of crisps could she have bought?

15·2 The graphs $x + y = k$ and $ax + by = k$

The equations (a) $x + y$ = a constant number
and (b) $ax + by$ = a constant number
both graph as straight lines. They can be drawn by finding two points of the graph and joining them with a straight line.

Example 1:
Draw the graph of $x + y = 5$.

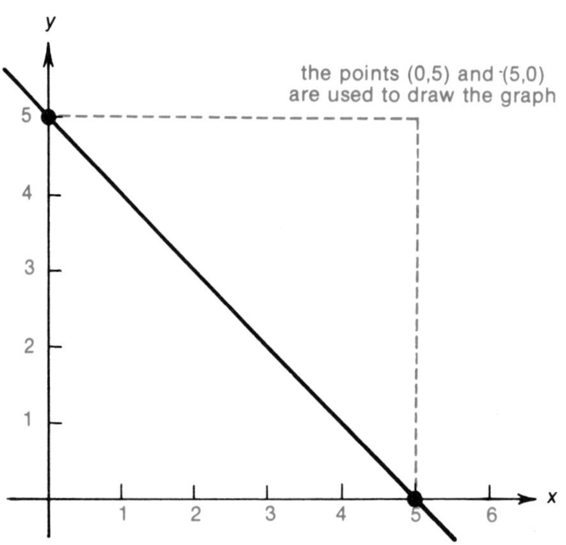

Two obvious points on the graph are (0, 5) and (5, 0). (Because $0 + 5 = 5 + 0 = 5$.)

The graph passes through all the points for which x and y are greater than 0 and $x + y = 5$.

Example 2:

Draw the graph of $2x + 5y = 15$.

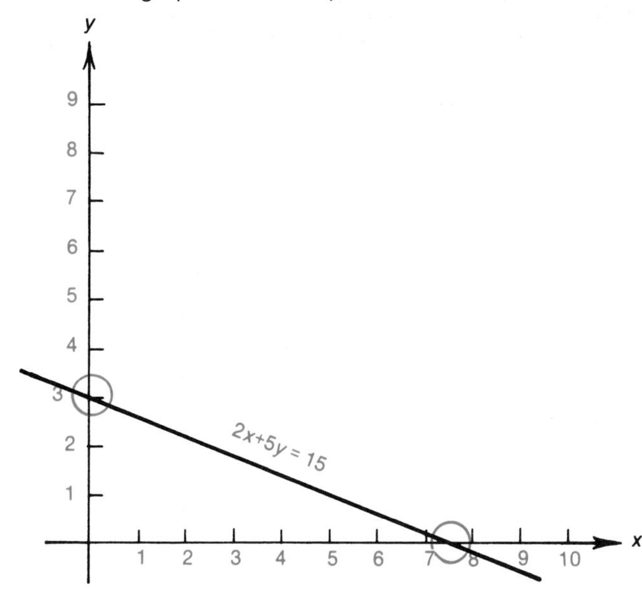

First find two points on the line:

(a) $x = 0 \Rightarrow 5y = 15$
$\Rightarrow y = 3$
(0, 3) is one point.

(b) $y = 0 \Rightarrow 2x = 15$
$\Rightarrow x = 7\frac{1}{2}$
$(7\frac{1}{2}, 0)$ is another point.

Mark the points and join them with a straight line. Make sure the axes are long enough

Example 3:

Draw the graph of $3x - 2y = 12$.

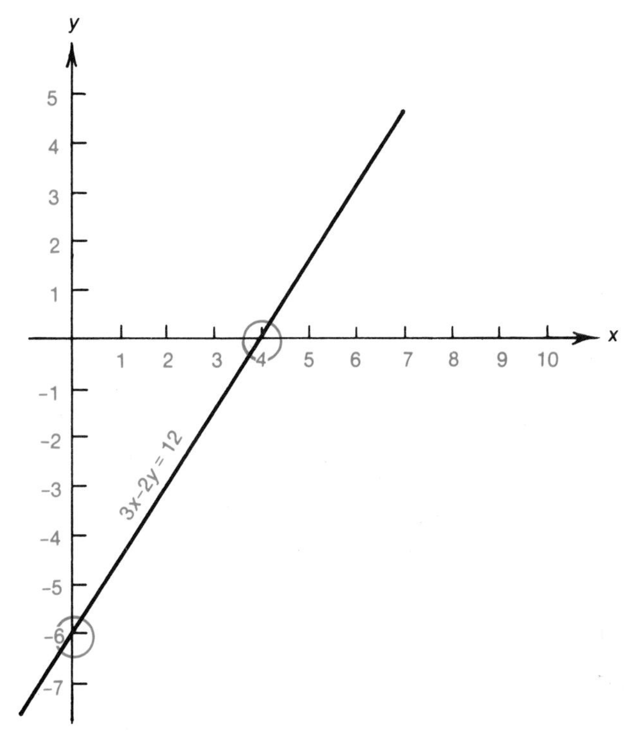

(a) $x = 0 \Rightarrow -2y = 12$
$\Rightarrow y = -6$

(b) $y = 0 \Rightarrow 3x = 12$
$\Rightarrow x = 4$

The points are (0, −6) and (4, 0).
Other points on this graph are:
(1, −4·5); (2, −3); $(3, -1\frac{1}{2})$.

Exercise 15·2

A **1** Draw on the same set of axes the graphs of:
(a) $x + y = 7$ (b) $x + y = 9$ (c) $x + y = 12$

2 Draw the graphs of:
(a) $x + 2y = 5$ (b) $x + 2y = 9$ (c) $x + 2y = 13$
on the same set of axes.

B **1** Draw the graphs of:
(a) $x - 2y = 5$ (b) $x - 2y = 10$ (c) $x - 2y = 14$
on the same set of axes.

2 Draw the graphs of:
(a) $3x - y = 4$ (b) $3x - y = 7$ (c) $3x - y = 12$
on the same set of axes.

C **1** Draw the graphs of:
(a) $2x - 3y = 7$ (b) $3x + 4y = 9$ (c) $4x - 2y = 6$
on the same set of axes.

2 A straight line graph goes through the points (0, 4) and (5, 0). Which of these relations could it be?:
$x + y = 5$, $2x + y = 4$, $4x + 5y = 20$, $5x + y = 20$.

15·3 Simultaneous equations

A pair of equations such as $x + y = 6$, $2x + 3y = 15$, can be **solved**. This means finding a pair of values for x and y that makes both relations true **at the same time**.

There are many ways of doing this. Three different ways are shown below.

(a) Tabulation

$x + y = 6$

x	y
0	6
1	5
2	4
3	3
4	2
5	1

$2x + 3y = 15$

x	y
0	5
1	4·333
2	3·666
3	3·000
4	2·333

We note that the pair (3, 3) occurs in both tables. So this is the solution required.

$x + y = 6$ $\quad$ $2x + 3y = 15$

$3 + 3 = 6$ $\quad$ $6 + 9 = 15$

(b) Graph

The solution pair will correspond to a point that lies on both lines. We draw both graphs on the same pair of axes and find the point on both lines.

$x + y = 6$

Points:

(0, 6); (6, 0)

$2x + 3y = 15$

Points:

(0, 5); ($7\frac{1}{2}$, 0)

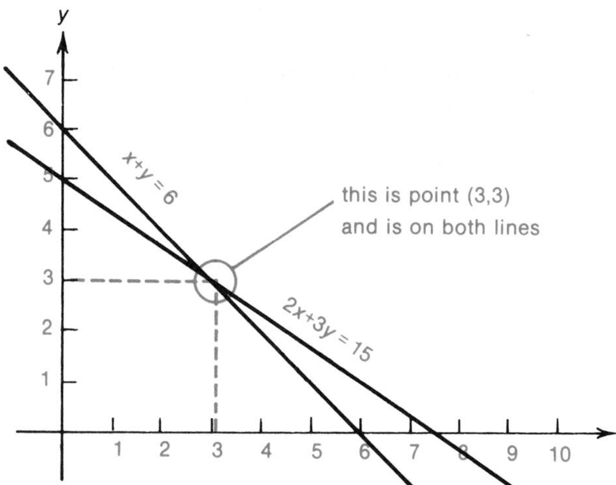

(c) Rules of Algebra

$$x + y = 6 \quad ①$$
$$2x + 3y = 15 \quad ②$$
$$2x + 2y = 12 \ldots \textit{ doubling equation } ①^*$$

Subtract: $y = 3$ . . . *You can subtract equal things from both sides of an equation.*

Go back to ① $x = 3$

Check in ② $2 \times 3 + 3 \times 3 = 15$

Note: We can find x by replacing y by the value we have just found.
Note how we check in the second equation, not the first.

Exercise 15·3

A Solve the following equations using the rules of algebra.

1 $x + y = 8$ ...①
$2x - y = 4$ ...②... note that we can 'lose' y by adding equation 1 to equation 2

2 $2x + y = 9$ ...①
$x + y = 5$ ...②... note that we can 'lose' y by subtracting equation 2 from equation 1

3 $2x - y = 5$ ...①
$3x + y = 5$ ...②

4 $x + 2y = 14$ ...①
$2x + y = 13$ ...②... Multiply ① by 2 then subtract ② from ① to 'lose' x

5 $x - 2y = 3$ ...①
$2y + x = 7$ ...② Rearrange ②, then add.

6 $2x + y = 15$ ...①
$x + 3y = 2$ ...② Multiply ② by 2, then subtract to 'lose' x

B Solve each of the six equations in section A above by drawing both relations on the same axes. The solution is to be found where the graphs meet.

C The following problems can be solved by forming simultaneous equations. The equations must then be solved to give the answers to the problems.

1 Two numbers add to 60. One number is 24 more than the other. Find the numbers.
2 Fred is 9 years older than his brother Sid. Their ages add to 31. How old are the brothers?
3 42 young people went on a club outing. There were two boys for every girl. How many boys and girls went on the outing?
4 Mrs Green bought 6 kg of potatoes and 4 kg of carrots for £1·28. Mrs Blue bought 4 kg of potatoes and 3 kg of carrots for £0·92. How much did 1 kg of carrots cost?

* We have adjusted the first equation so that it has the same number of x's as the second. We can now 'lose' the x's by subtracting. This leaves a simple equation in y to solve.

Unit M16 Tables

Tables are often used to give information. Everyone needs to know how to read them. They can help you make a journey, buy sensibly, save money, remember science, use machines correctly and many other things besides.

The tables we study in this unit are only a few of the many you will find if you read a newspaper or work in a shop or factory.

Make your own collection of tables. You will be surprised how often they crop up.

16·1 Tables of values

These are lists of things with a value attached. Sometimes the lists are arranged in alphabetical order. This helps you to find the thing you want.

Examples:

Telephone numbers

These are listed in alphabetical order of surnames. Initials are used to order people with the same surname.

280 Bleach

Bleach Michael, 6 Woodstock Cres N9	01-**804** 7560
Bleach T, 61 Grove Rd SW19	01-**540** 8958
Bleach T, 4 Manor Rd E15	01-**555** 1771
Bleacher B, Sunningdale,The Bishops Av N2	01-**458** 3115
Bleackley J, 86 Claxton Gro W6	01-**385** 8539
Bleak Hill Motors, Bleak Hl SE18	01-**854** 4874
Bleakley Dan D, 40 Michelson Ho,Black Prince Rd SE11	01-**582** 1445
Bleakley Francis, 8 Queens Rd N11	01-**889** 6027
Bleakley G.E, 181 Popes La W5	01-**579** 0486
Bleakley H, 55 Holsworthy Sq WC1	01-**278** 5164
Blean J, 34 Cavendisn Av N3	01-**349** 0212
Bleaney M, 35 Tottenham St W1	01-**637** 9598
Blearie K.S, 31 Alkham Rd N16	01-**806** 1735
Blears Mrs J, 7 Bickley St SW17	01-**672** 8816
Bleasby Maj H, 6 Cope Pl W8	01-**937** 2464
Bleasby K.G, 44 Beauchamp Rd E7	01-**552** 1136
Bleasby R, 78 Dorset Rd SW19	01-**540** 5507
Bleasby Robt O.M, 14 Thurlby Croft,Mulberry Clo NW4	01-**203** 1939
Bleasby S, 16 Shelley Ho,Roman Rd E2	01-**980** 1496
Bleasdale F, 22 Binyon Ho,Milton Gro N16	01-**254** 9464
Bleasdale John, 60a Cleveland Rd E18	01-**530** 2911
Bleasdale M, 32 South Hl Pk NW3	01-**435** 9547

Weather reports round the World.
(From *The Times*.)

Towns are listed alphabetically.

WEATHER REPORTS YESTERDAY MIDDAY :

c, cloud; f, fair; s, sun

		C	F			C	F			C	F			C	F
Ajaccio	f	27	81	**Copenhgn**	f	20	68	**Majorca**	s	28	82	**Rio de Jan**			
Akrotiri	s	25	77	**Corfu**	f	21	70	**Malaga**	s	38	100	**Rome**	s	26	79
Alexandria	c	28	82	**Dallas**	f	29	84	**Malta**	s	27	81	**Salzburg**	f	23	73
Algiers	f	27	81	**Dublin**	r	13	55	**Melbourne**	c	13	55	**Sao Paulo**			
Amsterdam	s	18	64	**Dubrovnik**	f	24	75	**Mexico C**	s	25	77	**S Francisco**	s	19	66
Athens	f	23	73	**Faro**	s	33	91	**Miami**	f	29	84	**Santiago***			
Bahrain	s	34	93	**Florence**	s	28	82	**Milan**	f	26	79	**Seoul**	f	24	75
Barbados	f	29	84	**Frankfurt**	f	22	72	**Montreal**	f	29	84	**Singapore**	th	30	86
Barcelona	s	25	77	**Funchal**	s	27	81	**Moscow**	c	22	72	**Stockholm**	f	23	73
Beirut	s	25	77	**Geneva**	c	19	66	**Munich**	c	17	63	**Strasbourg**	c	18	64
Belgrade	s	22	72	**Gibraltar**	s	35	95	**Nairobi**	c	23	73	**Sydney**	s	16	61

Exercise 16·1

A These questions refer to the tables above.

1. What is the telephone number of R. Bleasby, 78, Dorset Rd.?
2. What is the telephone number of M. Bleasdale, 32, South Hill Pk.?
3. I have been given the number 01–889–6027 for a Mr Bleakley. What is his address?
4. What is the name of the person whose phone number is 01–937–2464?
5. What was the temperature in Manchester, based on *The Times* weather report?
6. Which city had the highest temperature?
7. Name four cities where the temperature was below 20°C.
8. Which of these pairs of cities was warmer on the reported day:
   (a) London or Manchester (b) Paris or Edinburgh
   (c) Bristol or Birmingham (d) Florence or Naples
   (e) Madrid or Moscow (f) Athens or Rome

B 1 The weights of 1 cm^3 of certain metals are given in the table.
   (a) What is the weight of 1 cm^3 of silver?
   (b) How much more does 1 cm^3 of gold weigh than 1 cm^3 of silver?
   (c) Bronze is made from copper and tin. Would you guess it had more copper or tin in it?

Gold	19·64 g
Silver	14·00 g
Lead	11·32 g
Copper	9·00 g
Brass	8·00 g
Iron	7·654 g
Tin	7·320 g

These are listed in order of **density**.

2 The dosage for a cough mixture is given in this table. What is the correct dose for:
   (a) A baby 8 months old?
   (b) A child 4 years old?
   (c) A child 10 years old?
   (d) A young person aged 16 years old?
   (e) A new-born baby?

Age	*Dose*
Infants 3–12 mths	half a 5 ml sp
Children 1–6 yrs	one 5 ml sp
Children 6–12 yrs	$1\frac{1}{2}$ 5 ml spns
Adults over 12 yrs	two 5 ml spns

3 The standard sizes of paper are given in the table.
   (a) What are the length and breadth of an A4 size sheet of paper?
   (b) Which A size is nearest to this book?
   (c) Which size is a piece of paper 105 mm × 148 mm?
   (d) What size do I get if I cut an A4 piece of paper in half? (See figure.)

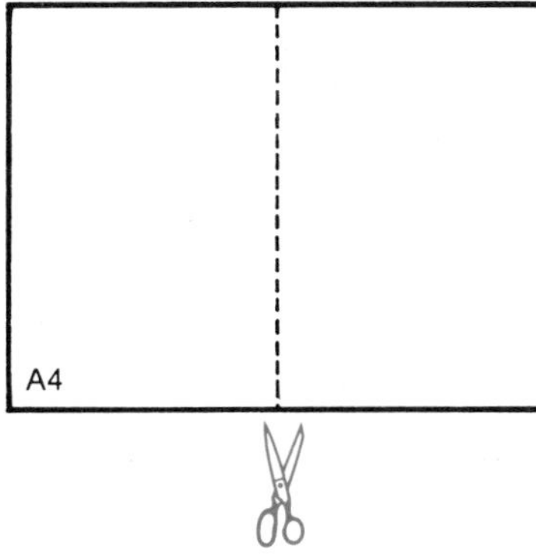

Name	*Size* (mm)
A0	841 × 1189
A1	594 × 841
A2	420 × 594
A3	297 × 420
A4	210 × 297
A5	148 × 210
A6	105 × 148
A7	74 × 105
A8	52 × 74

4 The Beaufort scale of wind force gives ways of testing the strength of the wind.

(a) What speed of wind would you expect in a fresh breeze?

(b) What type of wind blows at 35 mph?

(c) What would you expect to happen with a wind of 52 mph?

(d) Why do you think the winds are not arranged in alphabetical order?

(e) Find out all you can about the air movements that produce gales and hurricanes.

Beaufort Wind Number		*Effect on land*	*Speed mph*
0	Calm	Smoke rises vertically	less than 1
1	Light air	Smoke moves	1–3
2	Light breeze	Leaves rustle	4–7
3	Gentle breeze	Leaves and twigs move	8–12
4	Moderate breeze	Moves paper	13–18
5	Fresh breeze	Small trees sway	19–24
6	Strong breeze	Large branches move	25–31
7	Moderate gale	Whole trees move	32–38
8	Fresh gale	Twigs break off trees	39–46
9	Strong gale	Slates blown off roof	47–54
10	Whole gale	Trees uprooted	55–63
11	Storm	Buildings damaged	64–75
12	Hurricane	Violent damage	over 75

C Sometimes information is arranged in tables to help with comparisons.

1 The table shows the changes in traffic on British roads.

	*Thousand million vehicle-kilometres**		
	1968	1973	1978
Cars	148·13	196·49	220.28
Mopeds	0·90	0·91	0·93
Motor scooters	1·47	0·73	0·31
Motorcycles	2·50	2·31	5·62
Buses/coaches	4·02	3·82	3·72
Goods vehicles (lorries and vans)	36·80	42·87	43·94

* 1 vehicle-kilometre is 1 vehicle travelling for 1 km. Thus 100 vks could be 100 vehicles travelling for 1 km or 1 vehicle travelling for 100 km etc.

(a) How many vehicle-kilometres were travelled by motorcycles in 1973?
(b) How many vehicle-kilometres were travelled by buses or coaches in 1978?
(c) Study the table and describe the changes from 1968 to 1973 and from 1973 to 1978.

2 The table shows how much you have to pay each month if you buy something you want on hire purchase at 24% interest.

(a) Suppose you buy a cassette/radio for £100 and pay over 24 months. How much are the monthly payments?

(b) Suppose you buy a hifi for £300. How much are the monthly payments if you pay over 36 months?

Cost (£)	*12 mths*	*24 mths*	*36 mths*
50	5·17	3·20	2·65
100	10·34	6·40	5·30
150	15·51	9·60	7·95
200	20·68	12·80	10·60
250	25·85	16·00	13·25
300	31·02	19·20	15·90
350	36·19	22·40	18·55
400	41·36	25·60	21·20
450	46·53	28·80	23·85
500	51·70	32·00	26·50

(c) Suppose you buy a bike for £450. How much extra does it cost to buy over 36 months? (Work out 36 × £23·85.) How much extra does it cost to buy over 24 months?

16·2 Timetables and 24-hour clock

Trains, buses and aircraft travel at fixed times and these are published as timetables. You will find many examples in any travel agent. Your local railway station will also give away a number of timetables.

Examples:

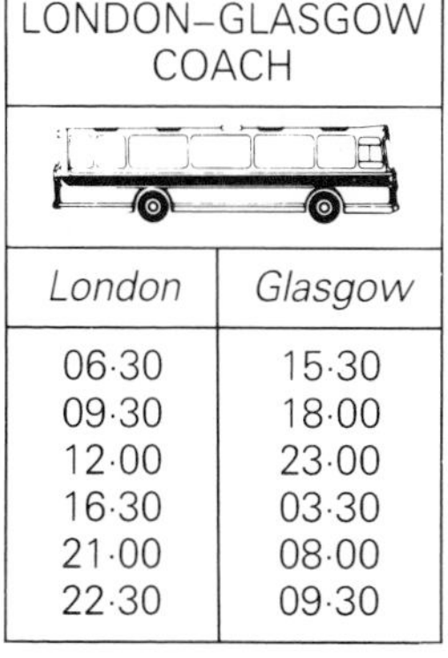

LONDON–GLASGOW COACH	
London	*Glasgow*
06·30	15·30
09·30	18·00
12·00	23·00
16·30	03·30
21·00	08·00
22·30	09·30

Flight times			
From London to New York		From New York to London	
Dep	*Arr.*	*Dep.*	*Arr.*
0600	0800	0600	1600
0900	1100	0400	1900
1500	1700	1500	0100
2100	2300	2100	0700

	Ferries from Portsmouth	Ferries from Isle of Wight
Mon To Fri.	0300, 0400, 0500, 0700 hourly until 1800, 1900, 2100 also every two hours 0630–1830	0045, 0400, 0600, 0700, 0800, hourly until 1900, 2000, 2200; also every two hours 0530 to 1930
Sat	0300, 0500, 0700 0800, hourly till 1800, 1900, 2100, 2300.	0700, 0900, 1000, 1100 1200 hourly until 1900, 2000, 2200

All timetables use 24-hour time. This is to make sure that people do not get confused between times before and after noon. The hours are counted from midnight, called 00·00 hours, through to one minute before midnight on the next night. This is 23·59 hours.

24-hour clock

Night ⟶				→ morning ⟶		
00·00	01·00	02·00	. . .	10·00	11·00	12·00
midnight	1 am	2 am		10 am	11 am	midday

afternoon ⟶				→ evening ⟶		
13·00	14·00	15·00	. . .	22·00	23·00	00·00
1 pm	2 pm	3 pm		10 pm	11 pm	midnight

Digital watches and clocks show 24-hour time (though not always).

Exercise 16·2

A These questions refer to the London–Glasgow coach (see example above).

1 What time does the first coach leave London?
2 What time does the last coach leave for Glasgow?
3 Work out the time each coach takes to Glasgow. Are the times the same? If not, why not?
4 Which coach could you take to be in Glasgow by 3 pm?
5 Which coach could you take to be in Glasgow by 6·30 pm?

B **1** Write the following times as 24-hour times.

(a) Two o'clock in the morning. (b) Half-past nine in the morning.
(c) Twenty to one in the afternoon. (d) Half-past six in the evening.
(e) 7·35 pm. (f) 10·10 pm.

2 Write the following 24-hour times as am/pm:

(a) 00·45 (b) 03·03 (c) 10·40
(d) 12·40 (e) 14·40 (f) 15·03
(g) 19·08 (h) 22·11 (i) 23·40

3 How long is it from

(a) 0400 to 1130 (b) 0700 to 2200 (c) 0930 to 2130
(d) 1330 to 1745 (e) 1620 to 2110 (f) 0425 to 1310
(g) 2100 to 0030 (next day) (h) 1900 to 0430 (next day) (i) 1840 to 0620 (next day)
(j) 2125 to 1250 (next day)
(*Hint*: Where the times cross midnight find: (i) the time to midnight, (ii) the time after midnight . . . and then add.)

C These questions refer to the tables on page 129.

1 How many ferry sailings are there on a weekday from Portsmouth to Isle of Wight?
2 Is there a ferry leaving Portsmouth at
(a) 14·30 on a Saturday? (b) 15·30 on a Tuesday? (c) 22·00 on a Saturday?
3 Look at the London–New York and New York–London flight times. How can you explain that one way takes 2 hours while the return flight seems to take 10 hours?

Exercise 16·3

The following are taken from tables in everyday use. Look at the tables carefully and answer the questions.

A Charges for telephone calls (1982)

Type of call	*Charge rate*	*Time allowed for 4·945 p*	*Cost of call*					
			1 min	2 min	3 min	4 min	5 min	10 min
Local calls	Cheap	8 min	5 p	5 p	5 p	5 p	5 p	10 p
	Standard	2 min	5 p	5 p	10 p	10 p	15 p	25 p
	Peak	1·5 min	5 p	10 p	10 p	15 p	20 p	35 p
Calls up to 56 km	Cheap	144 sec	5 p	5 p	10 p	10 p	15 p	25 p
	Standard	45 sec	10 p	15 p	20 p	30 p	35 p	69 p
	Peak	30 sec	10 p	20 p	30 p	40 p	49 p	99 p
Calls over 56 km	Cheap	48 sec	10 p	15 p	20 p	25 p	35 p	64 p
	Standard	16 sec	20 p	40 p	59 p	74 p	94 p	£1·88
	Peak	12 sec	25 p	49 p	74 p	99 p	£1·24	£2·47

Cheap: 1800–0800 Standard: 1300–1800, 0800–0900 Peak: 0900–1300

Questions

Work out the costs of these telephone calls:

1 5 minutes local call at 14·00 hrs.
2 2 minutes Nottingham to Leeds (100 km) at 11·30.
3 5 minutes Edinburgh to Cardiff (400 km) at 16·30.
4 10 minutes Southampton to Bournemouth (40 km) at 19·40.
5 20 minutes Local at 21·00.
6 0930–1030 Leeds to Liverpool.

B *Mileage charts*

Motoring books usually give a chart which shows distances between towns. The chart that follows shows 'great circle' routes between cities of the world. Since it is impossible to follow a *straight line* from one city to another, the great circle distance is the shortest.

For this reason aircraft are always flown along great circles.

Questions (see table on page 132)

1 What is the distance from
(a) London to Chicago? (b) Hong Kong to Delhi? (c) Moscow to Istanbul?

2 Which is nearer to London
(a) Nairobi or New York? (b) Moscow or Istanbul? (c) Oslo or Hamburg?

3 Which is the shorter of these flights?
(a) London → Lagos → Johannesburg *or* London → Nairobi → Johannesburg
(b) London → Paris → Geneva *or* London → Hamburg → Geneva
(c) London → Delhi → Darwin *or* London → Hong Kong → Darwin.

GREAT CIRCLE DISTANCES BETWEEN CITIES. (Miles)

	Calcutta	Canberra	Capetown	Chicago	Cologne	Colombo	Darwin	Delhi	Geneva	Hamburg	Hong Kong	Istanbul	Johannesburg	Lagos	Lisbon	London	Madrid	Moscow	Nairobi	New York	Oslo	Ottawa
Canberra	5640																					
Capetown	6026	6685																				
Chicago	7966	9379	8520																			
Cologne	4646	10276	5903	4248																		
Colombo	1232	5350	4890	8977	5102																	
Darwin	3756	1952	6962	9345	8334	3746																
Delhi	816	6440	5769	7472	3862	1513	4571															
Geneva	4747	10384	5597	4385	323	5105	8480	3946														
Hamburg	4504	10107	6074	4249	227	5019	8151	3732	540													
Hong Kong	1642	4596	7372	7788	5729	2523	2656	2344	5918	5536												
Istanbul	3647	9237	5224	5476	1239	3916	7404	2833	1190	1236	4989											
Johannesburg	5263	6703	790	8712	5475	4141	6602	4980	5189	5619	6661	4637										
Lagos	5734	9503	2974	5980	3069	5247	8847	5019	2745	3273	7357	2849	2811									
Lisbon	5637	11221	5333	3997	1149	5870	9390	4828	929	1366	6847	2003	5093	2359								
London	4962	10569	6010	3945	331	5416	8619	4183	468	463	5993	1562	5638	3109	972							
Madrid	5318	10915	5339	4192	883	5569	9070	4509	627	1107	6540	1686	5034	2380	319	774						
Moscow	3499	9013	6313	4956	1284	4106	7062	2702	1498	1096	4444	1106	5698	3886	2419	1565	2126					
Nairobi	3840	7407	2548	8022	4008	3019	6466	3366	3782	4100	5441	2966	1809	2381	4023	4250	3848	3944				
New York	7918	10090	7804	723	3765	8755	9983	7304	3852	3801	8055	5003	7972	5249	3358	3441	3580	4660	7352			
Oslo	4456	9937	6503	4044	639	5098	7990	3724	962	433	5341	1522	6028	3704	1694	723	1474	1012	4456	3668		
Ottawa	7619	10007	8026	651	3072	8530	9683	7055	3754	3652	7722	4872	8132	5363	3345	3323	3541	4437	7369	328	3480	
Paris	4876	10515	5803	4140	247	5295	8583	4091	245	459	5986	1393	5414	2913	894	215	641	1542	4026	3621	822	3518

4 A business-man flew round the world by flying from London to Istanbul to Hong Kong to Darwin to Capetown to Chicago and home again to London.
(a) How long was his total flight? (b) Which 'leg' was the longest?

5 Which is nearer to New York
(a) Moscow or Madrid? (b) Hong Kong or Colombo? (c) Lisbon or Cologne?

6 Why is it so much farther from London to Darwin than from London to Johannesburg?

C Make a collection of all the tables you can find in use in shops, offices and other places. Here are some suggestions.

Petrol stations and garages .... Cost, tyre pressures, new car prices
Furniture shops .... Hire purchase schemes
Offices .... Tax and insurance tables
Railway stations .... Timetables
Post office .... Letter and parcel rates

Unit M17 Binary numbers

17·1 Binary numbers (counting in base 2)

The electronic calculator, for all its brilliance, only counts up to 2. There are only two symbols, 0 and 1, but these, with place value, give a method of counting all numbers however large.

Symbols: 0, 1 Place value: Numbers have different values in different places. Zero is used as a place holder.

Decimal	Binary
0	0 . . . zero
1	1 . . . one unit
2	10 . . . a 2 and no units
3	11 . . . a 2 and a unit
4	100 . . . a 2^2, no 2's and no 1's
5	101 . . . a 2^2, no 2's and 1
6	110 . . . a 2^2, a 2 and no 1's
7	111
8	1000
9	1001

Binary numbers can be **made to correspond to a set of tiny cells which** are either on or off (electronically). **These cells are arranged on an integrated circuit** on a **micro-chip** inside your calculator.

This set of cells gives the number 1101001 (base 2)

= 105 (base 10).

1 1 0 1 0 0 1

64 + 32 + 8 + 1 = 105

Exercise 17·1

A 1 Write down all the binary numbers from 1 to $100\,000_2$ in base 2. Look out for patterns, to make the work easier.

2 Work out the value (in base 10) of these binary numbers. (Use your answers to question 1 to help.)

(a) 1101 (b) 10 101 (c) 110 011
(d) 1 010 111 (e) 11 010 111 (f) 1 000 000
(g) 1 101 011 011 (h) 10 111 010 111 (i) 11 011 011 011

3 What is the relationship between the first and second numbers in these examples? (Change them to base 10 to see.)

(a) 10 and 100 (b) 101 and 1010 (c) 1101 and 11 010
(d) 1011 and 10110 (e) 101 and 10100 (f) 1111 and 111 100?

4 Use the answers to question 3 to explain the effect of:

(a) Adding a zero to the end of a binary number (b) Adding two zeros.

B **1** Work out the values of all the powers of 2 up to 2^{20} in base 10.
$2^1 = 2$, $2^2 = 4$, $2^3 = 8$ ... etc. (Use your calculator if you like.)
How big a number would 2^{50} be?

2 Write these numbers in base 2, i.e. as binary numbers. (Take the biggest power of 2 out first, then the next and so on.)

(a) 11_{10} (b) 143 (c) 55
(d) 207 (e) 1415 (f) 4250

3 Show that the numbers 4, 8, 12, 16 ... 48 of the 4 times table all end in 00 when put into binary form. What is the reason for this?

C Try out the two methods given below for finding binary numbers from base 10 numbers on the calculator.

Example of method 1:

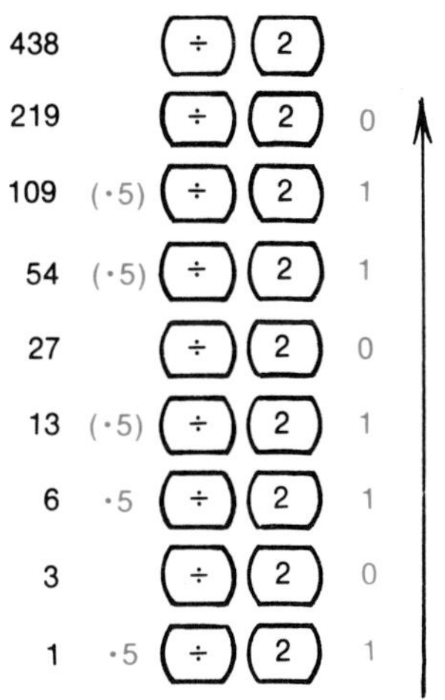

Divide by 2 and:
(a) If there is no decimal point after dividing write 0.
(b) If a ·5 appears after dividing write 1, and subtract ·5.
Continue until the process produces zero.
Read the number from the bottom up
$110\,110\,110_2 = 438$

Example of method 2 (by calculator):

438 ÷ 256 (2^8)

(a) Divide by the largest power of 2 that is less than 438
Write down the 1 and subtract it from the calculator display.
(b) Double the number left on display.
(i) If the result is less than 1 write 0 and double again.
(ii) If the result is 1·(something) write 1 and subtract the 1 before doubling again.

Stop when you reach zero. The binary number is 9 digits long (your first divisor was 2^8).

Use both methods to convert the following numbers to binary. Check that both methods give the same result.

(a) 48 (b) 77 (c) 150 (d) 588

D Use the rule given below to convert the following base 2 numbers to base 10.

(a) 1101 (b) 10101 (c) 11 101 (d) 11 011 011

Can you see why the rule works?

Example:

11011

1	1	0	1	1.
start	double +1	double	double +1	double +1
1	3	6	13	27

RULE
Start at the front of the number (highest power of 2).
Count 1 for the first figure
(a) If the second figure is 0 . . . double 1 (= 2)
(b) If the second figure is 1 . . . double 1 then add 1 (= 3)
Repeat for the next figure and on to the end of the number.

Check: 11 011
16 + 8 + 2 + 1 = 27

17·2 Addition and multiplication in binary

All calculations in binary are very simple because you only have 1 and 0 to work with. We can use the methods we use for base 10.
The basic facts are:

$1 \times 1 = 1$		$1 + 1 = 10$	(put down 0 and carry 1)
$1 \times 0 = 0$	$(= 0 \times 1)$	$1 + 0 = 1$	$(= 0 + 1)$
$0 \times 0 = 0$		$0 + 0 = 0$	

All this means that sums will be very easy indeed.

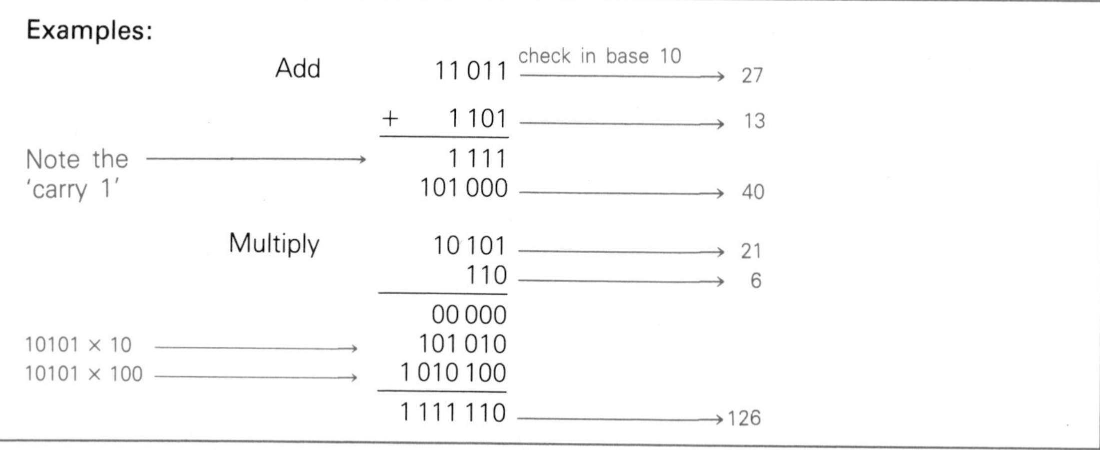

Exercise 17·2

A Complete the following binary additions:

1 1101 +111 **2** 10 101 +1 011 **3** 1110 +101 **4** 101 011 +11 011

Check each result by conversion to base 10.

B Complete the following binary multiplications:

1 101 ×11 **2** 1101 ×110 **3** 10 101 ×1 101 **4** 11 101 × 110

Check each result by conversion to base 10.

C Subtraction is possible using ordinary base 10 methods but other methods are better.

1 Subtract these by any method you like:

(a) 1100 −101 (b) 10 101 −1 101 (c) 11 011 −1 001

2 Follow the example carefully.

11 011 −101

First subtract* 11 011 from 11 111 . . . 00 100

Next add 101 − 101

01 001

Now subtract this result from 11 111*

. . . 10 110

Check in base 10

11 011	is	27
101	is	5
10 110	is	22

Use the method for the following subtractions:

(a) 1100 −101 (b) 10 101 −1 101 (c) 11 011 −1 001 (d) 100 011 −11 011

3 Show that the above method can be used in base 10 using 99999 instead of 11111. This leads to subtraction without borrowing! Describe your method carefully and give several examples to show it in action.

17·3 Arithmetic in other bases

There is no mystery about using a number base other than 10, although there is litle advantage in calculating in, say, base 6, for anything other than addition.

Example:

Calculate $34_6 \times 23_6$ and express the result in base 6.

$34_6 \longrightarrow (3 \times 6) + 4 = 22$

$23_6 \longrightarrow (2 \times 6) + 3 = 15$

$22 \times 15 = 330_{10} \rightarrow 1310_6$ †

*		
6	330	
6	55	R0
6	9	R1
6	1	R3
	0	R1

Example:

Add 1437_9 + 206_9 = 1644_9

It is simpler to leave this calculation in base 9.
$6 + 7 = 9 + 4 = 14_9$ . . . etc.

* Just change 1 for 0 and 0 for 1.

† For this method see Unit 18 in *IMS BOOKS A2* and *B2*

Exercise 17·3

A Calculate the following, giving the answer in the same base as the question.

1 (a) 143_9 $+66_9$ (b) 216_8 $+72_8$ (c) 1056_8 $+767_8$ (d) 1231_4 $+223_4$

2 (a) 23_6 $\times 4_6$ (b) 42_7 $\times 12_7$ (c) 55_9 $\times 16_9$ (d) 46_8 $\times 27_8$

B **1** Find the squares of the following numbers in the base of the question.

(a) 4_7 (b) 7_9 (c) 12_4 (d) 23_5

2 Find the square roots of these numbers:

(a) 100 (b) 121_7 (c) 220_8 (d) 1134_5

C Find the value of x in each of the following equations:

1 $x + 7 = 10_8$

2 $x - 3 = 14_6$

3 $2x = 14_8$

4 $2x + 4 = 22_6$

Unit M18

18·1 Matrix

A collection of numbers arranged in *rows* and *columns* is called a **matrix**. A matrix is usually shown inside a large pair of brackets.

col 1 col 2 col 3 col 4

$$\begin{matrix} \textit{row } 1 \\ \textit{row } 2 \\ \textit{row } 3 \end{matrix} \begin{pmatrix} 3 & 4 & 7 & 2 \\ 1 & 0 & 4 & 6 \\ 5 & 4 & 7 & 1 \end{pmatrix}$$

This matrix has 3 rows and 4 columns.

A matrix can be used as a store of information. In fact, many tables of information are really matrices. *

Example:
A girl records her clothes by colours
(a) If she adds across the rows she can find the total number of each type of garment.
(b) If she adds down the columns she can find the total number of garments of a given colour.
(c) The number 3 in the second row and second column tells you that she has three blue skirts.

	Red	*Blue*	*Green*	*Black*
Trousers	2	0	0	1
Skirts	1	3	1	2
Jumpers	2	1	0	1
Socks	0	2	1	0

Exercise 18·1

A 1 Write down:
(a) the second row (b) the third column (c) the number in the third row and second column of

$$\begin{pmatrix} 3 & 6 & 5 & 2 \\ 1 & 7 & 4 & 9 \\ 0 & 6 & 0 & 8 \end{pmatrix}$$

2 Write down a matrix with three rows and three columns in which:
(a) The second row is a row of zeros.
(b) Each number in the third row is double the number in the first row in the same column.

3 What number is in the second row and third column of these matrices?

$$\begin{pmatrix} 0 & 1 & 0 \\ 1 & 0 & 0 \end{pmatrix} \quad \begin{pmatrix} 1 & 2 & 3 \\ 4 & 5 & 6 \end{pmatrix} \quad \begin{pmatrix} 3 & 4 & 5 & 6 \\ 2 & 4 & 1 & 0 \\ 1 & 0 & 1 & 0 \end{pmatrix} \quad \begin{pmatrix} 3 & 6 & 5 \\ 4 & 0 & 9 \\ 5 & 1 & 2 \end{pmatrix}$$

* *Note*: matrices is plural of matrix.

4 Find (a) the sum of the second row for each of the matrices of question 3.
(b) the sum of the third column for the same matrices.

B **1** This matrix gives information about loaves of bread sold on a certain day.

$$\begin{array}{c} \\ \text{Large} \\ \text{Small} \end{array} \begin{array}{c} \begin{array}{cc} \text{Brown} & \text{White} \end{array} \\ \begin{pmatrix} 42 & 86 \\ 100 & 120 \end{pmatrix} \end{array}$$

(a) How many large white loaves were sold?
(b) How many small brown loaves were sold?
(c) How many brown loaves were sold altogether?
(d) How many small loaves were sold altogether?

2 There are four pumps on a garage forecourt selling petrol.
At the end of the day the supervisor fills up a matrix record card of sales.
(a) How many gallons of two star petrol were sold from pump 2?
(b) How many gallons of petrol were sold from pump 4?
(c) How many gallons of four star petrol were sold altogether?
(d) How many gallons of two star petrol were sold from pumps 3 and 4 together?

$$\text{Pump} \begin{array}{c} \\ 1 \\ 2 \\ 3 \\ 4 \end{array} \begin{array}{c} \begin{array}{cc} \star\star & \star\star\star\star \end{array} \\ \begin{pmatrix} 485 & 269 \\ 382 & 459 \\ 501 & 663 \\ 285 & 0 \end{pmatrix} \end{array}$$

Numbers in matrix are gallons of petrol sold.

3 Describe a situation where a matrix could be used as a store of information.

18·2 Row vector and column vector

A matrix with only one row is called a **row vector**.
A matrix with only one column is called a **column vector**.
(3 4 2 8) (0 1 0) (6 5) and (3 3 1 3 5) are all row vectors.

$\begin{pmatrix} 1 \\ 2 \end{pmatrix}$ $\begin{pmatrix} 0 \\ 0 \\ 0 \end{pmatrix}$ $\begin{pmatrix} 1 \\ 1 \\ 0 \\ 1 \end{pmatrix}$ $\begin{pmatrix} 5 \\ 5 \end{pmatrix}$ are all column vectors.

Vectors can be combined to give a product.

Example:

Suppose ... two star petrol costs 260 p per gallon
four star petrol costs 280 p per gallon
and we sell 120 gallons of two star petrol and 175 gallons of four star petrol.

(120, 175) Row, *quantity* vector $\begin{pmatrix}260\\280\end{pmatrix}$ Column, *cost* vector.

The product of the vectors (120, 175) $\begin{pmatrix}260\\280\end{pmatrix}$ is $(120 \times 260) + (175 \times 280) = 80\,200$ p

cost of ★★ (120 × 260); cost of ★★★★ (175 × 280)

In general the product of $(a, b)\begin{pmatrix}x\\y\end{pmatrix} = ax + by$.

This is very useful to know.

Exercise 18·2

A Find the products of these row vector, column vector pairs.

1 $(2, 0)\begin{pmatrix}1\\1\end{pmatrix}$

2 $(3, 5)\begin{pmatrix}6\\6\end{pmatrix}$

3 $(0, 0)\begin{pmatrix}5\\6\end{pmatrix}$

4 $(1, 1)\begin{pmatrix}0\\0\end{pmatrix}$

5 $(2, 3)\begin{pmatrix}5\\6\end{pmatrix}$

6 $(3, 2)\begin{pmatrix}1\\-1\end{pmatrix}$

B The equation $2x + 3y = 5$ can be written $(2, 3)\begin{pmatrix}x\\y\end{pmatrix} = 5$ using the idea of vectors.

Write in vector form:

1 $3x + y = 6$

2 $2x + 2y = 7$

3 $3x - y = 5$

4 $4x = 8$

5 $5y = 10$

6 $3x - 2y = 0$

C **1** A baker sells large loaves at 60 p each and small loaves at 35 p each. The matrix below shows how many of each he sold during a week.

	L	*S*
M	20	35
T	40	52
W	61	68
Th	43	59
F	86	75
S	106	124

$\begin{pmatrix}60\text{ p}\\35\text{ p}\end{pmatrix}$

How much money did he take each day?
How does this example show **vector** multiplication?

2 A hairdresser offers cutting at £4·50, shampoo and set at £2·80 and trimming at £2·30. The matrix of a week's work is shown below.

$$\begin{array}{c} \\ M \\ T \\ W \\ Th \\ F \\ S \end{array} \begin{array}{c} \begin{array}{ccc} C & S\&S & T \end{array} \\ \begin{bmatrix} 4 & 6 & 3 \\ 5 & 4 & 2 \\ 1 & 6 & 3 \\ 4 & 4 & 0 \\ 7 & 3 & 5 \\ 5 & 2 & 1 \end{bmatrix} \end{array} \quad \begin{array}{c} £ \\ \begin{bmatrix} 4{\cdot}50 \\ 2{\cdot}80 \\ 2{\cdot}30 \end{bmatrix} \end{array}$$

What was the total taken each day?
What was the total for the whole week?

3 Two farmers keep cattle, sheep and chickens.
Which of the two farmers has more money in animals?

$$\begin{array}{l} \\ \textit{Farmer Brown} \\ \textit{Farmer Green} \end{array} \begin{array}{c} \begin{array}{ccc} C & S & Ch \end{array} \\ \begin{pmatrix} 48 & 162 & 655 \\ 24 & 300 & 866 \end{pmatrix} \end{array}$$

Animal Values (£)

$$\begin{bmatrix} 120 \\ 45 \\ 10 \end{bmatrix}$$

18·3 The 2 × 2 matrix

A matrix with 2 rows and 2 columns is called a 2 × 2 matrix.

Examples:

$$\begin{pmatrix} a & b \\ c & d \end{pmatrix} \quad \begin{pmatrix} 3 & 1 \\ 2 & 5 \end{pmatrix} \quad \begin{pmatrix} 4 & 0 \\ 5 & 3 \end{pmatrix} \quad \begin{pmatrix} 0 & 1 \\ 1 & 0 \end{pmatrix}$$

Two 2 × 2 matrices can be added by adding numbers in corresponding rows and columns.

Example:

$$\begin{bmatrix} 2 & 3 \\ 4 & 5 \end{bmatrix} + \begin{bmatrix} 1 & 4 \\ 4 & 1 \end{bmatrix} = \begin{bmatrix} 3 & 7 \\ 8 & 6 \end{bmatrix}$$

Two 2 × 2 matrices can be multiplied as pairs of vectors.

Examples:

$$\begin{bmatrix} [2 & 3] \\ [4 & 5] \end{bmatrix} \times \begin{bmatrix} \begin{bmatrix}1\\4\end{bmatrix} & \begin{bmatrix}4\\1\end{bmatrix} \end{bmatrix} = \begin{bmatrix} [2\ \ 3]\begin{bmatrix}1\\4\end{bmatrix} & [2\ \ 3]\begin{bmatrix}4\\1\end{bmatrix} \\ [4\ \ 5]\begin{bmatrix}1\\4\end{bmatrix} & [4\ \ 5]\begin{bmatrix}4\\1\end{bmatrix} \end{bmatrix} = \begin{bmatrix} 14 & 11 \\ 24 & 21 \end{bmatrix}$$

Treat this one as a pair of row vectors

Treat this one as a pair of column vectors

Note: It is wrong to multiply two matrices by multiplying the numbers in corresponding rows and columns.

$$\begin{bmatrix} 1 & 2 \\ 3 & 4 \end{bmatrix} \times \begin{bmatrix} 2 & 5 \\ 1 & 4 \end{bmatrix} \neq \begin{bmatrix} 2 & 10 \\ 3 & 16 \end{bmatrix}$$

Exercise 18·3

A Add these pairs of matrices:

1 $\begin{bmatrix} 2 & 1 \\ 0 & 3 \end{bmatrix} + \begin{bmatrix} 4 & 1 \\ 0 & 2 \end{bmatrix}$

2 $\begin{bmatrix} 4 & -1 \\ 5 & 0 \end{bmatrix} + \begin{bmatrix} -3 & 2 \\ -4 & 0 \end{bmatrix}$

3 $\begin{bmatrix} 5 & 2 \\ 0 & 0 \end{bmatrix} + \begin{bmatrix} 1 & -1 \\ 3 & -2 \end{bmatrix}$

4 $\begin{bmatrix} 5 & 4 \\ 3 & 2 \end{bmatrix} + \begin{bmatrix} 0 & 0 \\ 0 & 0 \end{bmatrix}$

B Multiply these pairs of matrices:

1 $\begin{bmatrix} 1 & 2 \\ 3 & 4 \end{bmatrix}\begin{bmatrix} 1 & 3 \\ 5 & 6 \end{bmatrix}$

2 $\begin{bmatrix} 2 & 0 \\ 1 & 1 \end{bmatrix}\begin{bmatrix} 1 & 3 \\ 1 & 4 \end{bmatrix}$

3 $\begin{bmatrix} 0 & 2 \\ 1 & 2 \end{bmatrix}\begin{bmatrix} 3 & 1 \\ 4 & 2 \end{bmatrix}$

4 $\begin{bmatrix} 1 & 2 \\ 4 & 8 \end{bmatrix}\begin{bmatrix} 8 & 4 \\ 2 & 1 \end{bmatrix}$

C *A* is the matrix $\begin{bmatrix} 1 & 2 \\ 3 & 4 \end{bmatrix}$ *B* is the matrix $\begin{bmatrix} 1 & 2 \\ 2 & 1 \end{bmatrix}$

1 Find the matrices **A** × **B** and **B** × **A**. Are they the same?
2 Find the matrix **A** × **A** and the matrix **B** × **B**.
3 Work out **A** × (**A** +**B**). Is this the same as (**A** × **A**) + (**A** × **B**)?
4 Work out (**A** + **B**) × (**A** + **B**). Is this the same as (**A** × **A**) + (**B** × **B**)?

18·4 The unit matrix

The matrix $\begin{bmatrix} 1 & 0 \\ 0 & 1 \end{bmatrix}$ has special properties. It is called the Unit Matrix and given the sign *I*.

If you multiply any matrix **A** by **I**, the matrix **A** is unchanged.

Examples:

$$\begin{bmatrix}1 & 2\\3 & 4\end{bmatrix}\begin{bmatrix}1 & 0\\0 & 1\end{bmatrix} = \begin{bmatrix}(1\ \ 2)\begin{pmatrix}1\\0\end{pmatrix} & (1\ \ 2)\begin{pmatrix}0\\1\end{pmatrix}\\ (3\ \ 4)\begin{pmatrix}1\\0\end{pmatrix} & (3\ \ 4)\begin{pmatrix}0\\1\end{pmatrix}\end{bmatrix} = \begin{bmatrix}1 & 2\\3 & 4\end{bmatrix}$$

This is like multiplying an ordinary number by 1 . . . 235 × 1 = 235.

Inverse

If the product of two matrices is *I*, they are called inverses of each other.

Example:

$\begin{bmatrix}3 & 2\\4 & 3\end{bmatrix}$ and $\begin{bmatrix}3 & -2\\-4 & 3\end{bmatrix}$ are inverses because

$$\begin{bmatrix}3 & 2\\4 & 3\end{bmatrix} \times \begin{bmatrix}3 & -2\\-4 & 3\end{bmatrix} = \begin{bmatrix}1 & 0\\0 & 1\end{bmatrix} = I$$

Remember: $3 \times {}^-4 = {}^-12$, $2 \times {}^-2 = {}^-4$, etc.

Exercise 18·4

A **1** **I** is the unit matrix $\begin{bmatrix}1 & 0\\0 & 1\end{bmatrix}$ **A** is the matrix $\begin{bmatrix}5 & 0\\0 & 5\end{bmatrix}$

(a) Show that **A** × **I** = **I** × **A** = **A** by multiplying out.

(b) Show that $\begin{pmatrix}0.2 & 0\\0 & 0.2\end{pmatrix}$ is the inverse of **A**.

2 Given **I** is the unit matrix, find **I**, $\mathbf{I}^2$, $\mathbf{I}^3$ and $\mathbf{I}^4$. What do you notice?

3 **A** is the matrix $\begin{bmatrix}-1 & 0\\0 & -1\end{bmatrix}$ *Remember:* ${}^-1 \times {}^-1 = {}^+1$

(a) What is $\mathbf{A}^2$? (b) What is $\mathbf{A}^3$? (c) What is $\mathbf{A}^4$? (d) What is the inverse of **A**?

4 **B** is the matrix $\begin{bmatrix}1 & 0\\0 & -1\end{bmatrix}$

(a) Find $\mathbf{B}^2$ (b) Find $\mathbf{B}^3$ (c) Find $\mathbf{B}^4$ (d) What is the inverse of **B**?

B **1** The following six matrices form three pairs of inverses. Sort them into the pairs and show that the product of each pair is **I**.

$$\begin{bmatrix} 2 & 1 \\ 7 & 4 \end{bmatrix} \begin{bmatrix} -7 & 4 \\ 2 & -1 \end{bmatrix} \begin{bmatrix} -7 & 2 \\ 4 & -1 \end{bmatrix} \begin{bmatrix} 1 & 2 \\ 4 & 7 \end{bmatrix} \begin{bmatrix} 1 & 4 \\ 2 & 7 \end{bmatrix} \begin{bmatrix} 4 & -1 \\ -7 & 2 \end{bmatrix}$$

2 (a) Show that $\begin{bmatrix} 4 & -5 \\ -2 & 3 \end{bmatrix}$ and $\begin{bmatrix} 1{\cdot}5 & 2{\cdot}5 \\ 1 & 2 \end{bmatrix}$ are inverse matrices.

(b) Multiply $\begin{bmatrix} 1 & 2 \\ 3 & 4 \end{bmatrix}$ by $\begin{bmatrix} 4 & -5 \\ -2 & 3 \end{bmatrix}$ then multiply the result by $\begin{bmatrix} 1{\cdot}5 & 2{\cdot}5 \\ 1 & 2 \end{bmatrix}$

What is the final matrix?

3 Explain how inverse matrices behave in a similar way to reciprocal numbers. (Numbers whose product is 1, e.g. 9 and ·111 111 11 or $\frac{3}{4}$ and $\frac{4}{3}$).

C The Inverse Puzzle

It is an interesting puzzle to try to find an inverse to a 2 × 2 matrix. In the first four puzzles below we give you the numbers from which the inverse is made. In the last two you will have to guess the numbers for yourself.

1 $\begin{bmatrix} 2 & 1 \\ 5 & 3 \end{bmatrix} \begin{bmatrix} \dots & \dots \\ \dots & \dots \end{bmatrix} = \begin{bmatrix} 1 & 0 \\ 0 & 1 \end{bmatrix}$ The inverse is made up from the numbers 2, 3, −1 and −5.

2 $\begin{bmatrix} 1 & 0 \\ 1 & 1 \end{bmatrix} \begin{bmatrix} \dots & \dots \\ \dots & \dots \end{bmatrix} = \begin{bmatrix} 1 & 0 \\ 0 & 1 \end{bmatrix}$ The inverse has the numbers 1, 1, 0, −1.

3 $\begin{bmatrix} 0 & 2 \\ 5 & 3 \end{bmatrix} \begin{bmatrix} \dots & \dots \\ \dots & \dots \end{bmatrix} = \begin{bmatrix} 1 & 0 \\ 0 & 1 \end{bmatrix}$ The inverse has the numbers 0·2, 0·5, −0·3, 0.

4 $\begin{bmatrix} 2 & 2 \\ 3 & 8 \end{bmatrix} \begin{bmatrix} \dots & \dots \\ \dots & \dots \end{bmatrix} = \begin{bmatrix} 1 & 0 \\ 0 & 1 \end{bmatrix}$ The inverse has the numbers 0·2, −0·2, −0·3, −0·8.

5 $\begin{bmatrix} 3 & 2 \\ 5 & 4 \end{bmatrix} \begin{bmatrix} \dots & \dots \\ \dots & \dots \end{bmatrix} = \begin{bmatrix} 1 & 0 \\ 0 & 1 \end{bmatrix}$

6 $\begin{bmatrix} 2 & 1 \\ 3 & 2 \end{bmatrix} \begin{bmatrix} \dots & \dots \\ \dots & \dots \end{bmatrix} = \begin{bmatrix} 1 & 0 \\ 0 & 1 \end{bmatrix}$

Unit M19 Isometries

19·1 Isometries

Isometries is the name given to changes of position without change of shape.

Iso means 'the same', *metrics* means 'measurements'.

There are three types of isometries:

1 Translations—shapes are moved in straight lines without turning.
2 Rotations—shapes are turned around a fixed point.
3 Reflections—shapes are flipped over to a position which is the mirror image.

Translation

Every point is moved the same distance in the same direction.

Every translation has a *translation vector* which tells you the distance and direction of movement.

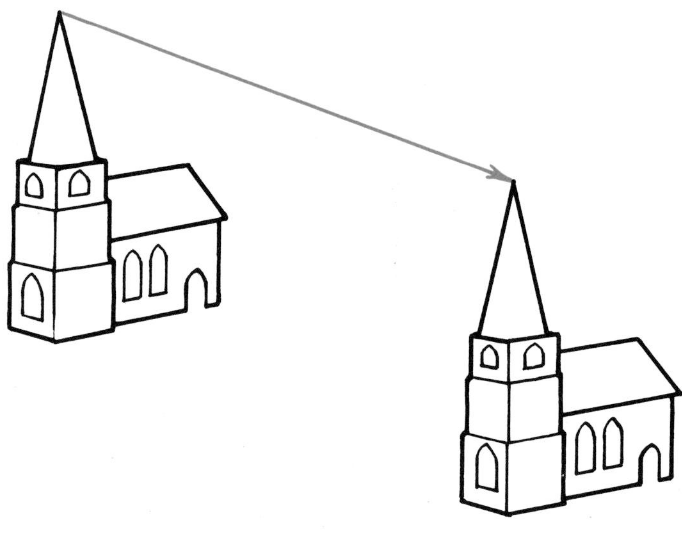

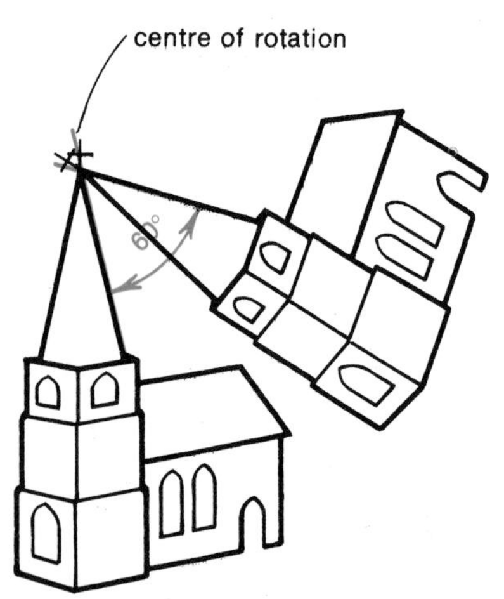

Rotation

Example: 60° about the top of the steeple.

One point is fixed and everything else is moved around that fixed point.

Every rotation has a fixed point called the **centre**, and an **angle** of **rotation**.

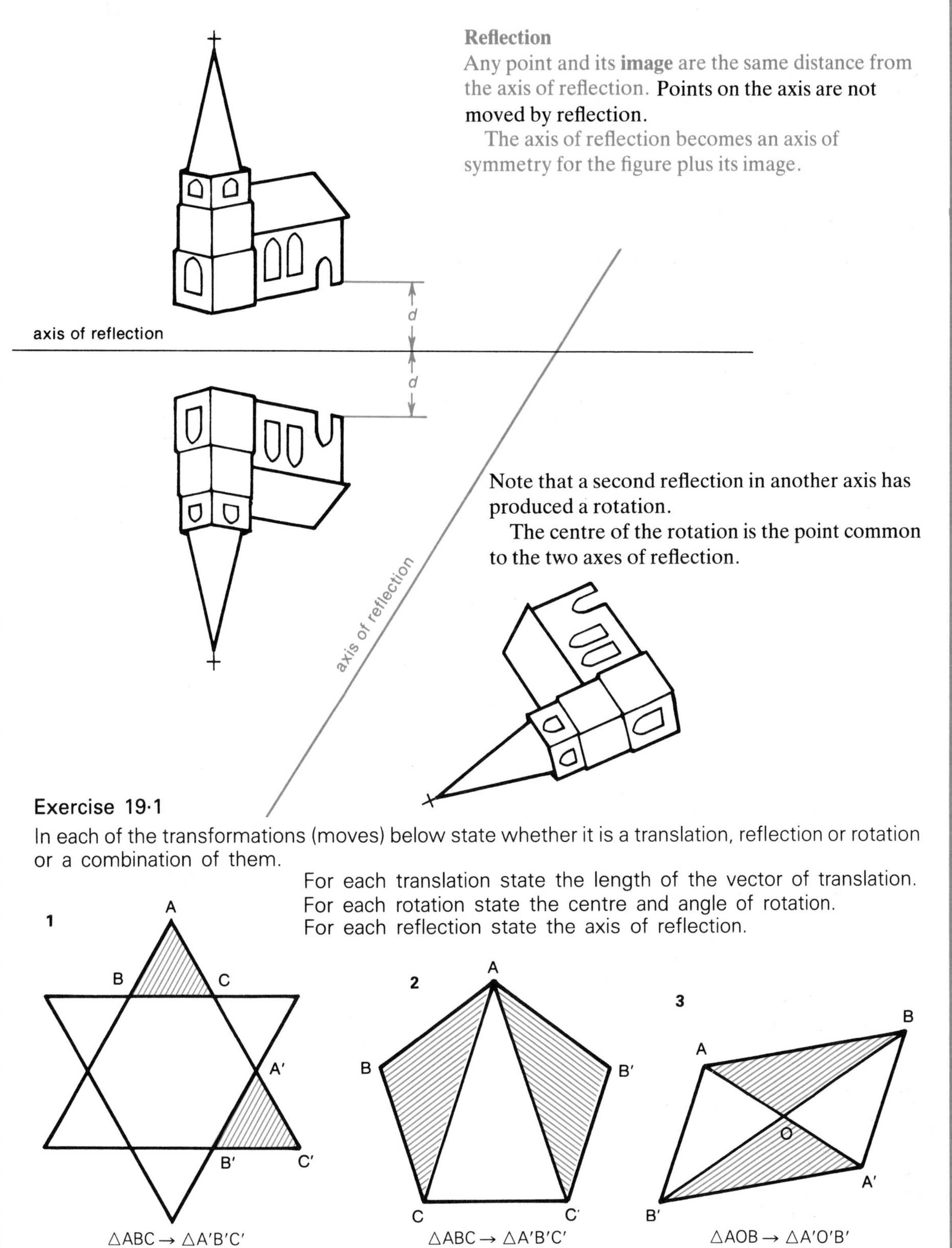

Reflection

Any point and its **image** are the same distance from the axis of reflection. **Points on the axis are not moved by reflection.**

The axis of reflection becomes an axis of symmetry for the figure plus its image.

Note that a second reflection in another axis has produced a rotation.

The centre of the rotation is the point common to the two axes of reflection.

Exercise 19·1

In each of the transformations (moves) below state whether it is a translation, reflection or rotation or a combination of them.

For each translation state the length of the vector of translation.
For each rotation state the centre and angle of rotation.
For each reflection state the axis of reflection.

1 $\triangle ABC \rightarrow \triangle A'B'C'$

2 $\triangle ABC \rightarrow \triangle A'B'C'$

3 $\triangle AOB \rightarrow \triangle A'O'B'$

4

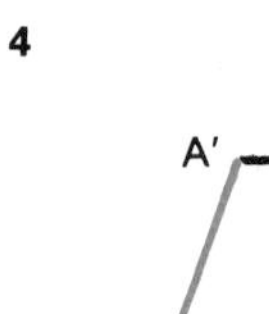

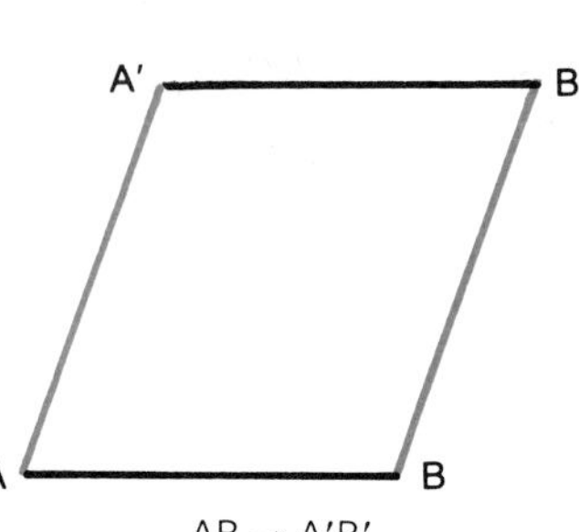

$AB \rightarrow A'B'$

5

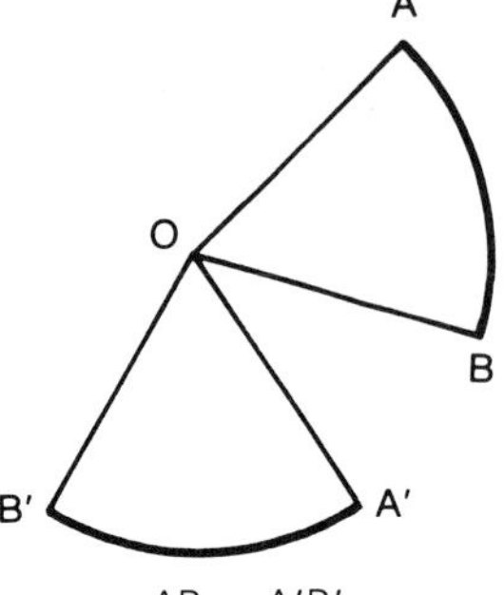

$AB \rightarrow A'B'$

6

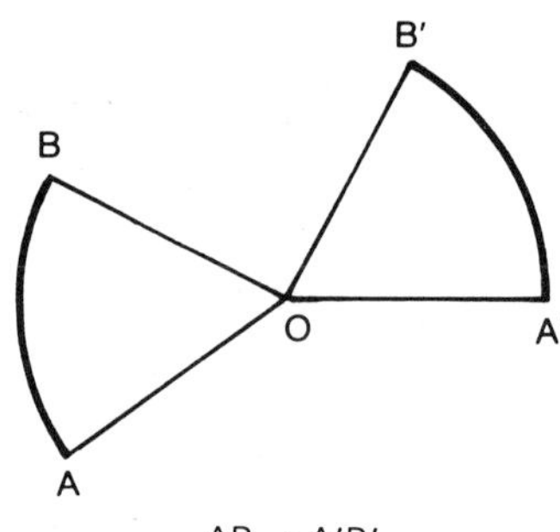

$AB \rightarrow A'B'$

7

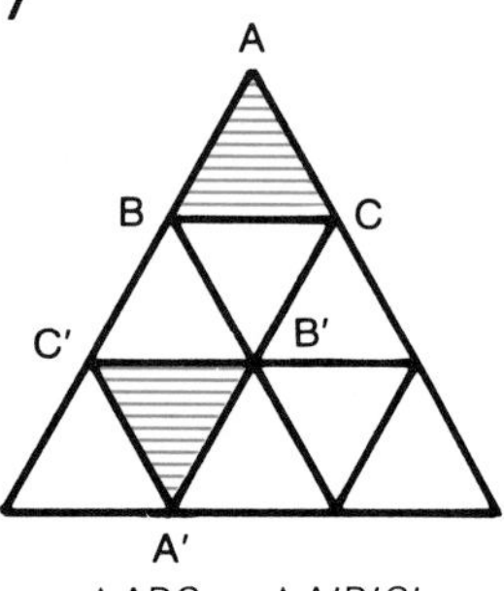

$\triangle ABC \rightarrow \triangle A'B'C'$

8

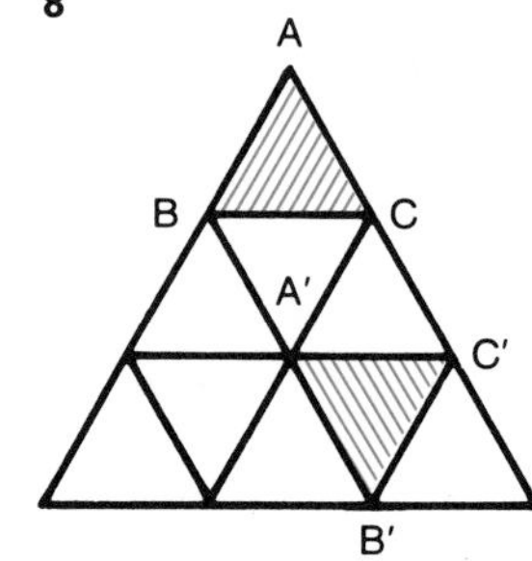

$\triangle ABC \rightarrow \triangle A'B'C'$

9

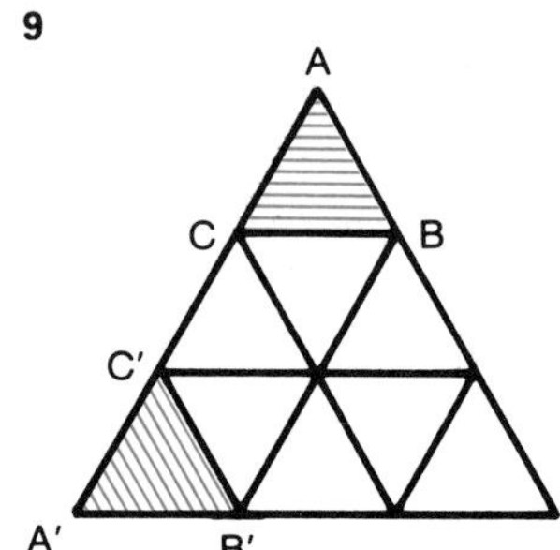

$\triangle ABC \rightarrow \triangle A'B'C'$

19·2 Translations by vector

Every translation can be described by a vector.

Example:

Every point of the triangle is moved 4 units in the x direction and 3 units in the y direction.

This translation vector is written

$$\begin{bmatrix} 4 \\ 3 \end{bmatrix}$$

The new position of any point whose position vector is $\begin{bmatrix} x \\ y \end{bmatrix}$ will be $\begin{bmatrix} x+4 \\ y+3 \end{bmatrix}$ under this translation.

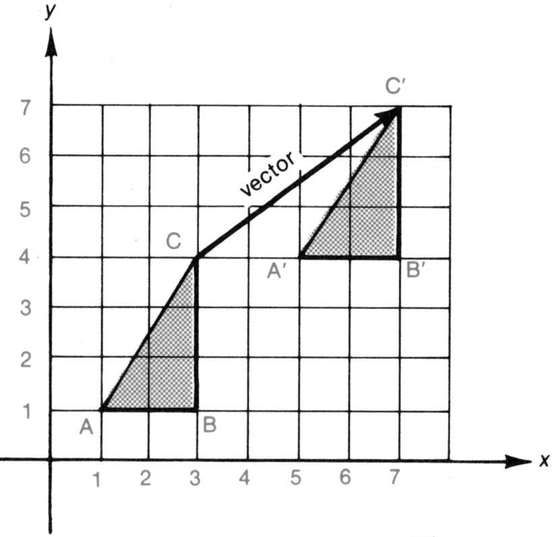

B's position vector is written $\begin{pmatrix} 3 \\ 1 \end{pmatrix}$

B moves to B′ $\begin{pmatrix} 3 \\ 1 \end{pmatrix} + \begin{pmatrix} 4 \\ 3 \end{pmatrix} = \begin{pmatrix} 7 \\ 4 \end{pmatrix}$

Position vector of B′ is $\begin{pmatrix} 7 \\ 4 \end{pmatrix}$

Example:

A triangle ABC with vertices A(0, 0); B(3, 1) and C(2, 3) is translated by vector $\begin{pmatrix}3\\2\end{pmatrix}$. What is the new position of the triangle?

$$A;\ \begin{pmatrix}0\\0\end{pmatrix} + \begin{pmatrix}3\\2\end{pmatrix} = \begin{pmatrix}3\\2\end{pmatrix} \ldots A' = (3, 2)$$

$$B;\ \begin{pmatrix}3\\1\end{pmatrix} + \begin{pmatrix}3\\2\end{pmatrix} = \begin{pmatrix}6\\3\end{pmatrix} \ldots B' = (6, 3)$$

$$C;\ \begin{pmatrix}2\\3\end{pmatrix} + \begin{pmatrix}3\\2\end{pmatrix} = \begin{pmatrix}5\\5\end{pmatrix} \ldots C' = (5, 5)$$

Note: To get from A(0, 0) to B(3, 1) you go 3 → and 1 ↑
To get from A′(3, 2) to B′(6, 3) you go 3 → and 1 ↑

Exercise 19·2

A 1 What translation vector moves:

(a) (0, 0) to (3, 6)?
(b) (1, 1) to (4, 5)?
(c) (2, 4) to (3, 8)?
(d) (0, 0) to (−1, −3)?
(e) (4, 5) to (2, 1)?
(f) (3, −6) to (0, 0)?

2 The line AB has A on the point (1, 1) and B on the point (3, 5).

(a) What translation vector would move A on to B?
(b) What would this vector do to B?
(c) Draw a diagram to check that C(2, 3) is the middle point of AB.
(d) What point is C′ under the same translation?
(e) Is C′ the middle point of A′B′? Remember A′ is B in this case.

3 (a) The point A(1, 2) is moved by a translation vector $\begin{pmatrix}3\\3\end{pmatrix}$

What are the coordinates of A′?

(b) A′ is moved by another translation vector $\begin{pmatrix}-2\\-1\end{pmatrix}$

What are the coordinates of the resulting point A″?

(c) What translation vector would have moved A direct to A″?

B 1 The point A is moved to A′ by a translation vector T_1. A′ is then moved by another vector T_2 to A″. This point is moved back to A by a third vector T_3. Find T_1, T_2 and T_3. What do you notice about $T_1 + T_2 + T_3$?

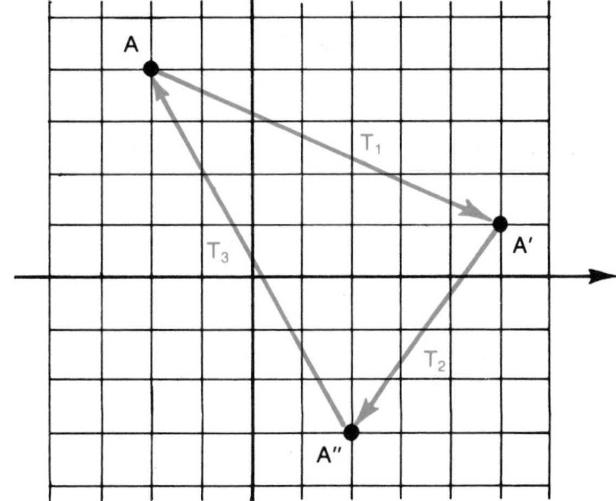

2 Find the translation vectors that would move:
(a) A″ to A′ (b) A′ to A (c) A to A″
Write each of these in terms of T_1, T_2 and T_3.

3 A translation moves every point of the grid to another one. No points are left where they are. Is this true of reflections and rotations?

C Make a list of all the translations you could make in the diagram below. (For example AB → IJ or AB → BC.) There are quite a lot.

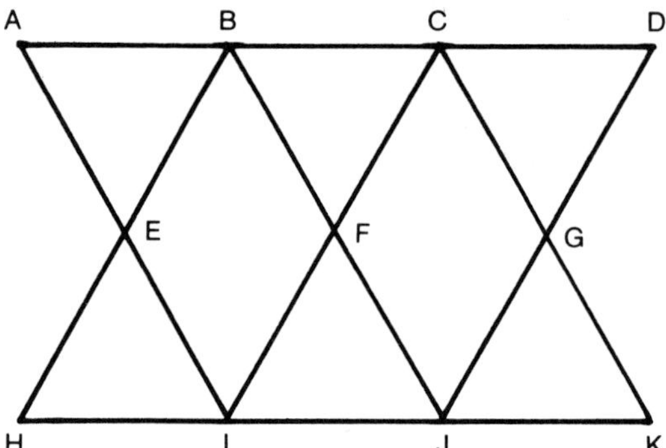

19·3 Rotations by matrix

The point (x, y) has position vector $\begin{pmatrix} x \\ y \end{pmatrix}$

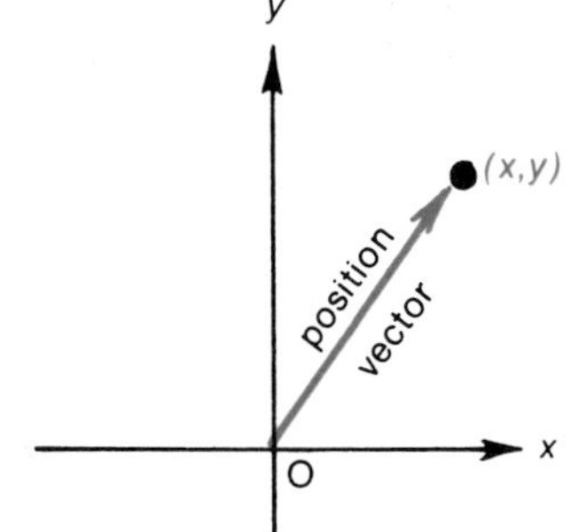

The position vector is rotated by multiplying it by a matrix as shown in the examples below.

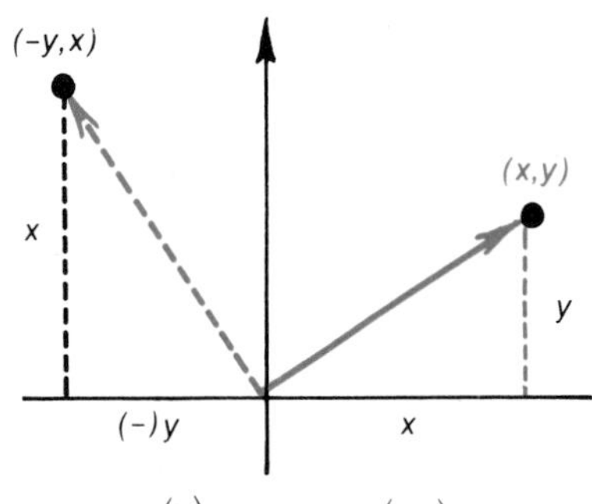

Vector $\begin{pmatrix} x \\ y \end{pmatrix}$ rotated to $\begin{pmatrix} -y \\ x \end{pmatrix}$

Rotation 90° anticlockwise

$$\begin{pmatrix} 0 & -1 \\ 1 & 0 \end{pmatrix} \begin{pmatrix} x \\ y \end{pmatrix} = \begin{pmatrix} -y \\ +x \end{pmatrix}$$

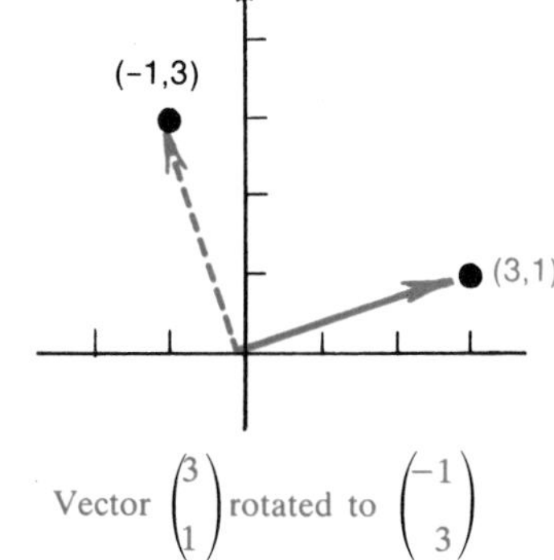

Vector $\begin{pmatrix} 3 \\ 1 \end{pmatrix}$ rotated to $\begin{pmatrix} -1 \\ 3 \end{pmatrix}$

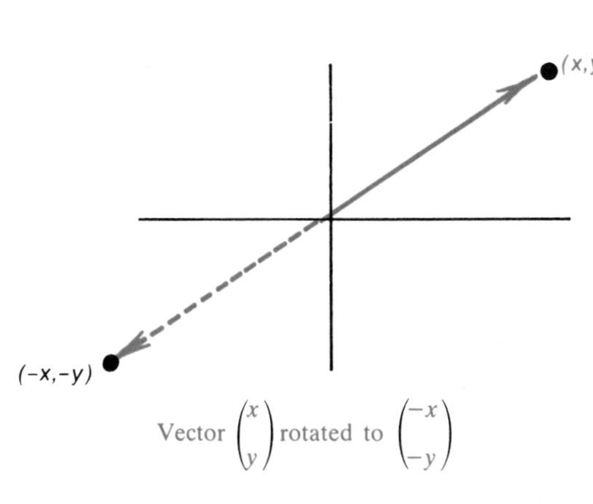

Vector $\begin{pmatrix} x \\ y \end{pmatrix}$ rotated to $\begin{pmatrix} -x \\ -y \end{pmatrix}$

Rotation 180° anticlockwise

$$\begin{pmatrix} -1 & 0 \\ 0 & -1 \end{pmatrix}\begin{pmatrix} x \\ y \end{pmatrix} = \begin{pmatrix} -x \\ -y \end{pmatrix}$$

(3,1)

(-3,-1)

Vector $\begin{pmatrix} 3 \\ 1 \end{pmatrix}$ rotated to $\begin{pmatrix} -3 \\ -1 \end{pmatrix}$

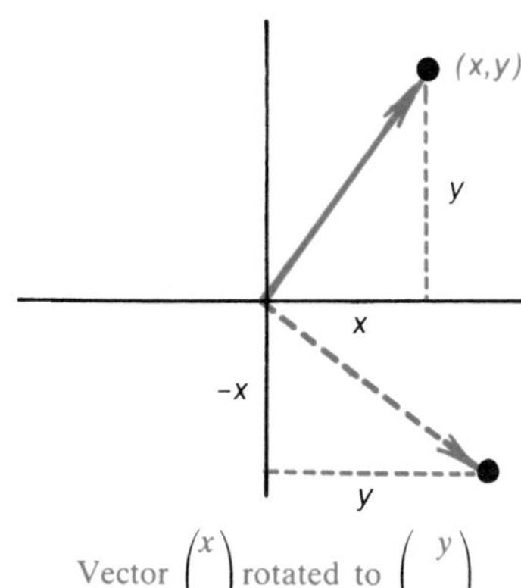

Vector $\begin{pmatrix} x \\ y \end{pmatrix}$ rotated to $\begin{pmatrix} y \\ -x \end{pmatrix}$

Rotation 90° clockwise

$$\begin{pmatrix} 0 & 1 \\ -1 & 0 \end{pmatrix}\begin{pmatrix} x \\ y \end{pmatrix} = \begin{pmatrix} y \\ -x \end{pmatrix}$$

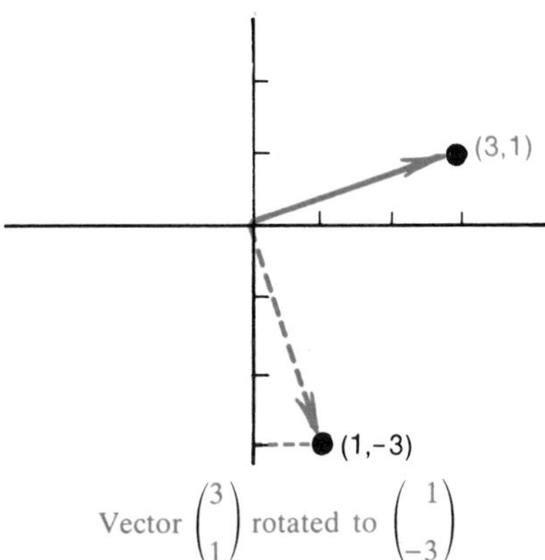

Vector $\begin{pmatrix} 3 \\ 1 \end{pmatrix}$ rotated to $\begin{pmatrix} 1 \\ -3 \end{pmatrix}$

Exercise 19·3

A Look carefully at the examples above and make sure that you understand . . .

1 How the matrix multiplication has moved the vector to produce the rotated vector.

2 The three different rotations; 90° clockwise, 180° and 90° anticlockwise. (Why do we have no separate clockwise and anticlockwise rotations for 180°?)

3 Why (x, y) becomes $(y, -x)$ when the vector is rotated 90° clockwise.

4 Check the matrix multiplication for each example.

B **1** The anticlockwise rotation matrix $\begin{bmatrix} 0 & -1 \\ 1 & 0 \end{bmatrix}$ corresponds to one of the commands 'right turn', 'left turn' and 'about turn'. Which one?

2 Which matrices correspond to the other two commands?

3 Which matrix would make the vector turn right round and back to its original position?

4 (a) Multiply the matrix $\begin{bmatrix} 0 & -1 \\ 1 & 0 \end{bmatrix}$ by itself. What do you notice?

(b) Multiply the matrix $\begin{bmatrix} -1 & 0 \\ 0 & -1 \end{bmatrix}$ by itself. What do you notice?

(c) Multiply the matrix $\begin{bmatrix} 0 & 1 \\ -1 & 0 \end{bmatrix}$ by itself. What do you notice?

C Write down the vectors resulting from multiplying:

1 $\begin{bmatrix} 0 & -1 \\ 1 & 0 \end{bmatrix}\begin{bmatrix} 2 \\ 3 \end{bmatrix}$ **2** $\begin{bmatrix} -1 & 0 \\ 0 & -1 \end{bmatrix}\begin{bmatrix} 4 \\ 5 \end{bmatrix}$ **3** $\begin{bmatrix} -1 & 0 \\ 0 & -1 \end{bmatrix}\begin{bmatrix} -3 \\ -2 \end{bmatrix}$

4 $\begin{bmatrix} 0 & 1 \\ -1 & 0 \end{bmatrix}\begin{bmatrix} -3 \\ 4 \end{bmatrix}$ **5** $\begin{bmatrix} 0 & 1 \\ -1 & 0 \end{bmatrix}\begin{bmatrix} -2 \\ -3 \end{bmatrix}$ **6** $\begin{bmatrix} 0 & -1 \\ 1 & 0 \end{bmatrix}\begin{bmatrix} 4 \\ 0 \end{bmatrix}$

Describe each of the results as a rotation of the original vector.

19·4 Reflection by matrix

Looking back over the work of this unit you would expect reflection to be connected with matrices. In fact, there are simple matrices which produce reflection and three of them are given below.

(a) Reflection in the y-axis

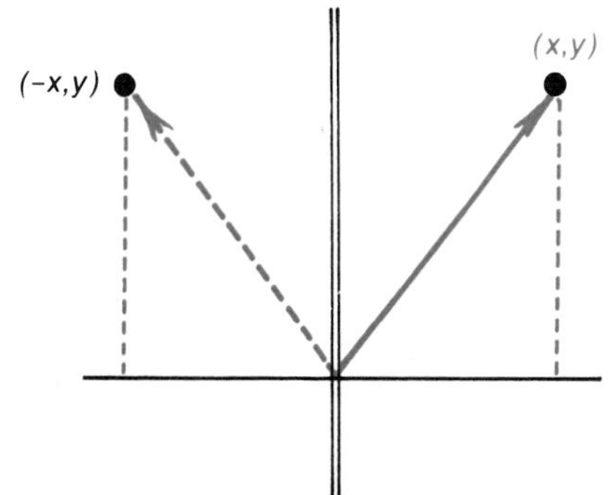

x becomes $-x$ and
y stays y.

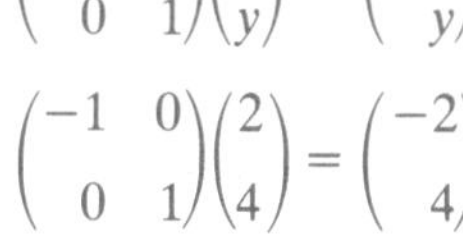

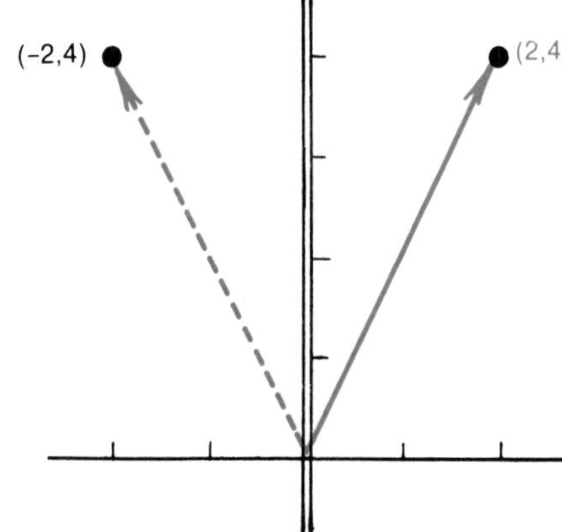

(b) Reflection in the x-axis

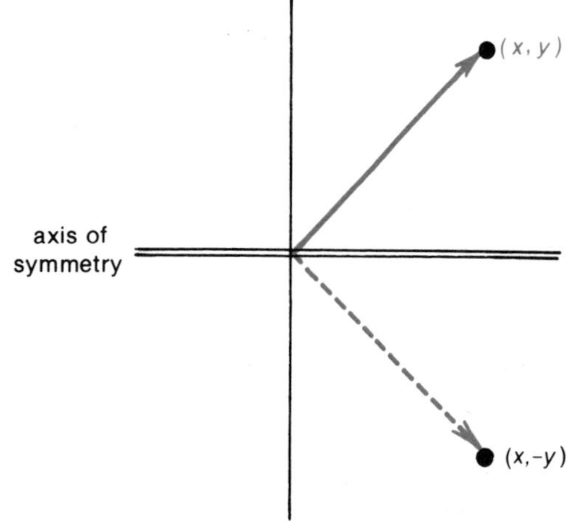

x stays x and
y becomes $-y$.

$$\begin{pmatrix} 1 & 0 \\ 0 & -1 \end{pmatrix}\begin{pmatrix} x \\ y \end{pmatrix} = \begin{pmatrix} x \\ y \end{pmatrix}$$

$$\begin{pmatrix} 1 & 0 \\ 0 & -1 \end{pmatrix}\begin{pmatrix} 2 \\ 4 \end{pmatrix} = \begin{pmatrix} 2 \\ -4 \end{pmatrix}$$

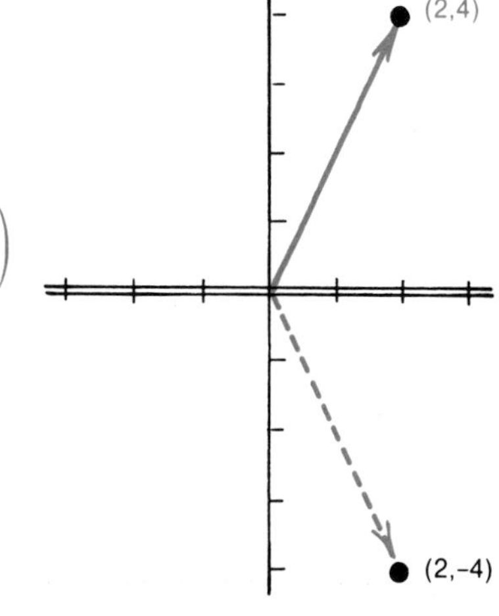

(c) Reflection in the line $y = x$

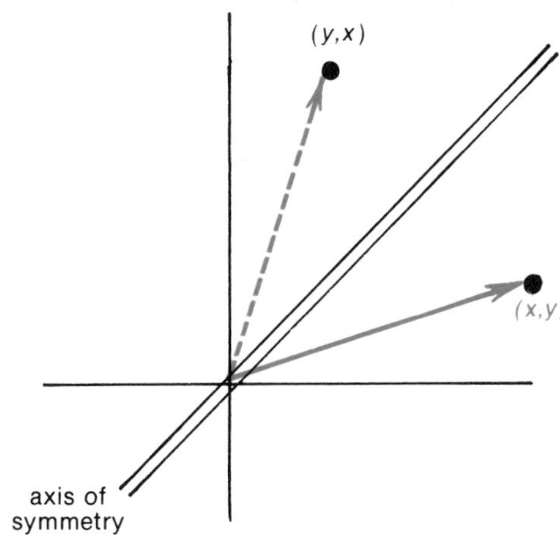

x becomes y and
y becomes x

$$\begin{pmatrix} 0 & 1 \\ 1 & 0 \end{pmatrix}\begin{pmatrix} x \\ y \end{pmatrix} = \begin{pmatrix} y \\ x \end{pmatrix}$$

$$\begin{pmatrix} 0 & 1 \\ 1 & 0 \end{pmatrix}\begin{pmatrix} 2 \\ 4 \end{pmatrix} = \begin{pmatrix} 4 \\ 2 \end{pmatrix}$$

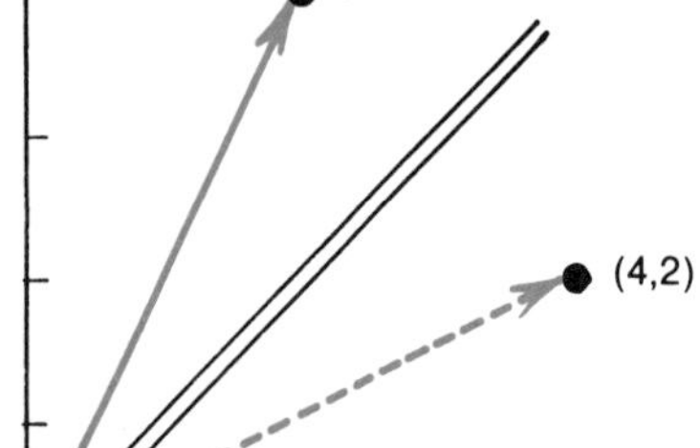

Exercise 19·4

A Look carefully at the examples above and make sure that you understand:

1 How the matrix multiplication has moved the position vector to produce the reflected vector.

2 The difference between reflections in the x-axis, in the y-axis and in the line $y = x$.

3 Exactly what has happened to the vector $\begin{pmatrix} 2 \\ 4 \end{pmatrix}$ in all three cases.

4 The connection between reflection in a line and axes of symmetry of geometrical figures (below.)

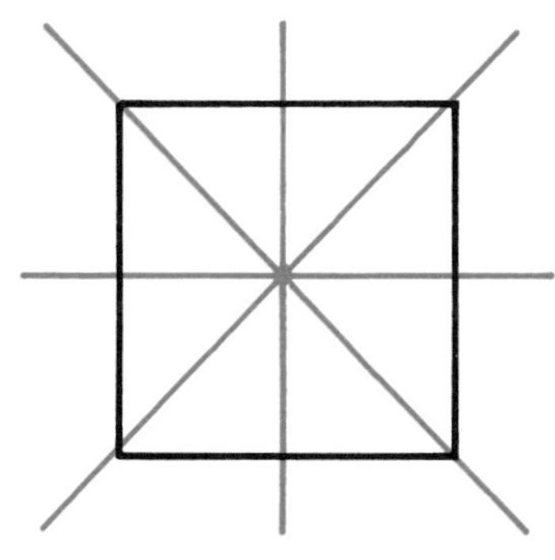

The square has four axes of symmetry.

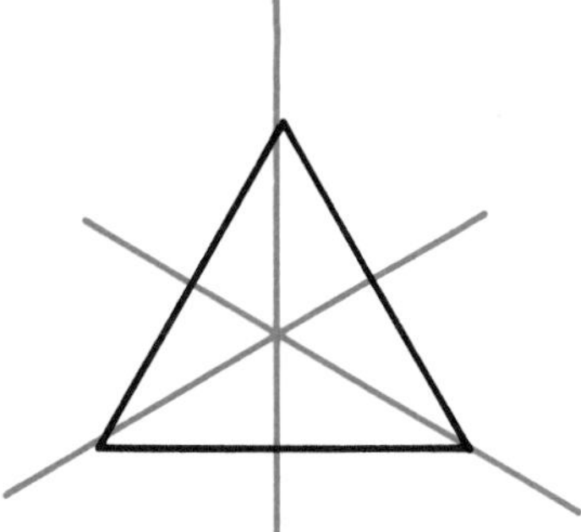

The equilateral triangle has three axes of symmetry.

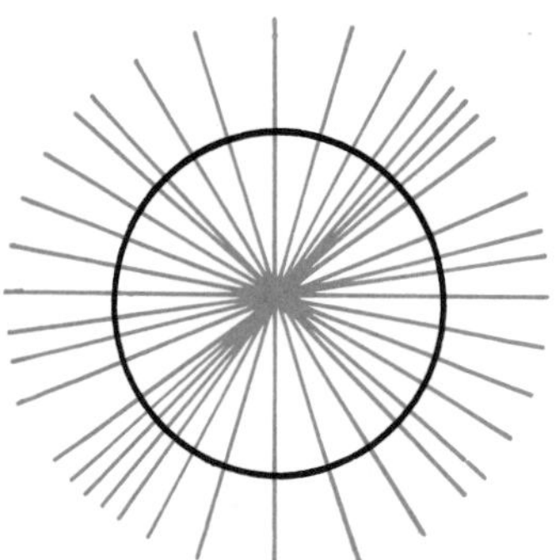

The circle has an infinite number of axes of symmetry.

B **1** Multiply the two matrices $\begin{pmatrix} -1 & 0 \\ 0 & 1 \end{pmatrix}$ and $\begin{pmatrix} 1 & 0 \\ 0 & -1 \end{pmatrix}$ and comment on the resulting matrix.

Does it suggest that a reflection in the x-axis followed by a reflection in the y-axis leads to a rotation of 180°?

2 Show that $\begin{pmatrix} -1 & 0 \\ 0 & 1 \end{pmatrix}\begin{pmatrix} -1 & 0 \\ 0 & 1 \end{pmatrix} = \begin{pmatrix} 1 & 0 \\ 0 & 1 \end{pmatrix}$ and $\begin{pmatrix} 1 & 0 \\ 0 & -1 \end{pmatrix}\begin{pmatrix} 1 & 0 \\ 0 & -1 \end{pmatrix} = \begin{pmatrix} 1 & 0 \\ 0 & 1 \end{pmatrix}$

What does this mean in terms of reflecting twice in the x-axis?

3 Work out these products and explain what has happened in terms of reflection.

(a) $\begin{pmatrix} -1 & 0 \\ 0 & 1 \end{pmatrix}\begin{pmatrix} 3 \\ -2 \end{pmatrix}$ (b) $\begin{pmatrix} 1 & 0 \\ 0 & -1 \end{pmatrix}\begin{pmatrix} -2 \\ -2 \end{pmatrix}$ (c) $\begin{pmatrix} -1 & 0 \\ 0 & 1 \end{pmatrix}\begin{pmatrix} -3 \\ 5 \end{pmatrix}$

(d) $\underbrace{\begin{pmatrix} -1 & 0 \\ 0 & 1 \end{pmatrix}\begin{pmatrix} 1 & 0 \\ 0 & -1 \end{pmatrix}}\begin{pmatrix} 4 \\ 3 \end{pmatrix}$ (e) $\begin{pmatrix} 1 & 0 \\ 0 & -1 \end{pmatrix}\begin{pmatrix} -1 & 0 \\ 0 & 1 \end{pmatrix}\begin{pmatrix} -2 \\ -3 \end{pmatrix}$

Work out this first

4 (a) **R** is the matrix $\begin{pmatrix} 0 & 1 \\ 1 & 0 \end{pmatrix}$ Find $\mathbf{R}^2$ and $\mathbf{R}^3$ and comment.

(b) Work out $\begin{pmatrix} 0 & 1 \\ 1 & 0 \end{pmatrix}\begin{pmatrix} 2 \\ 3 \end{pmatrix}$; $\begin{pmatrix} 0 & 1 \\ 1 & 0 \end{pmatrix}\begin{pmatrix} 3 \\ 2 \end{pmatrix}$; $\begin{pmatrix} 0 & 1 \\ 1 & 0 \end{pmatrix}\begin{pmatrix} -2 \\ -3 \end{pmatrix}$; $\begin{pmatrix} 0 & 1 \\ 1 & 0 \end{pmatrix}\begin{pmatrix} -3 \\ -2 \end{pmatrix}$

C 1 Each of the points ABCD is moved by multiplying the point's position vector by $\begin{pmatrix} -1 & 0 \\ 0 & 1 \end{pmatrix}$.

Copy the diagram and draw the image figure A′B′C′D′.

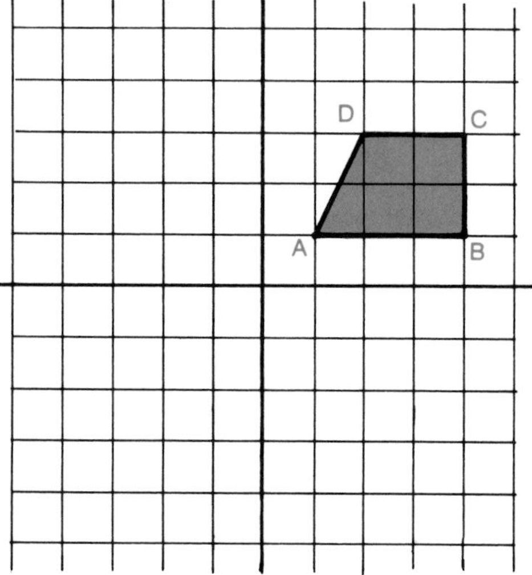

2 Find the image A″B″C″D″ that is obtained by reflecting ABCD in the *x*-axis.

3 What matrix transformation would move A′B′C′D′ on to A″B″C″D″??

4 The matrix transformation of question 3 is used on ABCD. Draw the figure that results. What is the line AD in the figure made up of ABCD and its image?

19·5 Transformations in sport and everyday life

When objects are moved, their movements can be described in terms of rotation and translation.

Example:

When a person walks upstairs, there is a translation of the whole body and also rotations as the legs are lifted to climb the stairs.

Exercise 19·5

A Explain the translations and rotations taking place in the following situations:

1 A girl is riding a bicycle along the road.
2 The driver of a car steers it round a corner.
3 A door is closed and locked.
4 A pair of shears is used to cut a hedge.

B Describe the translations and rotations that take place in these machines:

1 A lawn mower.
2 A sewing machine.
3 A kitchen mixer.
4 A crane moving a concrete block.

C **1** Describe the translations that take place when:

(a) A striker shoots at goal and the goalkeeper makes a 'great save'.
(b) A pole vaulter vaults 14 feet.
(c) A swimmer using breast stroke turns after a length.
(d) A player serves at tennis.

2 Choose a situation that interests you and describe the translations and rotations that take place. Can you think of any situations where reflection happens?

Unit M20

20·1 Pictorial statistics

Pictorial statistics are very easy to read if you use common-sense. We are starting this unit with a quiz. You will be able to answer most of the questions right away.

1 (a) In which year were most houses built?
(b) The number of homes built in 1982 was . . . ?

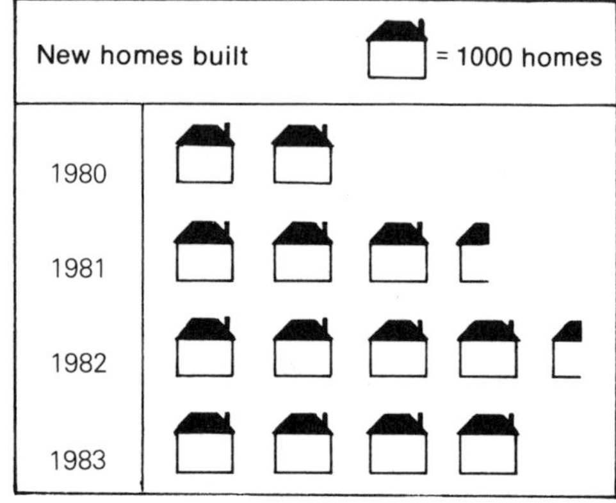

2 (a) The month with the most rain was . . .
(b) There were . . . cm of rain in May.
(c) The three driest months were . . .

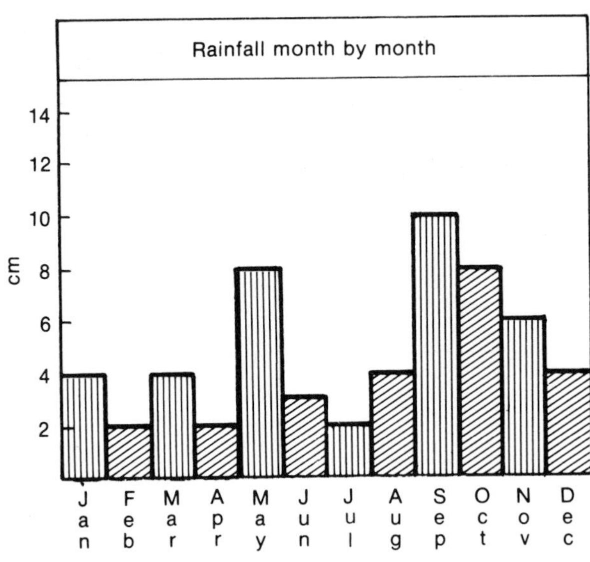

3 (a) In which month was steak the cheapest?
(b) What was the price per lb in September?
(c) In which month(s) was the price about £2·80/lb?

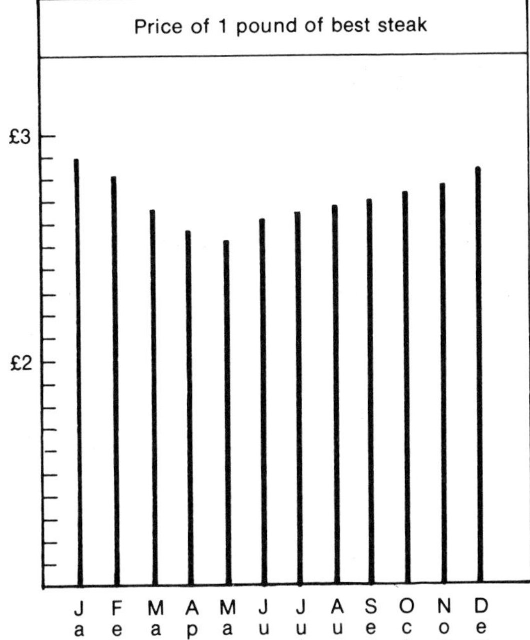

4 (a) Which service costs the most money?
(b) Is it true in this diagram, that health costs more than transport?

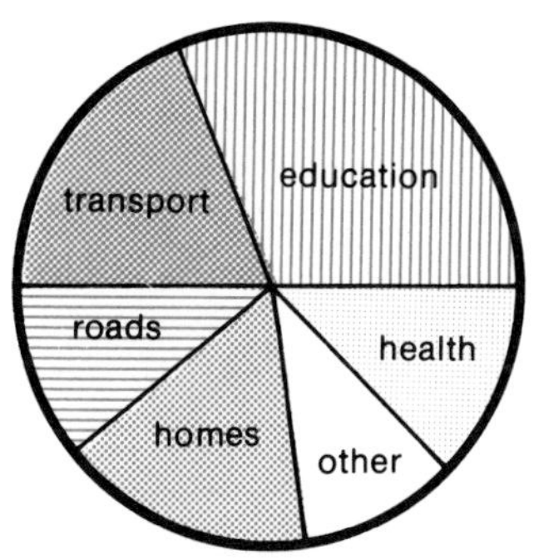

How the rates are spent in **Newtown**.

5 (a) Which of these is true (from the diagram)?
(1) Girls have more education than boys.
(2) Girls have less education than boys.
(b) The difference in length of education between men and women is getting (1) more (2) less?
(c) The time spent on education increased by about ... years from 1900 to 1975.

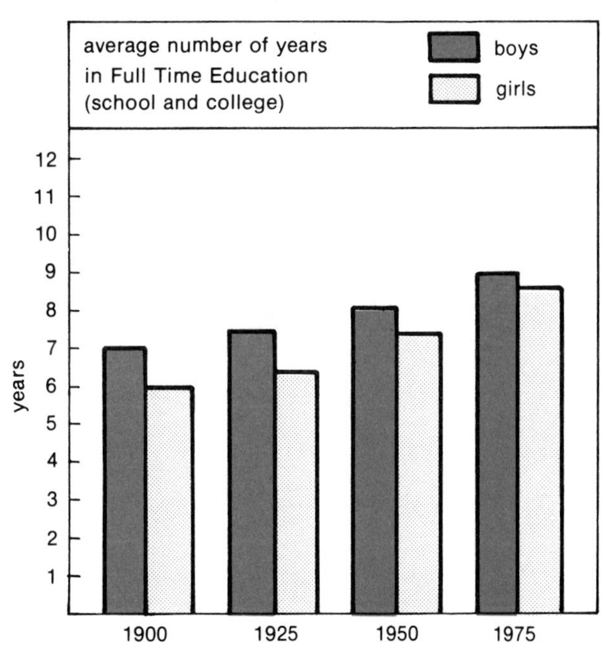

I hope you enjoyed the quiz. Now we will study the different forms of 'picture' used in statistics.

Note: A picture cannot give more information than the number it is taken from. Pictures draw attention to things, emphasise things which depend on the point of view of the person preparing the statistics. Sometimes they are used to give a wrong impression. We will discuss this later on in the course under the heading 'Misuse of Statistics'.

20·2 Pictogram

A pictogram is a diagram which uses little symbols or pictures to represent statistical data. The first table in the quiz is a pictogram. Each little house stands for 1000 new homes built. The parts of houses are not accurate.

This sort of diagram is often used when statistics are presented on TV or in the newspapers.

Exercise 20·1

A 1 How many of each country's cars were sold? (From the diagram.)

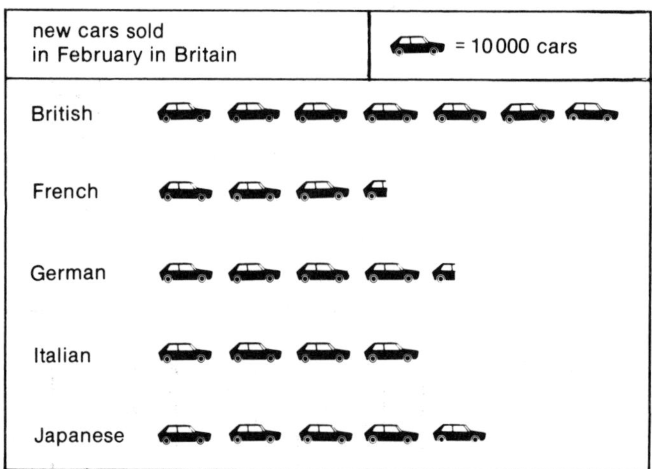

2 Which country sold fewest cars?
3 How many non-British cars were sold?
4 What percentage of the total number were British cars?

B

men and women at work in a town

= 100 women

= 100 men

mining

factory

shop

office

teaching

farming

1. How many men work in mining?
2. How many women work in factories?
3. Which jobs use more women than men?
4. How many more women office workers are there than men office workers?
5. Which industry employs six times as many men as women?
6. How many workers are listed altogether?
7. What important jobs have been left out of the list?
8. Do you think the pattern of employment is very different in your town?

C Draw pictograms to show the following data.

1. During one day the following vehicles were counted passing on a section of motorway. 5000 lorries, 6500 cars, 3500 coaches, 1500 motor cycles.
2. The information below gives yearly energy consumption per head of population (how much power is used by each person in 1 year.) The power is measured in units of kilowatt hours.

USA	50 000 kw hrs
Japan	30 000 kw hrs
EEC	21 000 kw hrs
USSR	16 000 kw hrs
India	3 000 kw hrs

Use one power station to represent 10 000 kilowatt hours per head to make a pictogram. Comment on the information. (How do you think Americans use all that power?)

20·3 Bar Chart

In a bar chart the height (or length) of the bar shows the quantity. A bar chart will show up outstanding values.

Example:

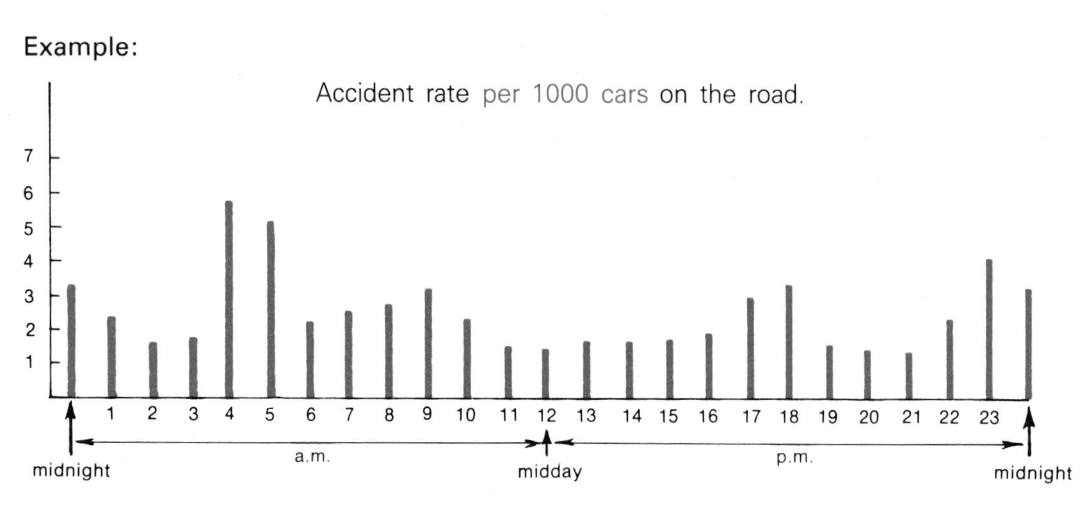

This very interesting bar chart is about road accidents. It shows that at 4 o'clock in the morning there are 6 accidents per 1000 cars on the road. So, although there are more cars about during the day, the *proportional* accident rate is highest very early in the morning.

The bar chart shows the more dangerous times, as follows:

4/5 am —	Probably dark with fast drivers taking risks
9 am —	Rush hour, morning peak
17/18 hrs which is 5/6 pm —	Rush hour, evening peak
23 hrs which is 11 pm —	Pub closing time, dangerous driving

Exercise 20·2

A The bar chart below shows the percentage of people absent from work during the first 15 weeks of the year.

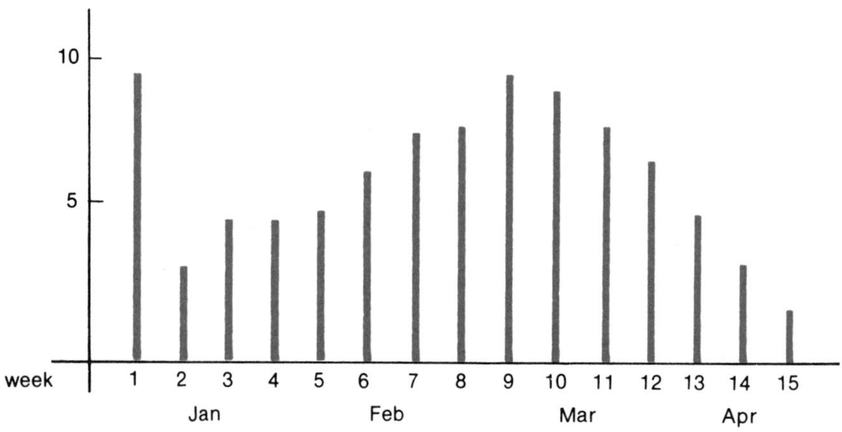

1 When was the 'peak' absence period? (Most people away sick.)
2 For which weeks were 5 people per 100 absent from work?
3 For which weeks were more than 6 people per 100 absent from work?
4 For which weeks were less than 6 people per 100 absent from work?
5 Discuss the shape of the bar chart. What 'story' does it tell?

B After an operation a girl's temperature was taken every 2 hours.

Time	*°C*	*Time*	*°C*
10·00	38·9	02·00	39·2
12·00	39·1	04·00	39·6
14·00	39·1	06·00	39·8
16·00	39·2	08·00	39·4
18·00	39·4	10·00	39·0
20·00	39·6	12·00	38·6
22·00	39·4	14·00	38·4
24·00	39·4	16·00	38·4

1 Draw a bar chart to show the girl's temperature.
2 If the doctor had said she had been worried twice during the night when would that have been?
3 For how long was the girl's temperature over 39°C?
4 When was the greatest rise in temperature over 2 hours?
5 When was there the greatest fall in temperature over 2 hours?

C 1 Bar charts are often used for grouped data. The bar is then given a 'thickness' to represent the group. The height or length of the bar corresponds to quantity. This type of diagram is sometimes called a 'block graph'.

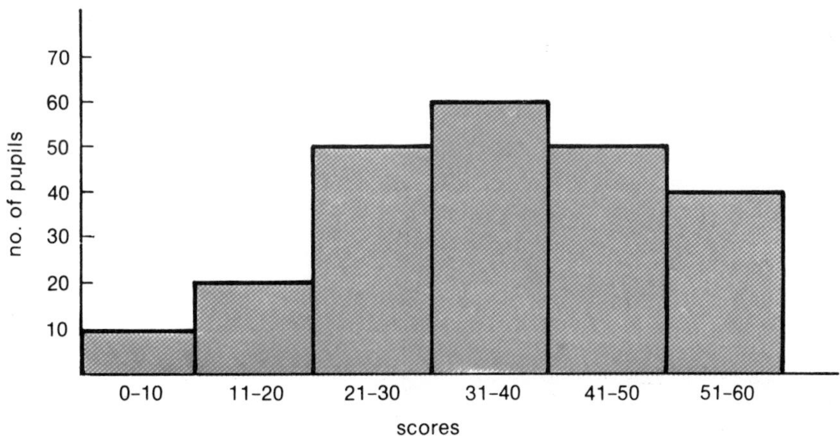

The 1st-year children were all given a reading test out of 60 marks when they started at Milldew Comprehensive.
(a) How many children scored between 11 and 20 marks in the test?
(b) How many children scored between 41 and 50 marks?
(c) How many children scored **over** 40 marks?
(d) How many children scored under 21 marks?
(e) Can you tell how many children scored full marks? Explain your answer.
(f) How many children took the test altogether?
(g) Estimate the average mark for the test.

2 The children also took a mathematics test and the results are given in the table below.

Mark	*No. of children*
0–10	15
11–20	36
21–30	44
31–40	68
41–50	73
51–60	12

(a) Draw a bar chart to show the information.
(b) How many children took the maths test?
(c) Estimate the average mark for the test.
(d) Do you think the children were better at maths or reading? Give reasons for your answer.

20·4 Comparisons by bar chart

The 'double' bar chart gives a quick picture of a situation in which two things are compared.

Example 1:

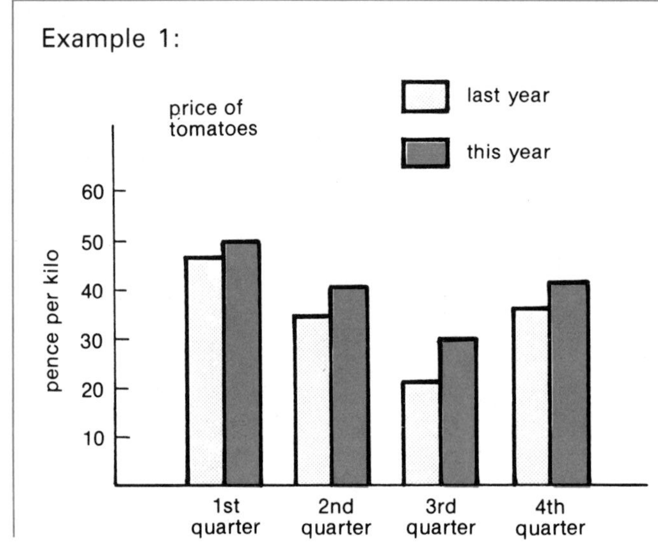

This bar chart compares this year's prices with last year's prices.
It also shows the way prices changed during this year and during last year. You can see that:

(a) The prices fell during the year and then rose again in the last quarter.
(b) This year tomatoes have been dearer than last year, especially during the cheapest time.

Example 2:

This chart compares population growth over the periods 1961–1970 and 1971–1980. It also compares different countries.
You can see that:

(a) USA and USSR have very similar growth.
(b) Africa and S. America have similar growth.
(c) The rate of growth in Africa and S. America is much larger than the rate in Europe.
(d) All countries listed have reduced their population growth except S. America.

USA
EEC
USSR
AFRICA
SOUTH AMERICA
1961-1970
1971-1980
1 2 3 4
percentage growth

This type of chart is used a great deal in **geography**.

Exercise 20·3

A 1 *How Britain's money was spent.*

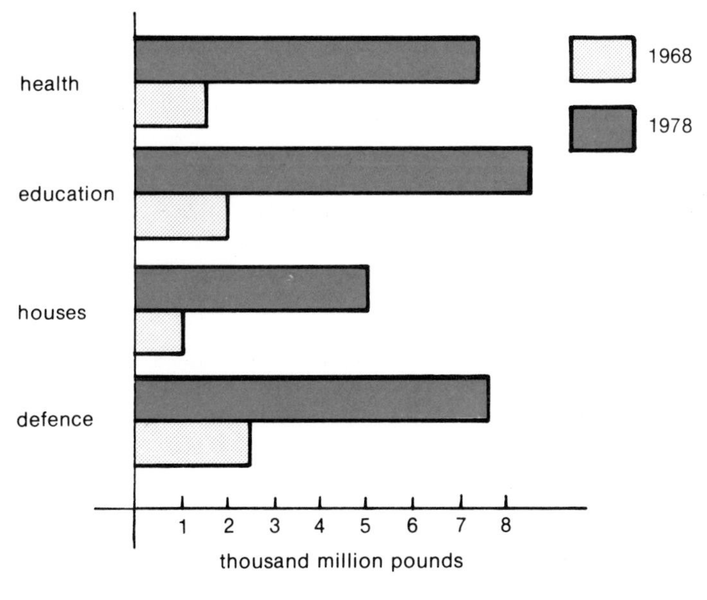

(a) Write down how much money was spent in 1968 on health, education, housing and defence. (Nearest 0·5 thousand million.)
(b) Write down how much money was spent on the same items in 1978.
(c) Was the most expensive item in 1968 the same as the most expensive item in 1978?
(d) Why was so much money spent in 1978?
(e) What fact stands out most clearly from the bar chart?

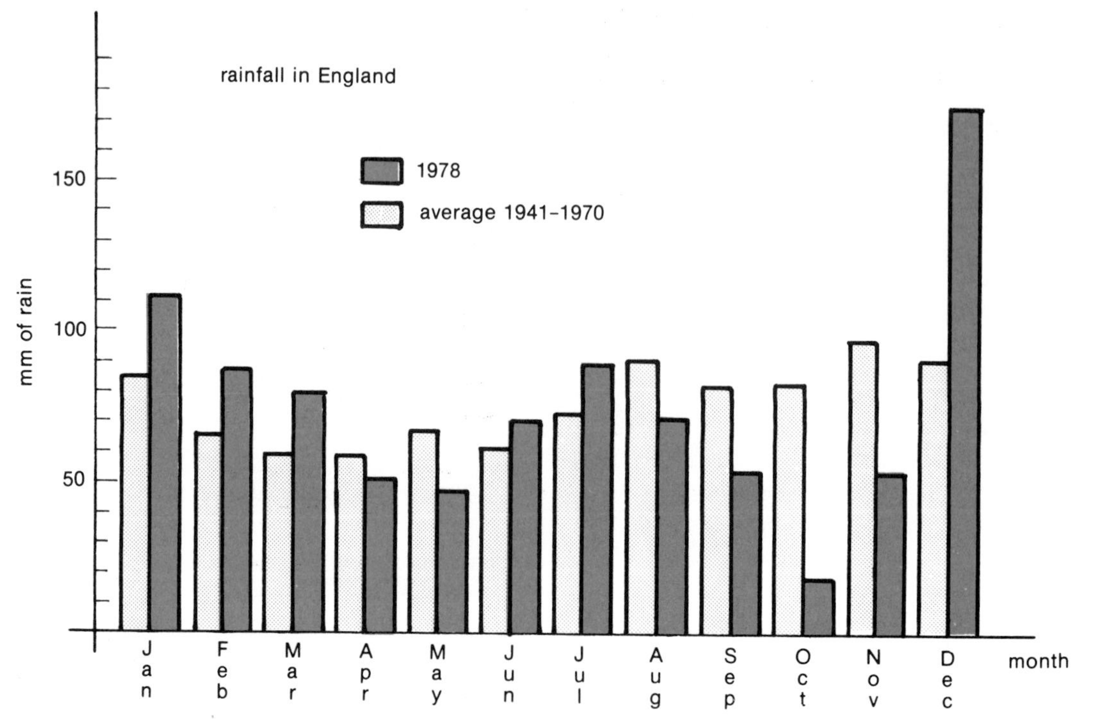

2 (a) What was the rainfall in January 1978?
(b) What was the average rainfall for January?
(c) For which month in 1978 was the rainfall about 20 mm?
(d) Which month had an average rainfall of 100 mm?
(e) Which months in 1978 had above average rainfall?
(f) Which two months in 1978 were very unusual?
(g) What is the difference between the wettest month in 1978 and the driest month in 1978 (in mm of rain)?
(h) What is the difference between the wettest month on average, and the driest month on average?
(i) Explain why you would expect the answer to (h) to be less than the answer to (g) above.

B Draw bar charts to help compare the facts from the following data. Write about interesting facts which show up clearly on the bar charts.

1 *Reported and solved crimes in a certain city* (1971–1978).

Year	*Reported crimes*	*Solved crimes*
1971	620	320
1972	660	300
1973	610	380
1974	720	350
1975	750	320
1976	780	340
1977	800	300
1978	850	350

2 Average weights of girls and boys in Britain aged $13\frac{1}{2}$ years.

Year	*Girls* (kg)	*Boys* (kg)
1910	38·0	36·6
1938	43·75	41
1949	45·45	42·75
1959	48·1	45·25
1966	48·75	45·35

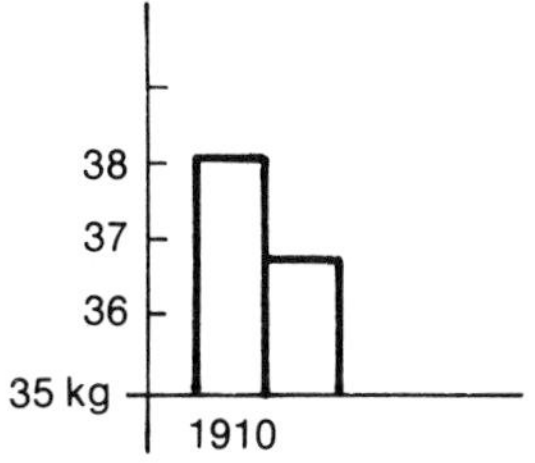

When you draw the bar chart use 35 kg as base.

20·5 Pie charts

A pie chart is a circular diagram which shows clearly how something is shared.

The angle of each sector (slice) corresponds to the size of the share. (The share is also shown by the **area** of the sector and the **length** of arc.)

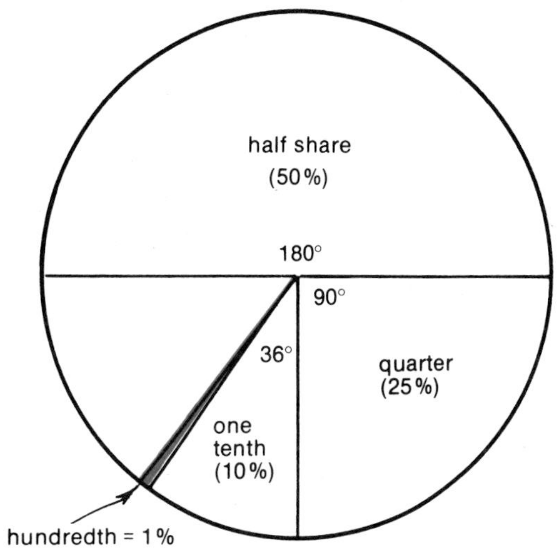

A half share will have an angle of 180° . . . (360/2).
A quarter share will have an angle of 90° . . . (360/4).
A tenth share will have an angle of 36° . . . (360/10).
A hundredth share will have an angle of 3·6° . . . (360/100).

Example:

A working mother works 8 hours a day at the factory. She spends 1 hour travelling to and from work, 2 hours on cleaning and washing and 2 hours preparing food and washing up.
She sleeps for 8 hours at night and the rest of the time she watches TV or makes clothes for the family.
Show her day on a pie chart.

24 hr = 360°   8 hr = 120°
2 hr = 30°
1 hr = 15°

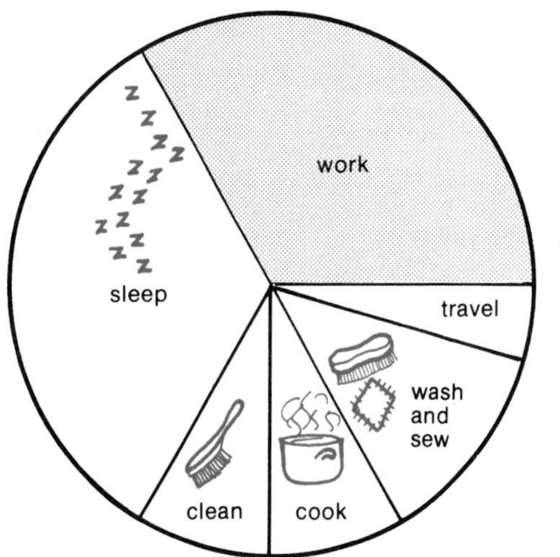

The pie chart shows how the mother has to crowd her home life into quite a small part of the day.

Population growth in different types of country

We can divide the world into four types of country by asking two questions:
Crowded or not crowded?
Fast population growth or slow population growth?

CROWDED	NOT CROWDED	
Examples China India A 1969: 1770 2000: 3500	*Examples* Africa Brazil B 1969: 640 2000: 1500	high growth
Examples Europe Japan C 1969: 560 2000: 700	*Examples* USA USSR D 1969: 500 2000: 750	low growth

You can see from the pie charts that:

(a) The world population will have grown from 1969 to 2000.
(b) That group A countries will have increased their share.
(c) That group B countries will represent a much larger proportion in AD 2000 than they did in 1969. (Equal to C and D added together.)
(d) That the order ABCD of size will have changed to ABDC with the developed countries having less than one quarter of the world's population.

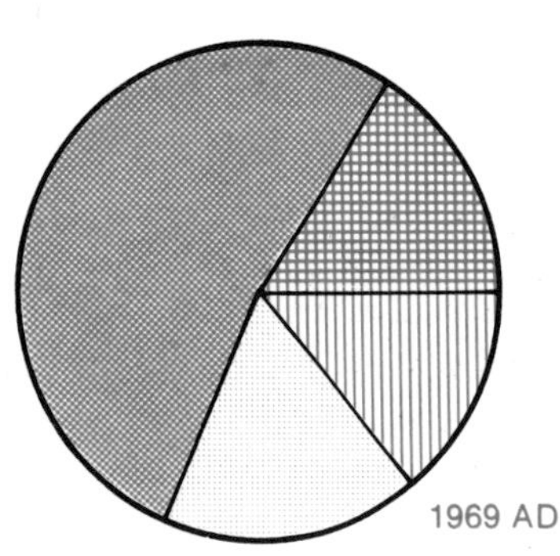

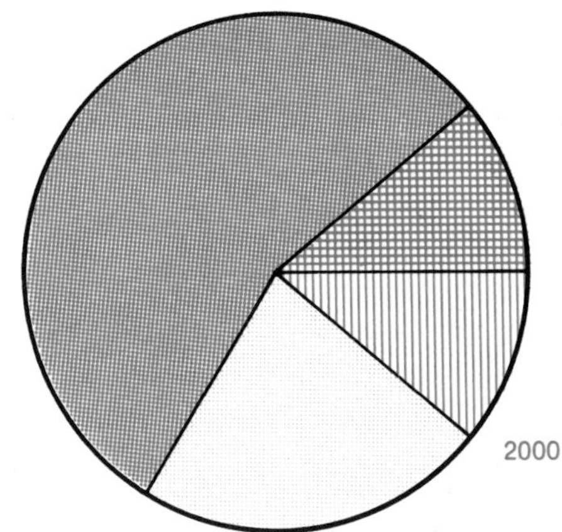

Exercise 20·4

A Comment on each of the pie charts below. In each case pick out facts which seem important.

1 How people were viewing on Saturday, 17th August.

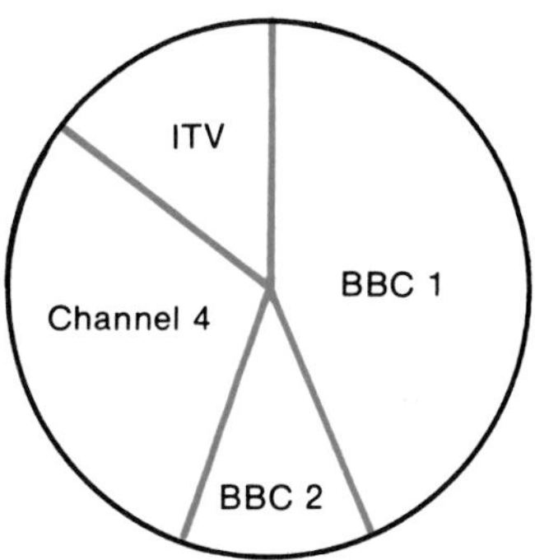

2 Method of coming to school for all children at a comprehensive.

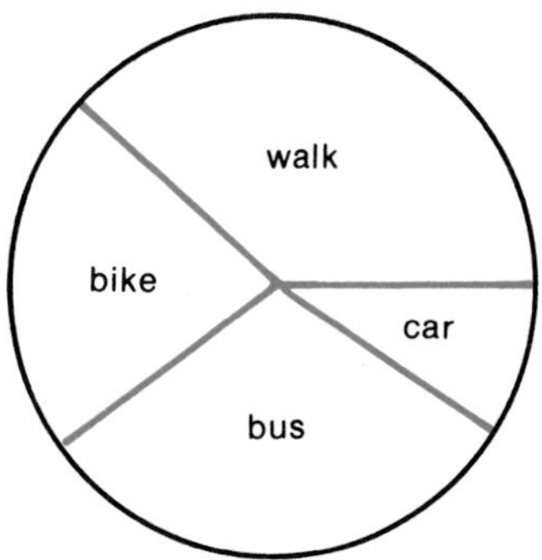

3 Pets kept by families in Newtown.

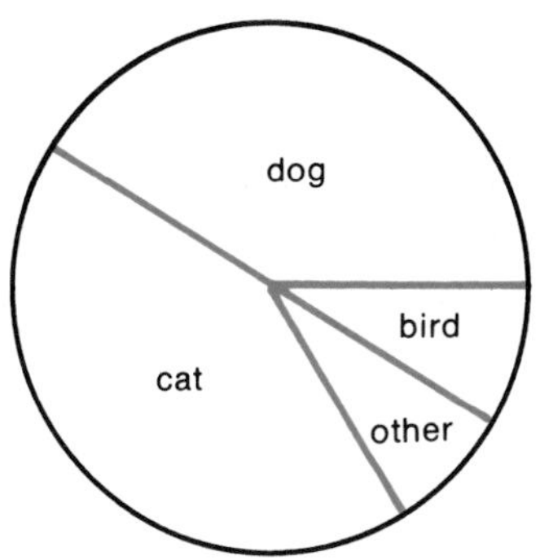

4 What teenagers do on a Saturday night.

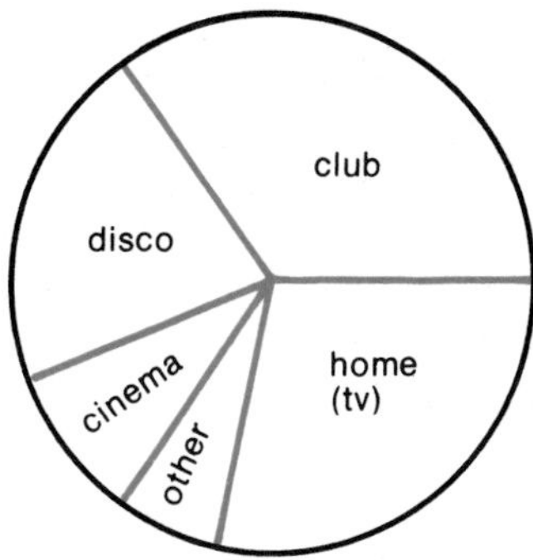

B Make a pie chart for each of the data sets below. Divide the circle into 24 equal parts before you start. Remember: 1% = 3·6° angle.

1 The Jones family spend their money on: housing (30%), food (27%), clothes (14%), hire purchase (12%), transport (8%), entertainment (5%), other (4%).

2 Gary Hughes goes to school from 9 am till 4 pm, has an evening job till 7 pm, does homework till 9 pm, goes to bed at 11 pm and gets up at 8 am.

3 100 children were asked which sport they liked best. The results were: football 48; hockey 30; tennis 6; swimming 16.

C **1** Make two pie charts about some information of your own choice. Explain why you think the charts are interesting.

2 Make pie charts which compare how you spend your days:
(a) During school days (b) At weekends (c) During school holidays

Unit M21 Volume and density

21·1 Quantity of substance

Every object occupies some space. The amount of space is called the **volume** of the object. Volume is measured in 'cubic units'. The space inside an object is also called volume but more often it is called cubic capacity. Cubic capacity is also measured in cubic units.

Examples:

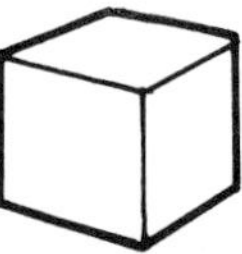

This cube is 1 cm long
1 cm wide
1 cm high
its volume is:
1 cubic centimetre
1 cm^3

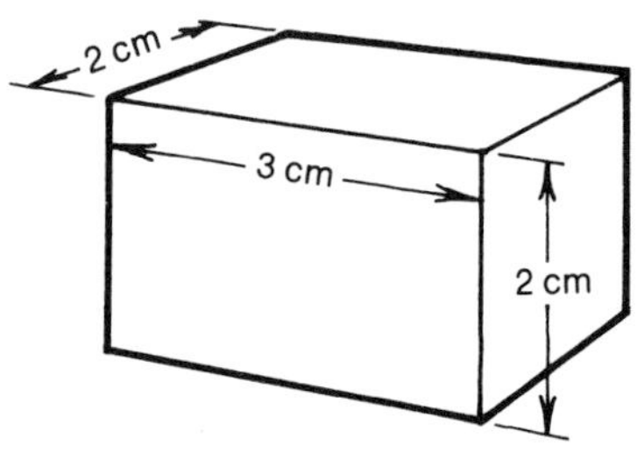

This cuboid is 3 cm long
2 cm wide
2 cm high
its volume is:
12 cubic centimetres
12 cm^3

This refrigerator has a **cubic capacity** of 6 cubic feet
(The space inside measures 3 ft × 2 ft × 1 ft.)

Exercise 21·1

A Explain what you understand from the following statements:

1 'Mrs Sharma arrived carrying an enormous suitcase. Its volume must have been half a cubic metre!'

2 The new van had a cubic capacity of 12 m^3.

3 The fire engine pumped 400 m^3 of water into the burning house.

4 A racing car engine with 2000 cm^3 capacity.

5 A moped with engine capacity 50 cm^3.

B Liquids are measured in litres.

1 litre = 1000 cm^3

1000 litres = 1 cubic metre.

(Sometimes 1 millilitre is used as a measure of 1 thousandth of a litre. 1 ml = 1 cm^3.)

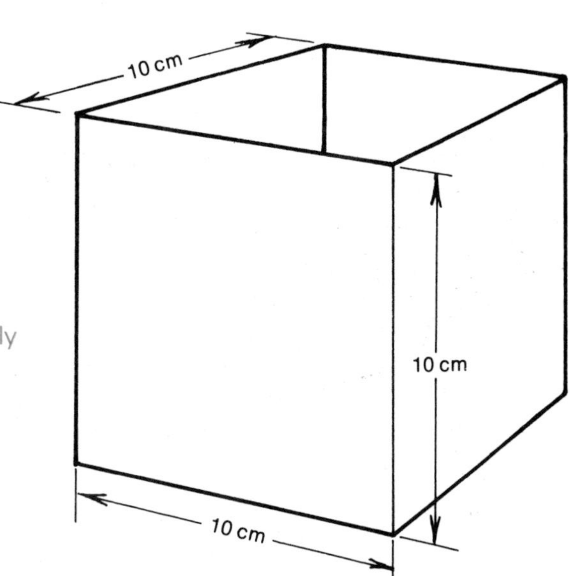

A box 10 cm × 10 cm × 10 cm will hold exactly 1 litre of liquid.

1 A tanker has a cubic capacity of 8 m^3. How many 1 litre bottles of wine could be filled from the tanker if it is:

(a) Full of wine (b) Half full (c) Carrying 5 m^3 only?

2 How many 5 ml doses of medicine can be poured from a half-litre bottle?

3 A water-tank is in the shape of a cuboid 2 m long, 1·4 m high and 1·6 m wide. Could this tank hold:
(a) 1000 litres of water? (b) 2000 litres of water? (c) 5000 litres of water?

4 How many litres of water would you expect in:
(a) A bucket full? (b) A full bath?
(c) A full cold water tank? (d) A full reservoir?
(Estimate).

5 A tap drips 1 cm^3 of water every 5 seconds into a sink. The cubic capacity of the sink is 20 litres. Would the sink overflow if the plug was left in and the tap dripped for 12 hours?

C 1 A 500 g packet of butter has a volume of 260 cm^3. How many blocks would you expect to find in a box, 60 cm long, 40 cm wide and 30 cm high?

2 A container has 60 m^3 capacity.
(a) How many boxes of butter could be carried in a full load?
(b) How many 500 g packets of butter would this be?
(c) What would the load weigh?

21·2 Measuring and calculating volume

Most objects are not regular in shape and so it is not easy to find their volumes. We will discuss some methods later.

If the shape is regular in cross-section, the volume is easy to calculate. We simply multiply the area of cross-section by length.

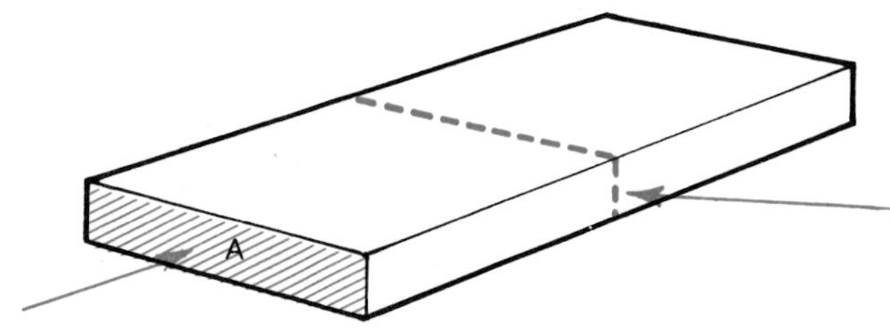

VOLUME = $A \times l$

area of cross-section *length*

Example:

Find the volume of a plank of wood 28 cm wide, 2 cm thick and 5 m in length.

Area of cross-section $28 \times 2 = 56$ cm^2

Volume = 56 cm^2 × 500 cm = 28 000 cm^3 = $\underline{\underline{0{\cdot}028}}$ m^3

Note: The 5 metres is changed to 500 cm before calculating the volume. **Always** work in the same units.

Example:

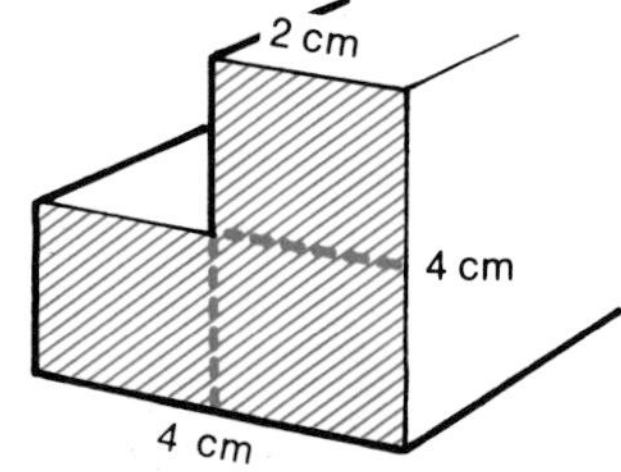

A concrete step has regular cross-section and is 60 cm long. Find its volume.

First find the area of the cross section.
Area = 12 cm^2 (3 squares 2 × 2 cm)
Volume of step = 12 cm^2 × 60 cm = 720 cm^3

Exercise 21·2

A Calculate the volumes of the following cuboids and cubes. Treat them as solids with regular cross-sections.

1. Length 3 cm, width 2 cm, height 1·6 cm.
2. Length 12 cm, width 8 cm, height 3·7 cm.
3. Length 1·2 m, width 44 cm, height 27 cm.
4. Length 0·38 m, width 0·45 m, height 0·31 m.
5. Length 11 cm, width 11 cm, height 11 cm.
6. Thickness 21 mm, width 104 mm, length 6 m.

B

1. Floor tiles which are squares 15 cm by 15 cm are 5 mm thick.
   (a) Find the volume of each tile.
   (b) Find the volume of a pile of 20 such tiles.
   (c) A dealer stores 10 000 tiles. How much space do they take up?
2. A packet of 400 sheets of paper is 4 cm thick. The paper is A4 in size (296 mm × 211 mm).
   (a) What is the volume of the pack?
   (b) What is the thickness of each sheet of paper?
3. A cornflakes packet is 20 cm wide, $6\frac{1}{2}$ cm thick and 29 cm high.
   What is the volume of the packet?
   Will the packet hold 2000 cm^3 of cornflakes?
4. A smaller packet is 15 cm wide, 5 cm thick and 20 cm high.
   Is the large packet more than double the volume of this smaller packet?

C Calculate the volumes of the objects drawn below. Find the area of the cross-section first. Which of the objects has the largest volume?

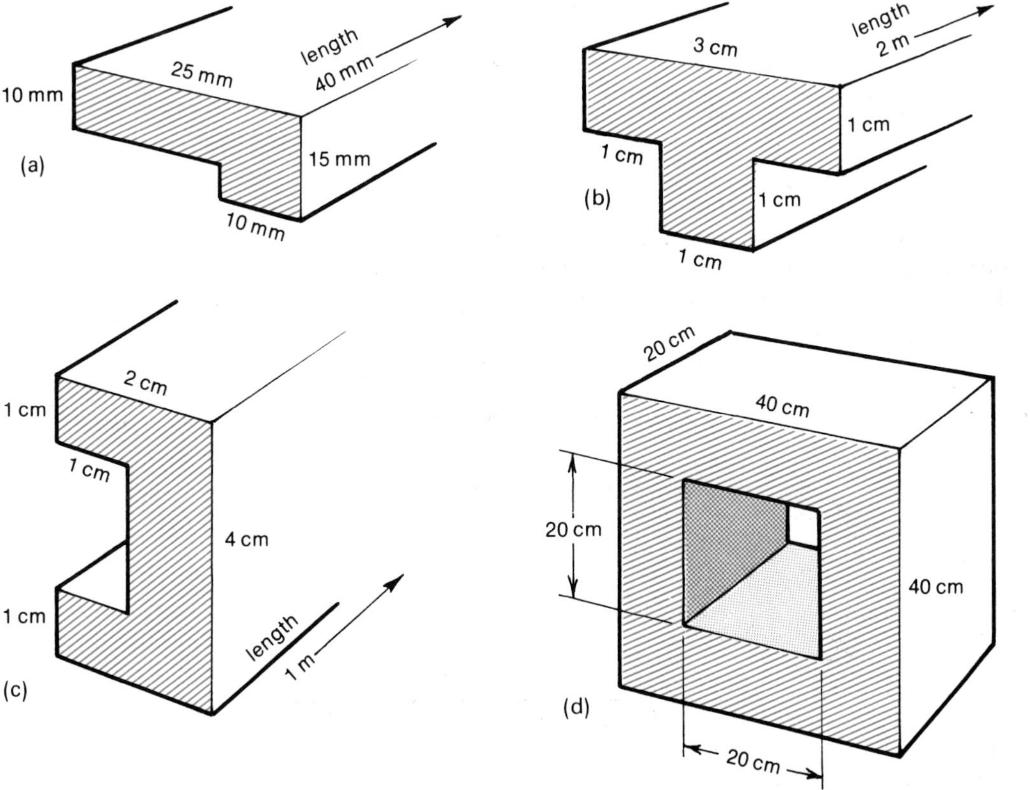

21·3 Cylinders and pipes

A cylinder has a regular circular cross-section so its volume may be found easily. First find the area of the cross-section, then multiply by the length (or height if the cylinder is standing up.)

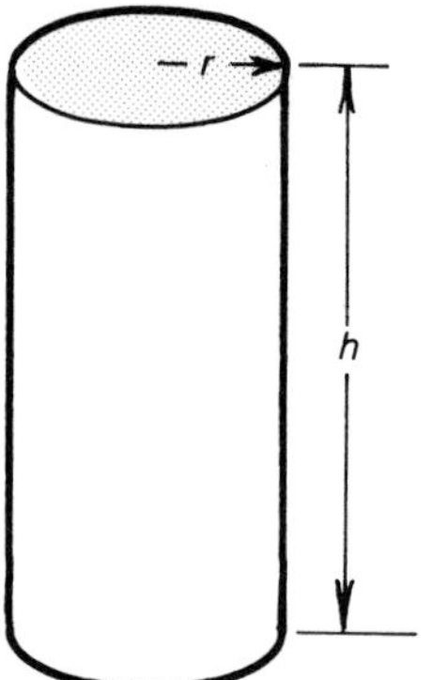

Cylinder: radius r, height h.
Area of section πr^2
Volume of cylinder $\pi r^2 \times h$

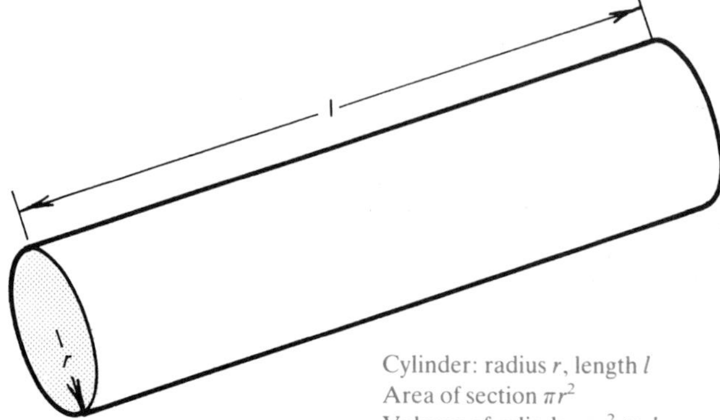

Cylinder: radius r, length l
Area of section πr^2
Volume of cylinder $\pi r^2 \times l$

If you know the size of r and h you can calculate the volume from the formula

$$V = \pi r^2 h$$

Example:
Find the volume of a cylinder radius 2·4 cm and height 12 cm.

$$V = \pi \times 2{\cdot}4 \times 2{\cdot}4 \times 12 = 217{\cdot}15 \text{ cm}$$

[C] [π]* [×] [2·4] [×] [2·4] [×] [12] [=]

Pipes

A pipe is treated as either (a) a cylinder of 'air' subtracted from a solid cylinder or (b) a solid with a regular cross-section made of a ring of metal.

Example:
Find the volume of metal in a pipe 4 m long, whose outside radius is 5 cm and whose inside radius is 4 cm.

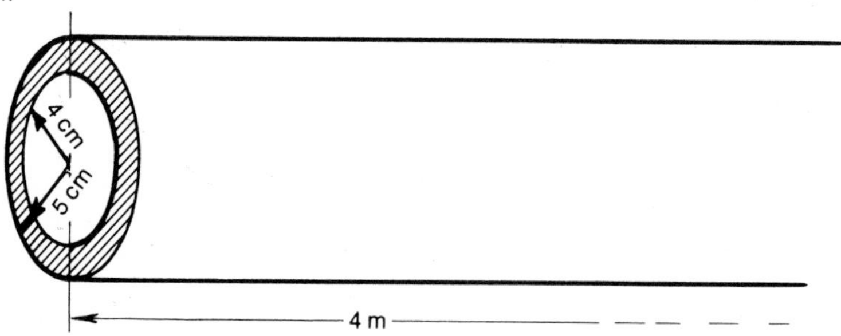

*If you do not have π on your calculator use 3·14.

First method: The outside volume of the pipe is $\pi r^2 l$, where $r = 5$ cm, $l = 400$ cm

$$\pi \times 5 \times 5 \times 400 = 31\,416 \text{ cm}^3$$

The inside volume of the pipe is $\pi r^2 l$, where $r = 4$ cm, $l = 400$ cm

$$\pi \times 4 \times 4 \times 400 = 20\,106 \text{ cm}^3$$

Volume of metal = $31\,416 \text{ cm}^3 - 20\,106 \text{ cm}^3 = 11\,311 \text{ cm}^3$

Second method: Find the area of the cross-section (metal only), then multiply by the length.

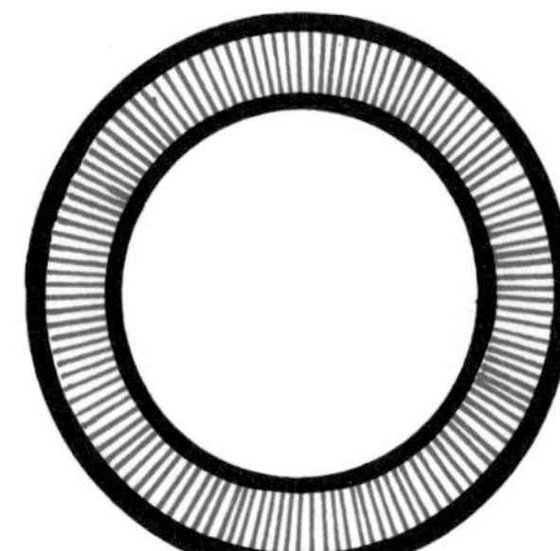

Area of outer circle = $\pi r^2 = \pi \times 25 = 78{\cdot}54 \text{ cm}^2$
Area of inside circle = $\pi r^2 = \pi \times 16 = 50{\cdot}26 \text{ cm}^2$
Area of ring = $78{\cdot}54 - 50{\cdot}26 = 28{\cdot}28 \text{ cm}^2$

Volume of pipe = $28{\cdot}28 \times 400 = 11\,312 \text{ cm}^3$*

Exercise 21·3

A Find the volumes of the following cylinders:

1. Radius 4 cm, length 10 cm.
2. Radius 10 cm, height 15 cm.
3. Radius 12 cm, height 22 cm.
4. Radius 1 mm, length 10 m (wire).
5. Radius 1·5 mm, length 50 m.
6. Radius 14 mm, height 2 mm (coin).

B

1. A tin of baked beans is a cylinder with 10 cm diameter and 11·5 cm height. What is the greatest volume of beans the tin could hold?
2. A giant size tin of beans has diameter 16 cm and height 14 cm. Could the giant size tin hold:
   (a) Twice as many beans as the tin in question 1?
   (b) Three times as many beans as the tin in question 1?
3. A cylindrical tin of radius 5 cm contains 1000 cm^3 (1 litre) of soup. What is the height of the tin?
4. A gold sovereign has 2 cm diameter. Its volume is 0·5 cm^3. What is the thickness of the coin?

C

1. A pipe has internal radius 12 cm and external radius 15 cm. What is the volume of metal in:
   (a) 1 m of this pipe? (b) 5 m?
2. The metal thickness of a copper pipe is 2 mm. Its external diameter is 14 mm. Calculate:
   (a) The internal and external radii of the pipe.
   (b) The volume of 15 m of copper pipe.

   Note: This question enables you to find the amount of copper in the pipe. This would help you to work out the cost.

* Note that different methods give a slight difference in volume. Why do you think this is?

21·4 Density

The weight of a cubic centimetre of a substance is called the density of the substance. Some densities are shown below.

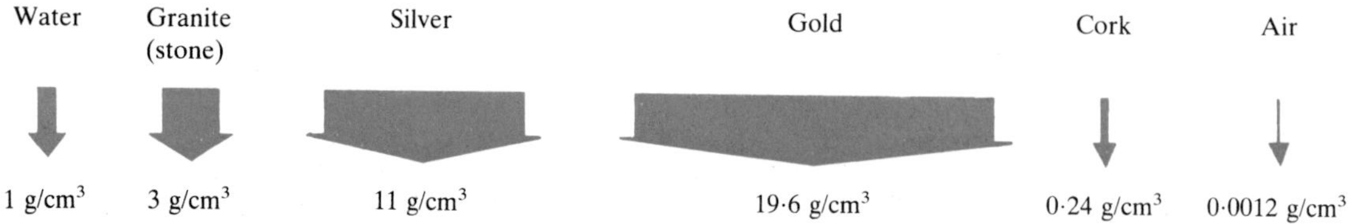

Density connects the two measures Weight and Volume for all substances. The relationship is given by the formula:

WEIGHT = VOLUME × DENSITY

This means that we can find the volume of an object if we know its weight and density.

Example:

A block of stone weighs 48 kg. Its density is 3 g/cm^3
Find the volume of the stone.

$$\underset{\text{(weight)}}{48\,000\text{ g}^*} = \text{volume} \times \underset{\text{(density)}}{3\text{ g}}$$

$$\text{Volume} = 16\,000\text{ cm}^3 = 0{\cdot}016\text{ m}^3$$

Example:

Estimate the weight of air in a classroom 6 m long, 5 m wide and 3 m high.
The volume of the room is $(6 \times 5 \times 3)^3 = 90\text{ m}^3 = 90\,000\,000\text{ cm}^3$
The density of air is 0·0012 g per cm^3
Weight = volume × density
= 90 000 000 × 0·0012
= 9000 × 12
= 108 000 g
= 108 kg

Exercise 21·4

A Find the weight of these solids:

1 40 cm^3 of gold (density 19·6 g/cm^3)
2 150 cm^3 of copper (density 9 g/cm^3)
3 1 m^3 of sand (density 1·52 g/cm^3)
4 50 m^3 of coal (density 1·25 g/cm^3)
5 15 m^3 of pine wood (density 0·55 g/cm^3)
6 45 mm^3 of carbon dioxide (density 0·0035 g/cm^3).

* Since density is given in grams per cm^3 we convert the weight to grams.

B Find the volumes of these solids:

1 A lump of pure gold weighing 1 kg
2 50 kg of scrap iron (density 7·6 g/cm^3)
3 1000 kg of coal (density 1·25 g/cm^3)
4 500 g of ivory (density 1·8 g/cm^3)
5 55 kg of brass (density 8 g/cm^3)
6 40 kg of glass (density 2·6 g/cm^3)

C *Problems*

1 A thief steals four bars of gold. Each one is 35 cm long, 14 cm wide and 12 cm high. What do they weigh altogether? Could he carrry them in a sack over his shoulder?
2 A wall is built from bricks. The wall is 40 m long, 50 cm thick and 3 m high. What weight of bricks have been used? (Density of brick: 2 g/cm^3.)
3 A necklace is made from gold wire, diameter 2 mm and length 50 cm. What weight of gold is this? If gold costs £9·50 per gram, what is the value of the gold in the necklace?
4 A silver ring is made from a cylinder 7 cm long, with radius 2 mm. What is the value of the silver in the ring at 45 p per gram?
5 A sheet of glass for a window is 6 mm thick, 90 cm wide and 180 cm high. What does the glass weigh? (Density of glass: 2·6 g/cm^3.)
6 A shop window is 3 m wide, 2·8 m high and 6 mm thick. What does it weigh? If glass costs about £2 per kg, what would it cost to replace a broken window of this size?
7 Find your volume, assuming your density to be the same as water (1 g/cm^3.)

21·5 Summary of facts about volume and density

Volumes

Shape	*Name*	*Volume*
	Cuboid	length × breadth × height $l \times b \times h$
	Prism (Regular cross-section)	Area of cross-section × length
	Cylinder	Area of cross-section × length $\pi r^2 h$
	Pipe	Area of circular ring × length $\pi R^2 l - \pi r^2 l$ (R = external radius, (r = internal radius)

Note: All these shapes are prisms.

Extra facts not dealt with in this unit:

Shape	Name	Volume
	Cone	$\frac{1}{3}\pi r^2 h$ One third of a cylinder with the same height and base radius
	Sphere	$\frac{4}{3} \times \pi r^3$ (Best learned off by heart.)

Density

1 Weight = Volume × Density

2 Densities of some ordinary substances:

Substance	Density
Gold	19·64 g/cm^3
Quicksilver (mercury)	14·00 g/cm^3
Silver	11·09 g/cm^3
Lead	11·325 g/cm^3
Copper	9 g/cm^3
Steel	7·85 g/cm^3
Iron	7·6 g/cm^3
Tin	7·32 g/cm^3
Granite	3 g/cm^3
Marble	2·7 g/cm^3
Glass	2·64 g/cm^3
Clay	2·16 g/cm^3
Brick	2 g/cm^3
Sand	1·52 g/cm^3
Coal	1·25 g/cm^3
Oak	0·925 g/cm^3
Apple wood	0·79 g/cm^3
Air	0·0012 g/cm^3

Unit M22 Factors

22·1 The rules of algebra

When two numbers are multiplied we get the same result whether we multiply by the first or the second number.

> Example:
> (a) $3 \times 8 = 24$, $8 \times 3 = 24$
> (b) $35 \times 136 = 4670$, $136 \times 35 = 4670$
> (c) $11{\cdot}9 \times 1{\cdot}06 = 12{\cdot}614$, $1{\cdot}06 \times 11{\cdot}9 = 12{\cdot}614$

This idea can be generalised into the rule:

$ab = ba$ . . . numbers are **commutative** for multiplication.

This rule says in a very short way what we said in the introduction to this unit.

The following rules are very important. Learn them, please.

1	$a + b = b + a$	Commutative law for addition
2	$ab = ba$	Commutative law for multiplication
3	$(a + b) + c = a + (b + c)$	Associative law for addition
4	$(ab)c = a(bc)$	Associative law for multiplication
5	$a(b + c) = ab + ac$	Distributive law

These laws have grand names but they are very simple. There are only these five laws to learn.

Exercise 22·1

A Look at the diagrams below. Each one represents one of the laws of algebra, you have to decide which.

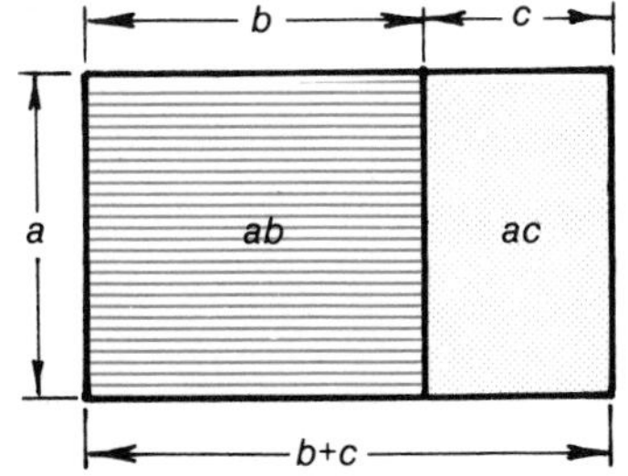

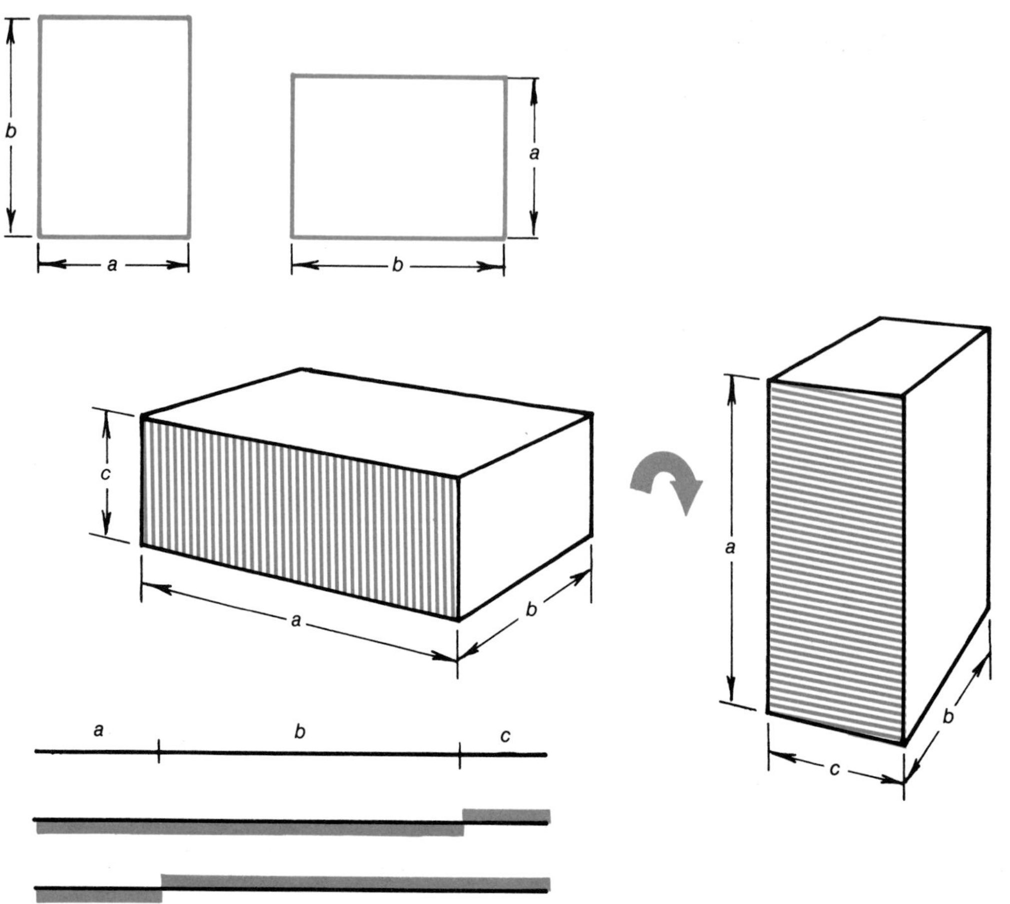

B Use your calculator to show that:

1 37 + 43 = 43 + 37 . . . [C] [37] [+] [43] [=]

[C] [43] [+] [37] [=]

2 139 + 62 = 62 + 139
3 4·65 + 0·27 = 0·27 + 4·65
4 29 × 63 = 63 × 29
5 3015 × 429 = 429 × 3015
6 1·32 × 7·08 = 7·08 × 1·32
7 (45 + 53) + 67 = 45 + (53 + 67)
↑
do this first
8 (4·95 × 6·15) × 2·88 = 4·95 × (6·15 × 2·88)

C Check that both sides of the equals sign are the same in $a(b + c) = ab + ac$ when
1 $a = 2$, $b = 3$, $c = 4$
2 $a = 24$, $b = 36$, $c = 49$
3 $a = 1{\cdot}2$, $b = 6{\cdot}7$, $c = 0{\cdot}5$
4 $a = 0{\cdot}85$, $b = 4{\cdot}23$, $c = 0{\cdot}17$
In each case work out $(b + c)$ before you multiply by a. (Use memory where possible.)

22·2 Multiplying out brackets

The distributive law $a(b + c) = ab + ac$ is used when you need to remove the brackets from an expression.

Example:

Remove the brackets from $2(x + 3)$

$2(x + 3) = (2 \times x) + (2 \times 3)$

$\quad = 2x + 6$

Do not forget to multiply the second number in the bracket by the number outside.

Example:

$x(x - 5) = (x \times x) - (x \times 5)$

$\quad = x^2 - 5x$

Note: (a) $x \times x = x^2$

(b) The −sign stays unchanged

(c) $x \times 5$ is written $5x$.

Exercise 22·2

A Multiply out the brackets in the following expressions:

1 $2(x + 3)$	**2** $3(a + b)$	**3** $4(2a + 2)$	**4** $5(a + 1)$
5 $7(x + 2)$	**6** $5(2x + 1)$	**7** $4(3x + 5)$	**8** $a(a + 1)$
9 $a(2a + 3)$	**10** $x(x + 4)$	**11** $2x(x + 3)$	**12** $3x(x + 1)$

B Multiply out the brackets in the following expressions. Take care with the negative sign.

1 $2(x - 2)$	**2** $4(x - 5)$	**3** $2(b - c)$	**4** $5(a - 1)$
5 $4(x - 2y)$	**6** $3(2a - b)$	**7** $a(a - 1)$	**8** $2a(a - b)$
9 $m(m - 1)$	**10** $2n(n - 3)$	**11** $5x(x - 2)$	**12** $3x(2x - 1)$

C Substitute the given numbers in each case to check whether the two sides of the sign are equal.

1 $3x(x + 5) = 3x^2 + 15x$ ... put $x = 2$

2 $2x(x + 3) = 2x^2 + 6x$ ... put $x = 3$

3 $3x(x - 2) = 3x^2 + 6x$ ... put $x = 5$

4 $x(2x + 1) = 2x^2 + x$ ... put $x = 0{\cdot}45$

5 $2x(2x + 3) = 4x^2 + 6x$ ... put $x = 1{\cdot}75$

6 $3x(2x - 3) = 6x^2 - 9$ ... put $x = 2{\cdot}8$

7 $x(x - 1) = x^2 - 1$ ... put $x = 0{\cdot}66$

8 $2x(3x - 2) = 6x^2 - 4x$ ... put $x = 1{\cdot}234$

22·3 Factorising

When we change a number into the product of two others we call it **factorising**.

Example:

24 ... which is really 20 + 4, can be changed into 4(5 + 1) by reversing the distributive law.

We do the same thing with letters in algebra.

Example:

Factorise $2x + 6$

Since 2 can be divided into each term we can write $2x + 6 = 2(x + 3)$. (This turns the **sum** $2x + 6$ into the **product** of **factors** 2 and $(x + 3)$)

We check in our heads by multiplying out the brackets.

Example:

Factorise $a^2 + 3a$

a can be divided into both a^2 and $3a$* so the factors are $a(a + 3)$.

Check: (a) $a(a + 3) = a^2 + 3a$ by multiplying out brackets.

(b) Put $a = 2$ (for example.)

We now have $a^2 + 3a = a(a + 3)$ Which gives 10 for both sides.

$4 + 6 \quad 2 \times 5$

Exercise 22·3

A Factorise these expressions:

1 $3x + 9$ **2** $4x + 2$ **3** $3x + 12$ **4** $2x + 18$
5 $3a + 9$ **6** $2m + 2n$ **7** $4a + 2b$ **8** $5b + 10$
9 $3m - 6$ **10** $4a - 2$ **11** $3x - x$ **12** $6a - 3b$

B Factorise these expressions:

1 $x^2 + x$ **2** $x^2 + 2x$ **3** $2x^2 + 3x$ **4** $3x^2 + 6x$
5 $2a^2 + ab$ **6** $3b^2 + 2bc$ **7** $a^2 + ax$ **8** $p^2 + 2pq$
9 $x^2 - x$ **10** $2x^2 - 4x$ **11** $ab - b$ **12** $3x^2 - 9$

C Use the values for x and y to check these factorisations:

1 $x^2 + 3x = x(x + 3)$ ... $x = 0{\cdot}45$
2 $2x^2 - 4x = 2x(x - 2)$ ... $x = 1{\cdot}72$
3 $3x^2 - 9x = 3x(x - 9)$ ... $x = 42$
4 $x^2 - 3x = x(x - 3)$ ... $x = 0{\cdot}08$
5 $x^2 + xy = x(x + y)$ ... $x = 4{\cdot}5,\ y = 3{\cdot}2$
6 $2x^2 - 4xy = 2x(x - y)$ ... $x = 0{\cdot}38,\ y = 0{\cdot}35$
7 $xy - x = y(x - y)$ ... $x = 2,\ y = 5{\cdot}7$
8 $2xy - x^2 = x(2y - x)$ ... $x = 3{\cdot}2,\ y = 2{\cdot}5$

Why is it better to check with numbers such as 1·72, 0·35 rather than simply with $x = 0$, $y = 1$?

22·4 Multiplying out a pair of brackets

When we multiply out a pair of brackets there are at least 4 products.

Example:

$(a + b)(c + d)$
$= (a + b)c + (a + b)d$ ... treating $(a + b)$ as one number
$= ac + bc + ad + bd$ ... multiplying each bracket out in turn.

* a is called a common factor of a^2 and $3a$ in this case.

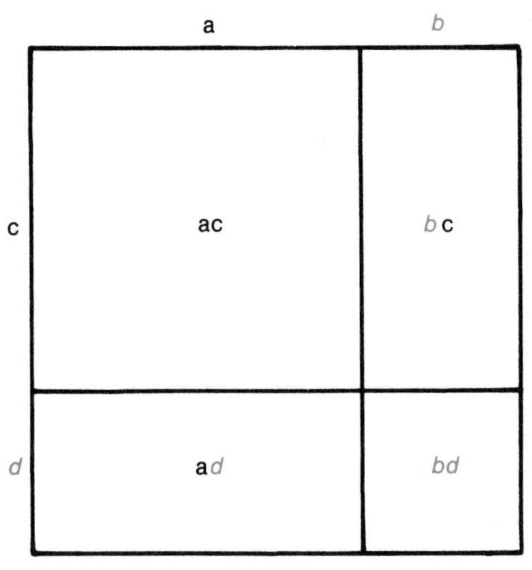

This diagram shows how the four products ac, bc, ad and bd are formed when $a + b$ is multiplied by $c + d$.

Example:

$74 \times 53 \quad = (70 + 4)(50 + 3)$
$\qquad\qquad = (70 \times 50) + (70 \times 3) + (4 \times 50) + (4 \times 3)$ four products
$\qquad\qquad = 3500 + 210 + 200 + 12$
$\qquad\qquad = 3922$ (checked on calculator.)

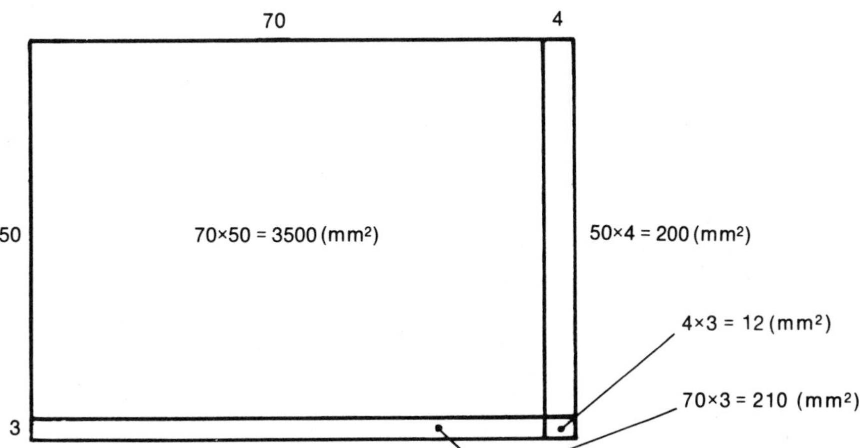

Example:

Multiply out $(x + 3)(x + 5)$

	x	5				
x	x^2	x	x	x	x	x
	x	1	1	1	1	1
3	x	1	1	1	1	1
	x	1	1	1	1	1

$$
\begin{aligned}
(x + 3)(x + 5) &= x(x + 5) + 3(x + 5) \\
&= x^2 + 5x + 3x + 15 \\
&= x^2 + 8x + 15
\end{aligned}
$$

(Gathering $5x$ and $3x$ together.)
The diagram shows all the different parts of the product.

Check: Choose any number for x, say 2·834. Put $x = 2{\cdot}834$

$(x+3)(x+5) \rightarrow 5{\cdot}834 \times 7{\cdot}834 \rightarrow 45{\cdot}7036$

$x^2 + 8x + 15 \rightarrow 8{\cdot}0316 + 22{\cdot}672 + 15 \rightarrow 45{\cdot}7036$

They come to the same number so the expansion is correct. The result can also be checked by putting $x = 1$ or some other easy number.

Put $x = 1$

$(x+3)(x+5) \rightarrow 4 \times 6 \rightarrow 24$

$x^2 + 8x + 15 \rightarrow 1 + 8 + 15 \rightarrow 24$

They come to the same so the expansion is correct.

Note: If the expansion is correct it will be correct for any value of x.

Exercise 22·4

A Multiply out these brackets. Check for the values given.

1 $(a+b)(p+q)$ ... $a = 1,\ b = 1,\ p = 2,\ q = 2$.
2 $(a+3)(b+4)$ ... $a = 2,\ b = 3$.
3 $(p+5)(q+7)$ ... $p = 2,\ q = 5$.
4 $(x+4)(y+5)$ ... $x = 0{\cdot}38,\ y = 0{\cdot}77$.
5 $(2a+b)(c+3)$ ... $a = 1,\ b = 2,\ c = 1$.
6 $(a+3b)(c+2d)$ ... $a = 3,\ b = 4{\cdot}5,\ c = 2{\cdot}6,\ d = 7$.

B Find the products of the numbers below by splitting them as shown. Check on your calculator or using tables.

1 $13 \times 15 \rightarrow (10+3) \times (10+5) \rightarrow (10 \times 10) + (10 \times 3) + (10 \times 5) + (3 \times 5)$.
2 $7 \times 9 \rightarrow (4+3) \times (5+4) \rightarrow$ etc.
3 $28 \times 47 \rightarrow (20+8) \times (40+7) \rightarrow$ etc.
4 $69 \times 41 \rightarrow (60+9) \times (40+1) \rightarrow$ etc.
5 $125 \times 125 \rightarrow (100+25) \times (100+25)$* $\rightarrow$ etc.
6 $237 \times 145 \rightarrow (200+37) \times (100+45)$* $\rightarrow$ etc.
7 $77 \times 183 \rightarrow (70+7) \times (100+83)$* $\rightarrow$ etc.
8 $8{\cdot}6 \times 7{\cdot}4 \rightarrow (8+0{\cdot}6) \times (7+0{\cdot}4) \rightarrow$ etc.

C Multiply out these pairs of brackets and collect up similar terms where possible (see example.)

1 $(x+2)(x+1)$ **2** $(x+3)(x+4)$ **3** $(x+4)(x+2)$
4 $(x+5)(x+1)$ **5** $(x+1)(x+1)$ **6** $(x+2)(x+2)$
7 $(x+3)(x+3)$ **8** $(x+4)(x+4)$ **9** $(a+2)(a+5)$
10 $(x+a)(x+a)$ **11** $(x+b)(x+b)$ **12** $(x+y)(x+y)$

* Use tables for the part products.

Unit M23 Squares and square roots

23·1 Squares using tables

The squares of the first 100 numbers are to be found along the diagonals of the calculating tables. (Bell & Hyman: *Basic Mathematics Tables*.) For larger numbers, use the distributive law.

Example:

Find the value of $(176)^2$ and $(17{\cdot}6)^2$
Treating 176 as $(170 + 6)$ we have

$170 \times 170 = 28\,900$ ... from 17×17
$170 \times 6 \quad = \quad 1\,020$ ... from $17 \times 6 \times 10$
$6 \times 170 \quad = \quad 1\,020$ ... as above
$6 \times 6 \quad = \quad 36$
$(176)^2 \quad = 30\,976$ and $(17{\cdot}6)^2 = 309{\cdot}76$

Example:

Find the value of $(23{\cdot}45)^2$

$23{\cdot}00 \times 23{\cdot}00 = 529{\cdot}0000$ ... we use 4 decimal places of 0s
$23{\cdot}00 \times 0{\cdot}45 \quad = \quad 10{\cdot}3500$ ... Take care that the decimal point is in the right place
$0{\cdot}45 \times 23{\cdot}00 \quad = \quad 10{\cdot}3500$
$0{\cdot}45 \times 0{\cdot}45 \quad = \quad 0{\cdot}2025$ ... 4 places of decimals
$549{\cdot}9025$ check on the calculator.

Exercise 23·1

A **1** Use the tables to find the values of:
(a) $(36)^2$ (b) $(43)^2$ (c) $(92)^2$ (d) $(66)^2$ (e) $(78)^2$

2 Use tables to find the values of:
(a) $(4{\cdot}5)^2$ (b) $(0{\cdot}38)^2$ (c) $(6{\cdot}9)^2$ (d) $(0{\cdot}53)^2$ (e) $(8{\cdot}8)^2$

3 Use tables to find the values of:
(a) $(20)^2$ (b) $(410)^2$ (c) $(530)^2$ (d) $(670)^2$ (e) $(4800)^2$

Check all results on the calculator.

B Use tables to find squares of the following. Work out answers to six figures.

1 (a) $(375)^2$ (b) $(283)^2$ (c) $(527)^2$ (d) $(639)^2$
2 (a) $(42{\cdot}5)^2$ (b) $(31{\cdot}7)^2$ (c) $(53{\cdot}3)^2$ (d) $(66{\cdot}4)^2$
3 (a) $(6{\cdot}15)^2$ (b) $(1{\cdot}34)^2$ (c) $(4{\cdot}65)^2$ (d) $(8{\cdot}88)^2$

Check all results on the calculator.

C Use tables to find the squares of the following. Work out answers to eight figures.

1 (a) $(4250)^2$ (b) $(3868)^2$ (c) $(1369)^2$ (d) $(5258)^2$
2 (a) $(37{\cdot}95)^2$ (b) $(41{\cdot}26)^2$ (c) $(44{\cdot}08)^2$ (d) $(36{\cdot}07)^2$
3 (a) $(234{\cdot}5)^2$ (b) $(421{\cdot}6)^2$ (c) $(219{\cdot}7)^2$ (d) $(3{\cdot}162)^2$

Check all results on the calculator.

23·2 Squares of sums and differences

You can soon check that $(20 + 5)^2$ is not equal to $20^2 + 5^2$.

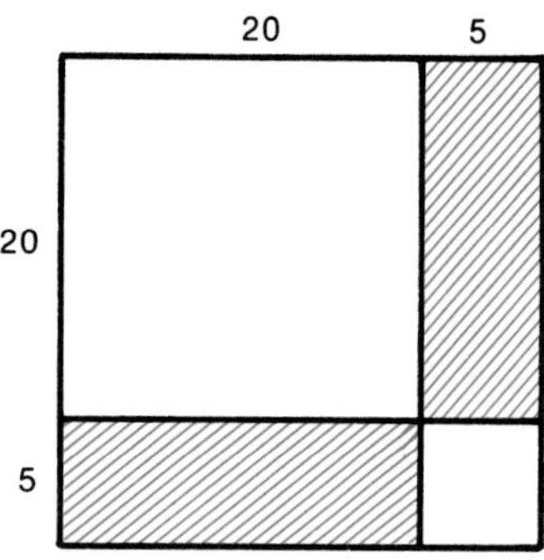

$(20 + 5)^2$ $\quad$ $20^2 + 5^2$ $\quad$ This is shown clearly on the diagram.

$$\begin{array}{ccc} (20+5)^2 & 20^2 & 5^2 \\ \downarrow & \downarrow & \downarrow \\ 25^2 & 400 & 25 \\ \downarrow & \multicolumn{2}{c}{\downarrow} \\ 625 & \multicolumn{2}{c}{425} \end{array}$$

$$(20 + 5)^2 = 20^2 + 5^2 + \underbrace{2 \times 20 \times 5}_{\uparrow}$$

The missing bit

$(a + b)^2 = a^2 + b^2 + 2ab$	Square of a sum
$(a - b)^2 = a^2 + b^2 - 2ab$	Square of a difference

These results should be memorised.

Example:
Use the result $(a - b)^2 = a^2 + b^2 - 2ab$
to calculate 17^2 (in your head if you can)

17 is 20 − 3

$$\begin{aligned}(20 - 3)^2 &= 20^2 + 3^2 - (2 \times 20 \times 3)\\ &= 400 + 9 - 120\\ &= 289\end{aligned}$$

If you subtract the square of the difference of two numbers from the square of their sum, the result is 4 times the product.

$$(a + b)^2 - (a - b)^2 = 4ab$$

Example:
$a = 9$, $b = 5$

$$\begin{aligned}(a + b)^2 &= (14)^2 = 196\\ (a - b)^2 &= (4)^2 = 16\\ & \qquad\quad\ \ 180\end{aligned}$$

$4 \times 9 \times 5 = 180$

The Romans used tables of squares and the above result to multiply numbers.

Example:
Find 37×19

$a + b = 56$ $\quad$ $(a + b)^2 = 3136$ (tables)
$a - b = 18$ $\quad$ $(a - b)^2 = 324$ (tables)
$\qquad\qquad\qquad\qquad\qquad\quad 2812$

Dividing by 4 gives 703. This is equal to 37×19

Exercise 23·2

A Check that the results $(a+b)^2 = a^2 + b^2 + 2ab$ and
$(a-b)^2 = a^2 + b^2 - 2ab$ are true by testing with these pairs of values:

1 $a = 42, b = 3$ **2** $a = 21, b = 0{\cdot}3$ **3** $a = 1{\cdot}1, b = 1{\cdot}1$
4 $a = 345, b = 16$ **5** $a = 138, b = 27$ **6** $a = 207, b = 45$

B Use tables of squares and the result $(a+b)^2 - (a-b)^2 = 4ab$ to find the following products. (This is only an exercise to show the properties of squares. We would not multiply this way. The Romans, however, with their numeral system would have found multiplying very complicated by our methods.)

1 27×19 **2** 43×6 **3** 52×51 **4** 73×18
5 37×42 **6** 45×26 **7** $12 \times 1{\cdot}4$ **8** $3{\cdot}8 \times 1{\cdot}5$

C **1** Show that $(a+b)(a-b) = a^2 - b^2$. Make a drawing which shows this.
2 Use the result to calculate, without a calculator or tables:
(a) $17^2 - 3^2$ (b) $28^2 - 22^2$ (c) $3{\cdot}1^2 - 2{\cdot}9^2$ (d) $4{\cdot}2^2 - 4{\cdot}8^2$

23·3 The square numbers

The numbers 1, 4, 9, 16 . . . which are formed by squaring 1, 2, 3, 4 . . . are called the **square numbers**.

They have many interesting properties which you will investigate in the next exercise.

Exercise 23·3

A The numbers 1, 4, and 9 can be made up as

$$1 = 1$$
$$4 = 1 + 3$$
$$9 = 1 + 3 + 5$$

1 Check that the pattern continues for 16, 25 and 36.
2 Work out the value of $1 + 3 + 5 + 7 + \ldots + 19$. Does this come to a square number?
3 What would you expect the sum of $1 + 3 + 5 + 7 + \ldots + 29$ to be?
4 Here is another way of building square numbers

$$1 = 1$$
$$4 = 1 + 2 + 1$$
$$9 = 1 + 2 + 3 + 2 + 1$$

Does this continue for all square numbers? Can you explain how the pattern works?
5 Write out the squares as dot patterns up to 10^2.

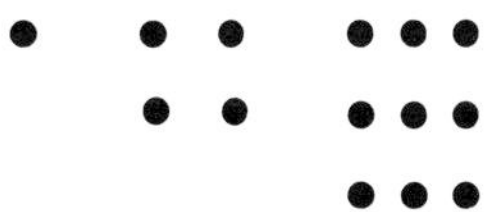

How does this explain the results of question 2 and question 4?

B Explore the square numbers to answer these questions.
1 Is it true that if you multiply any two square numbers, the result is another square number?
2 $9 + 16 = 25$. Both 9 and 16 are square numbers and so is their sum. Find two more square numbers whose sum is also a square.

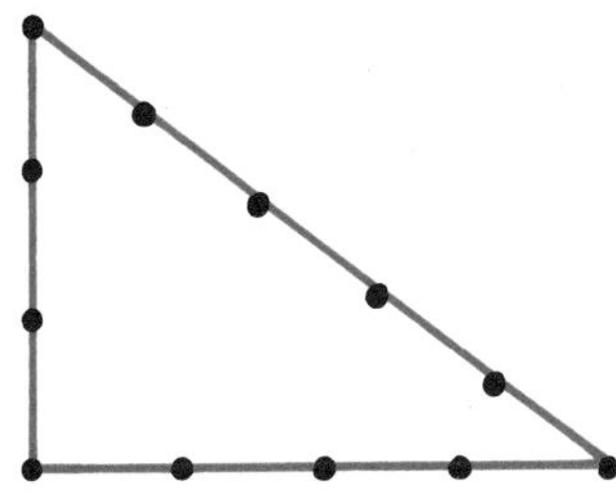

Sets of numbers like these are called **pythagorean triples**. They fit the sides of right-angled triangles. The 3, 4, 5 triangle was used by ancient Egyptians to form a perfect right angle.

3 Find two more sets of Pythagorean triples by searching the squares in the calculating tables.
4 Is it true that if you add any two square numbers the result is a square number?
5 Can you find a square number which is exactly double another square number?
6 Is it true that squares of odd numbers are odd and squares of even numbers are even?

C **1** Explain why $(10 \times n)^2 = 100 \times n^2$. (If one number is ten times larger than another, then its square is 100 times larger than the square of the other.)
2 Show by working them out that:
(a) $(30)^2 = 100 \times 3^2$ (b) $(450)^2 = 100 \times 45^2$
(c) $(52)^2 = 100 \times (5{\cdot}2)^2$ (d) $(36)^2 = 100 \times (3{\cdot}6)^2$
3 Show that:
(a) $(4{\cdot}6)^2 = 46^2 \div 100$ (b) $(0{\cdot}38)^2 = 3{\cdot}8^2 \div 100$ (c) $(0{\cdot}62)^2 = 6{\cdot}2^2 \div 100$
4 Use tables of squares to write down the squares of:
(a) 0·77 (b) 650 (c) 3800 (d) 0·066.
Check on the calculator.

23·4 The graph of $y = x^2$

The graph of $y = x^2$ is a very important one. The curve, which is called a **parabola**, occurs often in science.

Notes
1 The graph never comes below the x axis.
2 The y-axis is an axis of symmetry.
3 The graph rises steeply as x increases.
4 The graph has a **minimum** value when $x = 0$.
5 The graph gives two values of x for every positive value of y, e.g. if $y = 9$, $x = +3$ or -3.

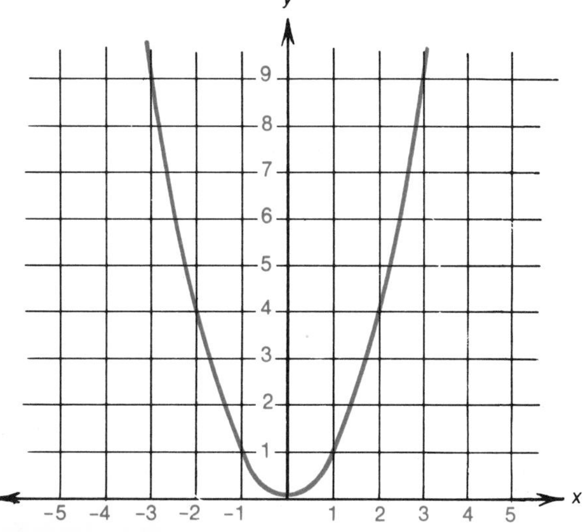

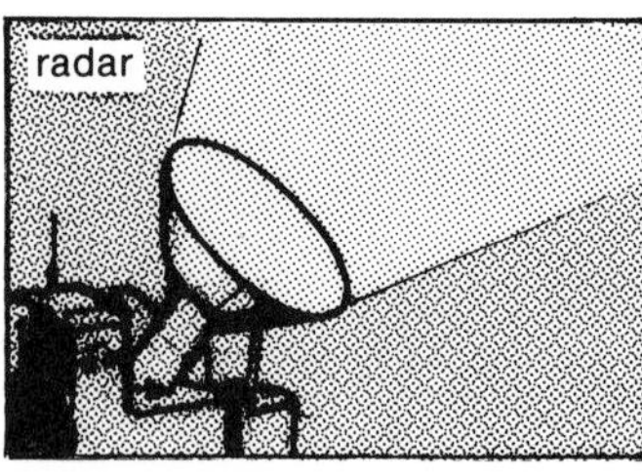

Exercise 23·4

A Draw a careful graph of $y = x^2$ on 1 mm^2 graph paper from $x = -4$ to $x = 4$.

1 What is the minimum value of y for this graph?

2 What is the value of y when

(a) $x = 2{\cdot}5$ (b) $x = 1{\cdot}6$ (c) $x = 2{\cdot}8$ (d) $x = 3{\cdot}2$

(e) $x = -0{\cdot}8$ (f) $x = -1{\cdot}3$ (g) $x = -2{\cdot}6$ (h) $x = -3{\cdot}5$

3 Does the graph become nearly straight between $x = 3$ and $x = 4$?

B Use your graph from section A to find values of x if:

1 (a) $y = 3$ (b) $y = 5$ (c) $y = 8$

2 (a) $y = 3{\cdot}6$ (b) $y = 4{\cdot}5$ (c) $y = 7{\cdot}5$

3 (a) $y = 0{\cdot}8$ (b) $y = 0{\cdot}6$ (c) $y = 1{\cdot}3$

C Draw an enlarged version of the graph $y = x^2$ by taking 10 cm = 1 unit on the x-axis and 10 cm = 1 unit on the y-axis. (Draw the graph from $x = -1$ to $x = 1$.)

1 Use your graph to find the value of x^2 if:

(a) $x = 0{\cdot}3$ (b) $x = 0{\cdot}7$

(c) $x = 0{\cdot}15$ (d) $x = 0{\cdot}48$

(e) $x = 0{\cdot}62$ (f) $x = 0{\cdot}55$

(g) $x = 0{\cdot}85$ (h) $x = 0{\cdot}64$

2 Use your graph to find the value of x for which:

(a) $y = 0{\cdot}04$ (b) $y = 0{\cdot}16$

(c) $y = 0{\cdot}36$ (d) $y = 0{\cdot}64$

(e) $y = 0{\cdot}3$ (f) $y = 0{\cdot}7$

(g) $y = 0{\cdot}85$ (h) $y = 0{\cdot}46$

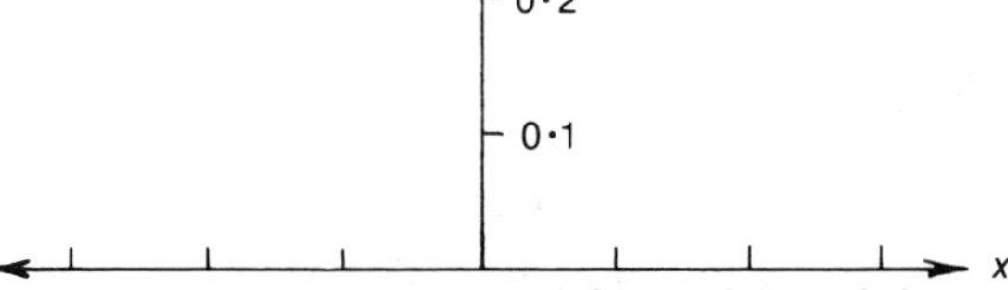

You will need to make a table of values first.

x	0	0·1	0·2
y	0	0·01	0·04 etc.

(Use calculator.)

23·5 Square roots

If x^2 equals a number n, then x itself is the **square root** of n. The square root is written $\sqrt{n}$ or $n^{1/2}$

> Example:
> If $x^2 = 64$, $x = 8$ so $8 = \sqrt{64}$

Only square numbers have exact square roots.*

> Example:
> If $x^2 = 45$, $x = 6{\cdot}708\,203\,9$ (calculator)
> So $\sqrt{45}$ equals 6·71 approximately.
> If you square 6·71 on the calculator
>
> [C] [6] [·] [7] [1] [×] [=]
>
> you get 45·0241 which shows that 6·71 is very near $\sqrt{45}$, but not exactly equal to it.

* Considering whole numbers only. But 1·44 (for example), has an exact square root, 1·2.

Square roots can be found

(a) From the calculator using [√]

(b) From tables of square roots

(c) From tables of squares (in reverse)

If none of these are available, you can still use a pencil-and-paper divide-and-average method (see below).

Example:

Find the value of $\sqrt{61}$ correct to 2 decimal places.

1 *Calculator* [C] [6] [1] [√] . . . 7·81

check by [×] [=], you should get 61 (or a number very close, back again in the display.

2 *Tables of square roots*

First find the number 61. Then look along the function line. The line gives the square roots of 61·0, 61·1, 61·2, 61·3.

$\sqrt{61}$ = 7·81 (correct to 3 figures).

	Function	0·0	0·1	0·2	0·3
60	Log	1·778	1·779	1·780	1·780
	Sine	0·866	0·867	0·868	0·869
	Cosine	0·500	0·498	0·497	0·495
	Tangent	1·732	1·739	1·746	1·753
	$1/x$	0·0167	0·0166	0·0166	0·0166
	$\sqrt{x}$	7·746	7·752	7·759	7·765
61	Log	1·785	1·786	1·787	1·787
	Sine	0·875	0·875	0·876	0·877
	Cosine	0·485	0·483	0·482	0·480
	Tangent	1·804	1·811	1·819	1·827
	$1/x$	0·0164	0·0164	0·0163	0·0163
	$\sqrt{x}$	7·810	7·817	7·823	7·829
62	Log	1·792	1·793	1·794	1·794
	Sine	0·883	0·883	0·883	0·883

3 *Tables of squares in reverse*

Look for 6100 in the calculation tables. The nearest square is 6084. This gives 78 as $\sqrt{6100}$ and 7·8 as $\sqrt{61}$ to the first decimal place.

Note: We can look up 61 or 6100 but **not** 610. Can you see why? When you have found a square root of a number you should always check by squaring it. You should then get back the number whose square root you want.

Example:

Suppose I wanted $\sqrt{75}$

I looked it up in the tables and found that apparently

$\sqrt{75} = 2·74$.

Check: $2·74^2 = 7·5076$.

I have found $\sqrt{7·5}$ by mistake.

2·74 is not $\sqrt{75}$. The correct value of $\sqrt{75}$ is 8·66.

Exercise 23·5

A Write down the values of these square roots:

1 100	**2** 64	**3** 49	**4** 25
5 4	**6** 400	**7** 6400	**8** 8100
9 2500	**10** 0·16	**11** 0·09	**12** 0·36

Check each one on the calculator.

B Use the calculator (if it has a $\sqrt{\ }$ key) to find the square roots of the following numbers correct to 2 decimal places:

1 48	**2** 39	**3** 7	**4** 66
5 120	**6** 250	**7** 382	**8** 495
9 6·4	**10** 10	**11** 3·6	**12** 48·9
13 0·45	**14** 0·72	**15** 0·05	**16** 0·08

B Use square root tables to find the square roots of the numbers in Section B above. When you have found them all compare table results and calculator results. Pay special attention to the position of the decimal point.

D (a) If you multiply $\sqrt{a}$ by $\sqrt{b}$, the result is $\sqrt{ab}$.

(b) If you divide $\sqrt{a}$ by $\sqrt{b}$, the result is $\sqrt{a/b}$.

1 Show that statement (a) is correct for the values of *a* and *b* given in the table below.

	I a	II b	III ab	IV $\sqrt{a}$	V $\sqrt{b}$	VI $\sqrt{a} \times \sqrt{b}$	VII $\sqrt{ab}$
e.g.	4	10	40	2	3·16	6·32	6·32
e.g.	5	9	45	2·24	3	6·72	6·71
	8	10					
	4	25					
	7	·6					
	14	·2					

Note:
The number in col. VI is found by multiplying the numbers in col. IV and col. V

The number in col. VII is found by 'square rooting' the number in col. III.

2 Choose numbers for *a* and *b* to check statement (ii) about dividing square roots. Draw a similar table to the one above (question 1).

Unit M24 Applications of square/square root

24·1 The right-angled triangle

Pythagoras's theorem states the relationship between the sides of any right-angled triangle.

$$a^2 + b^2 = c^2$$

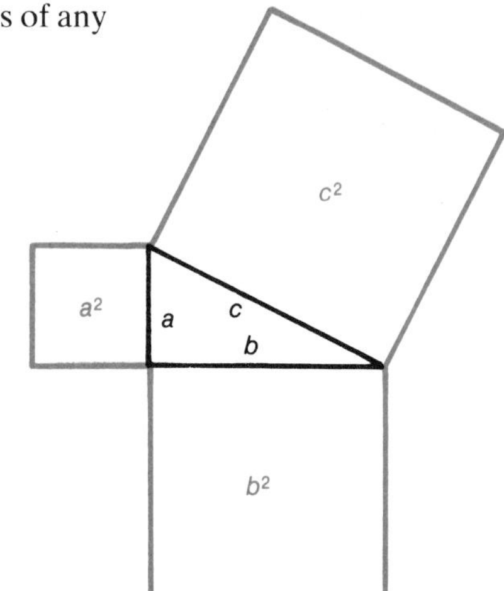

This means that if we know two sides of a right-angled triangle we can calculate the third side. (We can also check that a triangle is right-angled by seeing whether $a^2 + b^2 = c^2$.)

Example:

Calculate the length of AC in this diagram.

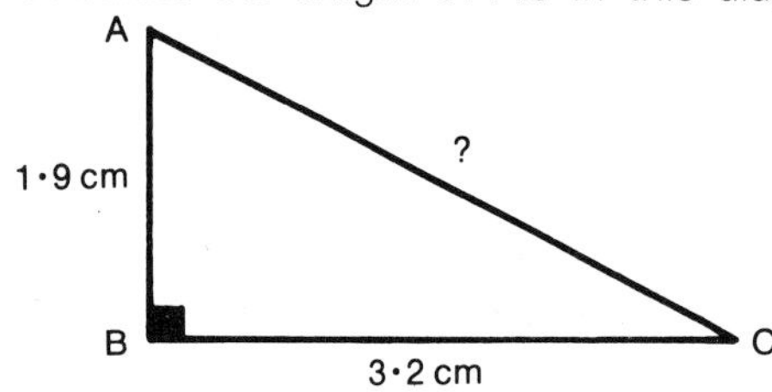

Since AC is the longest side of a right-angled triangle

$$AB^2 + BC^2 = AC^2$$
$$\downarrow \quad \downarrow$$
$$(1{\cdot}9)^2 + (3{\cdot}2)^2$$
$$\downarrow \quad \downarrow$$
$$3{\cdot}61 + 10{\cdot}24 = AC^2 = 13{\cdot}85$$
$$AC = \sqrt{13{\cdot}85} = 3{\cdot}72 \text{ cm}$$

Example:

Calculate the length of AC

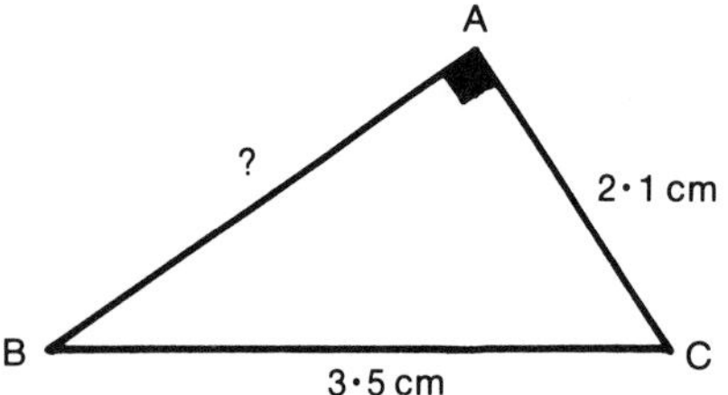

Since BC is the longest side of the triangle

$$AB^2 + AC^2 = BC^2$$
$$AB^2 = BC^2 - AC^2$$
$$\downarrow \quad \searrow$$
$$(3{\cdot}5)^2 - (2{\cdot}1)^2$$
$$\downarrow \quad \downarrow$$
$$12{\cdot}25 - 4{\cdot}41$$
$$AB^2 = 7{\cdot}84$$
$$AB = \sqrt{7{\cdot}84} = 2{\cdot}8 \text{ cm}$$

Exercise 24·1

A Find the length of the third side in each of the following triangles. Make a careful drawing to check your calculation.

1	AB = 4·6 cm	AC = 5·2 cm	A = 90°
2	AB = 3 cm	AC = 3 cm	A = 90°
3	AC = 5 cm	AB = 5 cm	A = 90°
4	AB = 4 cm	BC = 5 cm	B = 90°
5	AC = 3 cm	BC = 2·5 cm	C = 90°

B Make a drawing of each of the triangles below. Measure the third side and check its length by calculation.

Example:

AB = 5 cm, AC = 7 cm, $\hat{B} = 90°$

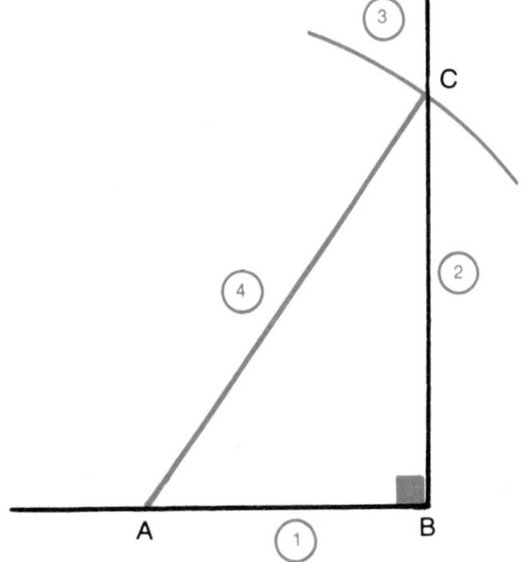

10 Draw AB 5 cm long.
20 Draw a line perpendicular to AB from B.
30 Draw an arc of a circle, centre A, radius 7 cm.
40 Draw AC.
50 Measure BC.

BC = 4·85 cm measurement.

Since AC is the longest side

$AB^2 + BC^2 = AC^2$

$(5)^2 + (4{\cdot}85)^2$

$25 + 23{\cdot}5225 = 48{\cdot}5225$ ... This is nearly 49, the correct value for AC^2. (The error is introduced because it is impossible to measure BC with sufficient accuracy.)

1	AB = 3 cm	AC = 5 cm	B = 90°
2	AB = 5 cm	AC = 8 cm	B = 90°
3	AB = 3·5 cm	AC = 4·8 cm	B = 90°
4	AB = 6 cm	AC = 10 cm	B = 90°

C Use Pythagoras's theorem to check which of the following triangles are right-angled. State which angle is the right angle in each case.

1	AB = 5 cm	BC = 12 cm	CA = 13 cm
2	AB = 6 cm	BC = 8 cm	CA = 10 cm
3	AB = 14 cm	BC = 11 cm	CA = 13 cm
4	AB = 10 cm	BC = 7·5 cm	CA = 12·5 cm
5	AB = 85 cm	BC = 58 cm	CA = 102 cm

24·2 Applications

Pythagoras's theorem is useful in many different situations. Some examples are given below.

Example:

A rectangle has sides 12 cm and 15 cm. Find the length of its diagonal.

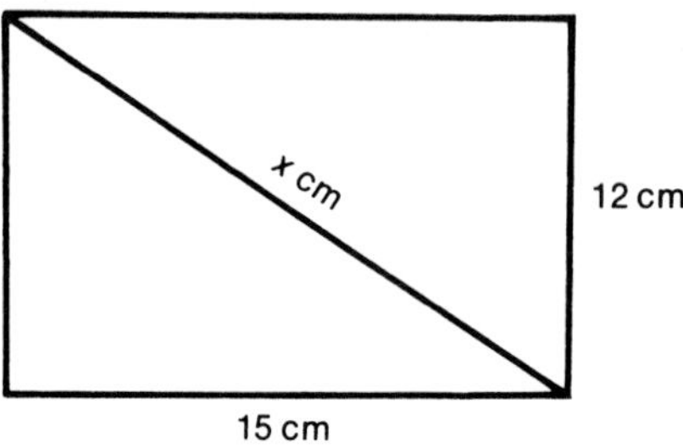

$$x^2 = 12^2 + 15^2$$
$$= 144 + 225$$
$$= 369$$
$$x = \sqrt{369} = 19{\cdot}21 \text{ cm}$$

Example:

A ship steams 450 km North and then 280 km East. How far has the ship travelled?

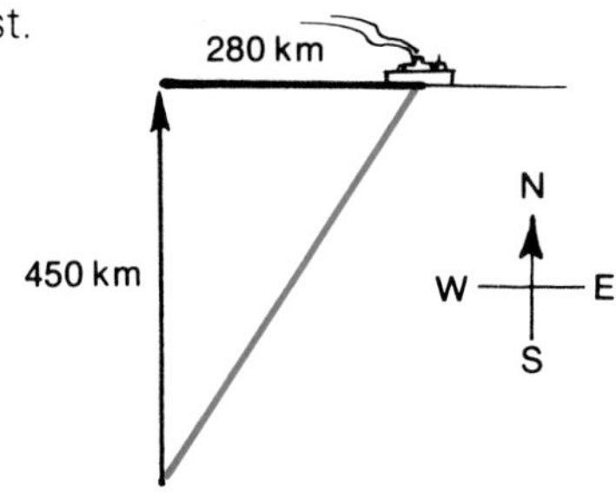

$$x^2 = 280^2 + 450^2$$
$$= 78\,400 + 202\,500$$
$$= 280\,900$$
$$x = \sqrt{280\,900} = 530 \text{ km}$$

Example:

Find the distance between the points (2, 5) and (5, 7) on a graph.

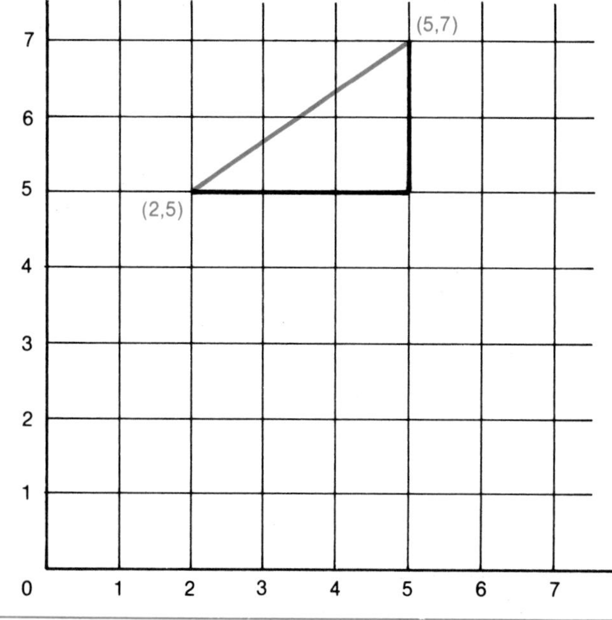

In the right-angled triangle the vertical side is 2 units the horizontal side is 3 units.

$$d^2 = 2^2 + 3^2$$
$$= 4 + 9$$
$$d = \sqrt{13} = 3{\cdot}61$$

Exercise 24·2

A **1** Find the length of diagonal of rectangles whose sides are:
(a) 5 cm and 10 cm (b) 8 cm and 15 cm (c) 1 m and 0·5 m
(d) 16 m and 14 m (e) 3·4 km and 2·9 km (f) 67 km and 159 km
(g) 7800 km and 2930 km (h) 9520 km and 14 km.

2 A rectangle has **perimeter** 120 m. What is its breadth if its length is:
(a) 10 m? (b) 15 m? (c) 20 m? (d) 25 m? (e) 30 m?
Calculate the diagonal length in each case.

3 A swimming pool is 15 m long and 8 m wide. What is the distance from one corner to the opposite corner?

B **1** A boy who is fishing with 20 m of line sits on a pier 8 m above the sea. What is the greatest distance from the pier that he can reach with his line and rod.

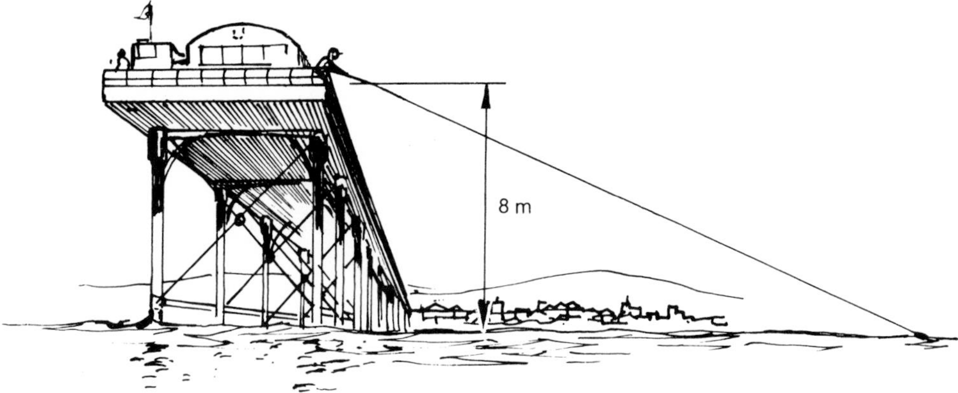

2 A kite has 50 m of string. It is flying above a point 20 m from the girl holding the string. What is its height? (rough)

3 (a) A ship sails 140 km due North and then 52 km due West. How far has it sailed altogether? How far is it from the starting-point?
(b) An aircraft flies 350 km direct from airport A to airport B (which is North and East of B). If airport B is 100 km North of A. how far is it East of A?

4 A tent has a vertical end pole 1·5 m high. This is held up by two guy ropes. The feet of the guy ropes must be at least 2 m from the foot of the pole. What is the minimum length of each guy rope?

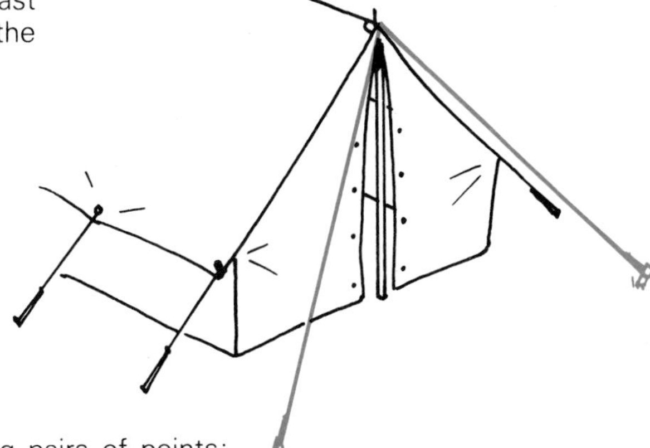

C Find the distances between the following pairs of points:

1 (0, 0) and (1, 5)
2 (0, 0) and (3, 6)
3 (0, 0) and (4, 4)
4 (0, 2) and (3, 3)
5 (3, 0) and (2, 4)
6 (4, 2) and (3, 7)
7 (5, 3) and (5, 8)
8 (4, 2) and (2, −1)

24·3 The cuboid

The lengths of diagonals on a cuboid are found using Pythagoras's theorem.

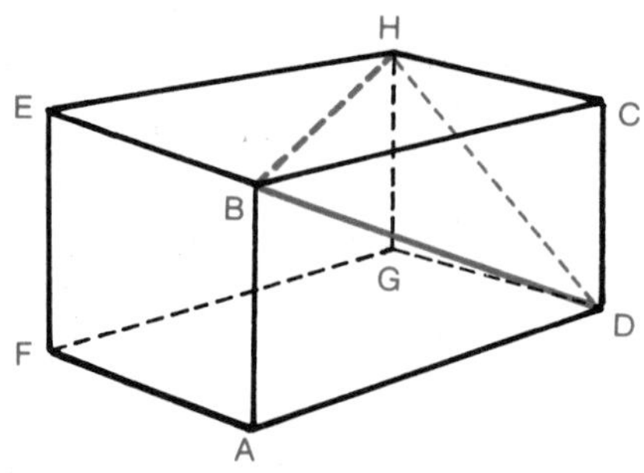

Three diagonals on faces.

There are three different sized diagonals on the faces of the cuboid.

There are also four diagonals through the centre of the cuboid. These are ED, AH, BG and CF in the diagram. (CF has not been drawn.)

All four long diagonals through the centre are the same length = $\sqrt{x^2 + y^2 + z^2}$

All four diagonals pass through the centre of the cuboid.

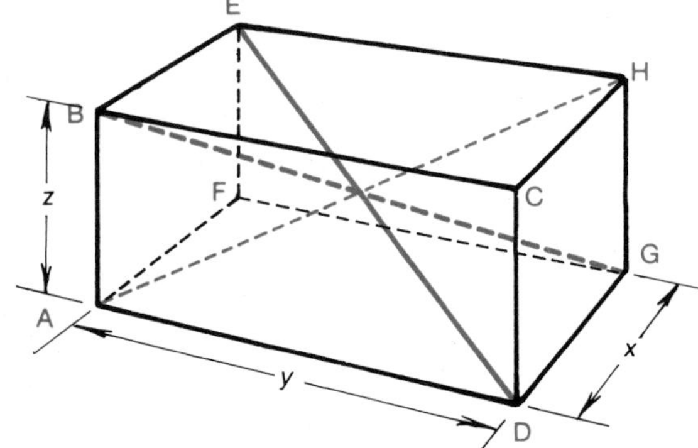

The three long diagonals of a cuboid.

> **Example:**
> A cuboid has length 12 cm
> breadth 5 cm
> height 4 cm
> Calculate the lengths of all the diagonals.
> There are 12 diagonals on the faces annd 4 long diagonals.
> 12 × 5 faces ... length of diagonals $\sqrt{12^2 + 5^2} = \sqrt{169} = 13$ cm
> 5 × 4 faces ... length of diagonals $\sqrt{5^2 + 4^2} = \sqrt{41} = 6{\cdot}4$ cm
> 12 × 4 faces ... length of diagonals $\sqrt{12^2 + 4^2} = \sqrt{160} = 12{\cdot}65$ cm
> Long diagonals $\sqrt{4^2 + 5^2 + 12^2} = 13{\cdot}6$ cm

Exercise 24·3

A **1** A cuboid has length 10 cm, breadth 8 cm and height 6 cm.
Calculate:
(a) The lengths of the diagonals on the faces.
(b) The lengths of the long diagonals.

2 A cuboid has length 15 cm and a square section, side 5 cm.
Calculate:
(a) The lengths of the diagonals on the faces.
(b) The lengths of the long diagonals.

3 An aircraft takes off from the airport and climbs, in a straight line, to a height of 10 km. It is then above a point 50 km North and 60 km East of the airport. Calculate the actual distance flown by the aircraft.

4 A container is 8 m long, 2·4 m wide and 3 m high.
Which of the following could be carried in the container:
(a) A pole 8·5 m long?
(b) A pole 9·5 m long?
(c) A sheet of glass, 7·5 m long and 4 m wide?

B 1 A cuboid has sides x, y and z cm in length.
The diagonals measure 10 cm, 8·94 cm and 7·07 cm across the faces.
(a) Shows that $x = 8{\cdot}06$
$y = 5{\cdot}92$
$z = 3{\cdot}87$ are possible values for x, y and z.
(b) What are the lengths of the four diagonals through the centre of the cuboid?

2 A cornflakes box measures 31·5 cm by 22·3 cm by 7·5 cm.
(a) What is the volume of the box?
(b) What are the lengths of the diagonals of the box?

3 A pyramid has height 4 m and the sides of the square base are all 5 m long. The apex (top) of the pyramid is vertically over the centre of the base.
(a) Find the lengths of the diagonals of the base AC and BD. (Remember ABCD is a square.)
(b) Now find the length AX.
(c) Use triangle PAX to find the length of PA, the slanting edge of the pyramid ($P\hat{X}A = 90°$.)
(d) Cut out a net of a pyramid so that you can make a model of the pyramid above. (1 m: 1 cm)
Make PA = PB = PC = PD equal to the length you have just found.
(e) Measure the height of the pyramid you have made. It should be 4 cm!

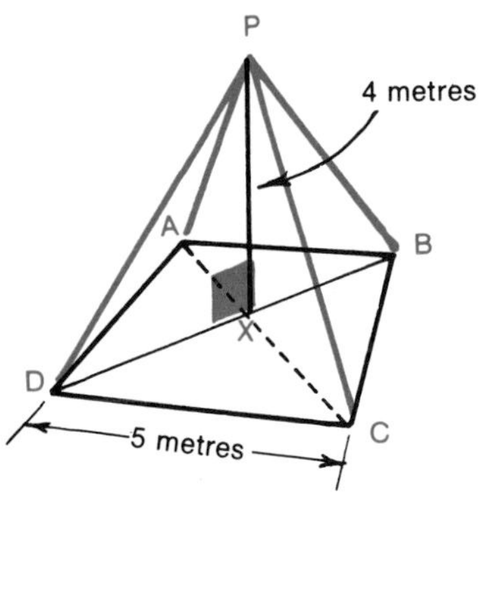

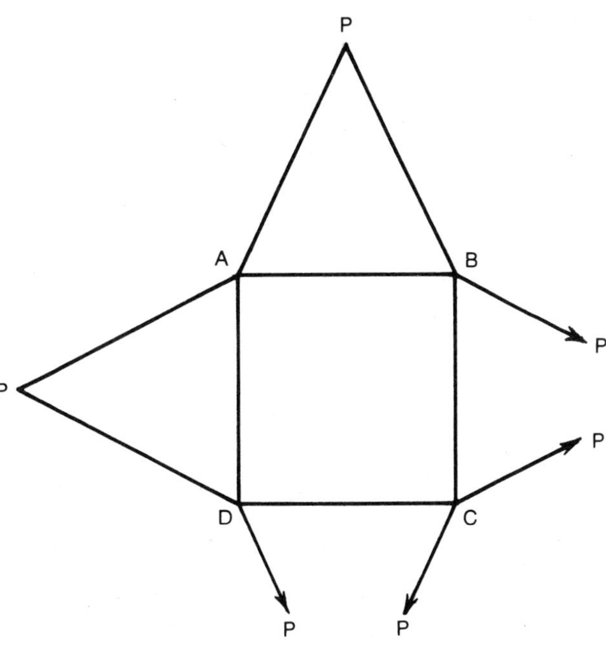

4 The spire of a church is a pyramid on a square base. The sides of the base measure 8 m and the height of the spire is 28 m. What is the length of the slanting edge of the spire?

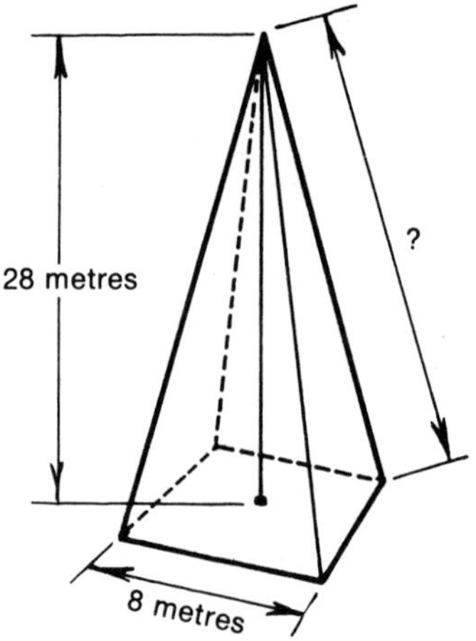

24·4 Circles

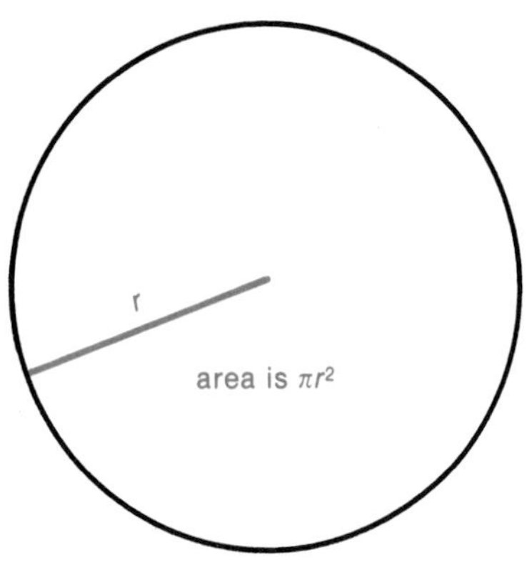

Since the area of a circle involves the square of the radius we expect to use squares and square roots in circle problems.

Example:

Find the area of a circle whose radius is 7·2 cm.

$$\text{Area} = \pi \times r^2$$
$$= \pi \times (7{\cdot}2)^2$$
$$= 3{\cdot}1416 \times 51{\cdot}84$$
$$= 16{\cdot}286 \text{ cm}$$

[C] [7] [·] [2] [×] [=] [×] [π] [=]

Example:

The area of a circle is 10 cm^2. Find the radius and circumference. What do you notice about radius × circumference?

Area $= \pi r^2$ $\quad A = 10$ cm

$$r^2 = \frac{10}{\pi} \text{ cm}$$

$$r = \sqrt{\frac{10}{\pi}} \text{ cm}$$ [C] [1] [0] [÷] [π] [=] [√] or use tables

$= 1{\cdot}784$ cm

Circumference $= 2\pi r$

$= 2 \times \pi \times 1{\cdot}784$

$= 11{\cdot}209$ cm [C] [2] [×] [π] [×] [1] [·] [7] [8] [4] [=]

Circumference × radius = 1·784 × 11·209 = 19·999

This suggests that circumference × radius = 2 × area.

Exercise 24·4

A Find the area of a circle given that:

1 The radius is 6·7 cm.
2 The radius is 0·45 cm.
3 The radius is 2·8 m.
4 The diameter is 5·6 m.
5 The diameter is 14·3 cm.

B Find the radius of a circle given that:

1 The area is 20 cm^2.
2 The area is 14·2 m^2.
3 The area is 45 m^2.
4 The area is 102 cm^2.
5 The area is 0·14 cm^2.
6 The area is 0·08 cm^2.

C Find the circumference of a circle given that:

1 The area is 12 cm^2.
2 The area is 0·14 cm^2.
3 The area is 28 m^2.
4 The area is 440 m^2.

D Find the area of a circle given that:

1 The circumference is 18 cm.
2 The circumference is 35 cm.
3 The circumference is 254 mm.
4 The circumference is 18·2 m.
5 The circumference is 26·3 m.

24·5 General problems

Squares and square roots occur in many problems in science and mathematics.

Example:

The heat given out by a wire depends on the square of the current passed (in amps). $[H = kI^2]$
A current of 2·0 A produces 4000 units of heat in a certain wire. What current would produce
(a) 6000 units of heat? (b) 1500 units of heat?

First find k

$$H = kI^2$$

Put

$H = 4000$, $I = 2$

$$4000 = k \times 4$$

Therefore $k = 1000$

Now we can answer the questions.

(a) $6000 = k \times I^2 = 1000 \times I^2$

$$I^2 = 6$$

$$I = \sqrt{6} = 2{\cdot}45 \text{ amps}$$

(b) $1500 = 1000 \times I^2$

$$I^2 = 1{\cdot}5$$

$$I = \sqrt{1{\cdot}5} = 1{\cdot}225 \text{ amps}$$

Exercise 24·5

A **1** The area of a circle depends on the size of its radius. A circle radius 10 cm has area 314·6 cm^2. What radius will produce a circle with area:
(a) 100 cm^2? (b) 500 cm^2? (c) 1400 cm^2?

2 The area of an equilateral triangle depends on the square of its side. An equilateral triangle with side 5 cm has an area of 10·825 cm^2. What is the side of an equilateral triangle with area:
(a) 50 cm^2? (b) 100 cm^2? (c) 0·4 cm^2?

B The distance fallen by a falling object depends on the square of the time taken to fall.

1 A stone falls 122·5 m in 5 seconds. How far would it fall in:
(a) 10 seconds? (Not twice as far) (b) 20 seconds? (c) 50 seconds?

2 How long would it take a stone to fall:
(a) 1000 m (b) 500 m (c) 50 m.

3 A man jumps from an aeroplane.
(a) It takes 15 seconds for his parachute to open. How far does he fall in this time?
(b) How far would he fall if his parachute takes 40 seconds to open?
(c) If the aeroplane is at 10 000 m and his parachute opens after 40 seconds, will he be saved?

Unit M25 Formulae

25·1 Introduction

A formula is an expression in letters which describes a relationship.
When the letters are replaced by numbers, a value is found.
Formulae are used in science, engineering and mathematics and also in many other subjects and activities.

Example:
Formula for the volume of a cone . . . $V = \frac{1}{3}\pi r^2 h$

If we know (by measurement) that
$r = 5$ cm, $h = 6{\cdot}5$ cm
we can find the value of V

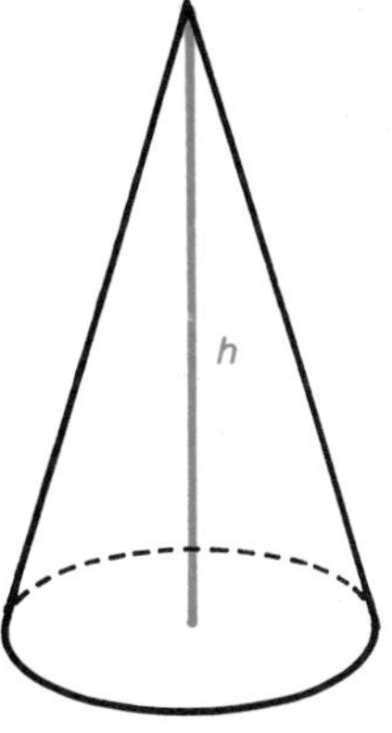

h is the height of the cone and r is the radius of its base.
The formula tells you that the volume of the cone is . . . one third of . . . π times the square of the radius times the height

Example:
Formula for the cost of a piece of meat . . . $C = p \times w$
p = Price per kilograms, w = weight in kilograms.
If we know the price per kilo is £1·40 and the weight of the meat is 1·6 kg.
we can find the *value* of C

Exercise 25·1

A Write these relationships as formulae.

1 The area of any rectangle is found by multiplying length (l) times breadth (b).
2 The cost of a 'fill-up' of petrol is the cost per litre times the number of litres.
3 The weight of a lump of metal is the density (d) of the metal times the volume (v) of the lump.
4 The time of a journey in hours is the distance travelled (d) divided by the speed (s). Distance and speed must be in the same units.
5 The volume of a pyramid on a square base is one third of the area of the base (a) times the height of the pyramid (h).

B Write sentences in place of the following formulae.

1 $d = \frac{w}{v}$, where d = density, w = weight in g and v = volume in cm^3.

2 $d = v \times t$, d = distance in metres, v = velocity in metres per second and t = time in seconds.

3 $V = l \times b \times h$, where V = volume of cuboid, l = length, b = breadth and h = height.

4 $A = \pi r^2$, where A = area of circle, $\pi = 3{\cdot}1416$ and r = radius.

25·2 Substitution

Replacing the letters by numbers and finding a value for the quantity on the left-hand side of the formula is called **substitution**.

Example:

$y = 2x^2 + 3x$ Substitute $x = 3$

$y = 2 \times (3)^2 + (3 \times 3)$

$y = (2 \times 9) + 9$

$y = 18 + 9 = 27$

Example:

$V = \pi r^2 h$ Substitute $\pi = 3{\cdot}1416$, $r = 5$, $h = 2{\cdot}6$

$V = 3{\cdot}1416 \times (5)^2 \times 2{\cdot}6$

* Using calculator [3] [·] [1] [4] [1] [6] [×] [5] [×] [5] [×] [2] [·] [6] [=]

$V = 204{\cdot}204$

Exercise 25·2

A Find the value of the *subject*† of the formula

1 $y = 3x^2 + 5 \ldots x = 7{\cdot}2$

2 $y = 17 - 2x \ldots x = 0{\cdot}8$

3 $y = \sqrt{3 - x^2} \ldots x = 1{\cdot}14$

4 $y = x^2 - 2x + 1 \ldots x = 0{\cdot}4$

B Find the value of the volume in each case.

1 $V = d^3$, where $d = 1{\cdot}8$ cm ... this is a cube.

2 $V = a^2 l$, where $a = 2{\cdot}4$ cm, $l = 3{\cdot}5$ cm ... this is a cuboid with square cross-section.

3 $V = a \times b \times c$, where $a = 3{\cdot}5$ cm, $b = 2{\cdot}8$ cm, $c = 6{\cdot}6$ cm ... this is a cuboid.

4 $V = \pi r^2 h$, where $\pi = 3{\cdot}1416$, $r = 8{\cdot}4$ cm, $h = 14$ cm ... this is a cylinder.

5 $V = \pi R^2 h - \pi r^2 h$, where $\pi = 3{\cdot}1416$, $R = 5{\cdot}6$ cm, $r = 5{\cdot}0$ cm and $h = 200$ cm. ... this is a cylindrical pipe, thickness 6 mm.

6 $V = \frac{1}{3}\pi r^2 h$, where $\pi = 3{\cdot}1416$, $r = 0{\cdot}82$ cm and $h = 12$ cm ... this is a cone.

* Care must be taken that the calculation follows the formula exactly.

† The letter on the left-hand side of the equals sign.

C Find the value of the subject of the formula in each case.

1 $E = \frac{1}{2}mv^2$, where $v = 16$ cm per second, $m = 22$ g. ...this is the formula for kinetic energy.

2 $p = \frac{2.7}{v}$, where $v = 302$ cm^3. ...this is the formula relating pressure and volume of gas.

3 $t = \frac{2\pi\sqrt{l}}{\sqrt{9.8}}$, where $\pi = 3.1416$, $l = 0.3$ m. ...this is the formula relating length and time of swing for a pendulum.

4 $F = ma$, where $m = 65$ g, $a = 981$ cm/sec^2. ...this is the formula relating *Force*, *Mass* and *Acceleration* discovered by Sir Isaac Newton.

Note: It is possible to find the value of the subject of a formula even if you do not know how the formula was formed.

25·3 Change of subject

It is sometimes convenient to change a formula round so that a different letter becomes the subject. This can be done by treating the formula as an equation. The rules are then followed to get the wanted letter on its own.

General examples:	RULES
$a = b \Rightarrow a + c = b + c$	**1** Equal quantities may be added to both sides of an equation.
$a = b \Rightarrow a - c = b - c$	**2** Equal quantities may be subtracted from both sides of an equation.
$a = b \Rightarrow ka = kb$	**3** Both sides may be multiplied by equal quantities.
$a = b \Rightarrow a/k = b/k$	**4** Both sides may be divided by equal quantities.
$a = b \Rightarrow a^2 = b^2 \Rightarrow a^3 = b^3$ etc.	**5** Both sides may be squared, cubed or raised to any power.
$a = b \Rightarrow \sqrt{a} = \sqrt{b}$	**6** Both sides may be square rooted, cube rooted or rooted to any power. (Care must be taken with signs.)

Example 1:

$A = l \times b$ ... make b the subject of the formula.
$A = lb$ ... divide by l (rule 4)

$\frac{A}{l} = b$ ... since b is alone, b is the subject.

$b = \frac{A}{l}$ change sides to put the subject on the left-hand side.

Example 2:

Given that $v = u + at$ and $v = 10$, $u = 8$ and $a = 12$ make t the subject of the formula and find the value of t.

$v = u + at$
$v - u = at$ subtract u from both sides

$$\frac{v-u}{a} = t \qquad \text{divide both sides by } a$$

$$t = \frac{v-u}{a} \qquad \text{change sides to put } t \text{ on the left}$$

The value of t is $\dfrac{10-8}{12} = \dfrac{2}{12}$

$$= \frac{1}{6}$$

Exercise 25·3

A **1** Make p the subject of $pv = k^2$.
2 Make l the subject of $A = l \times h \times b$.
3 Make v the subject of $E = \frac{1}{2}mv^2$.
4 Make t the subject of $S = \frac{1}{2}gt^2$.
5 Make r the subject of $V = \frac{1}{3}\pi r^2 h$.
6 Make r the subject of $A = \pi r^2 + d$.

B **1** Make x the subject of $y = 3x^2 + 2$ and find the value of x if $y = 3$.
2 Make z the subject of $y = x^2 + xz$ and find the value of z if $x = 2$ and $y = 8$.
3 Make h the subject of $V = \pi r^2 h$ and find the value of h if $V = 60 \text{ cm}^3$, $\pi = 3{\cdot}1416$, $r = 2{\cdot}8$ cm.
4 Make t the subject of $S = \frac{1}{2}gt^2$ and find the value of t if $S = 400$ m, $g = 10$ m per sec^2. g is roughly the acceleration due to gravity.

25·4 Changing the subject by inverting

A formula can be treated as a function or a series of functions in a program.

$y = 3x^2 + 2$ can be read

10 start with x	x .... say,	5
20 square it	x^2	25
30 multiply by 3	$3x^2$	75
40 add 2	$3x^2 + 2$	77
50 print y =		

Whatever number you put in for x, the output will be y, equal to $3x^2 + 2$. For example, if you put in $x = 5$, $3x^2 + 2$ will be 77.

If you start with y and **invert** the functions you will end up with x.
The **inverse** of square it is square root it,
of multiply by 3 is divide by 3,
of add 2 is subtract 2.

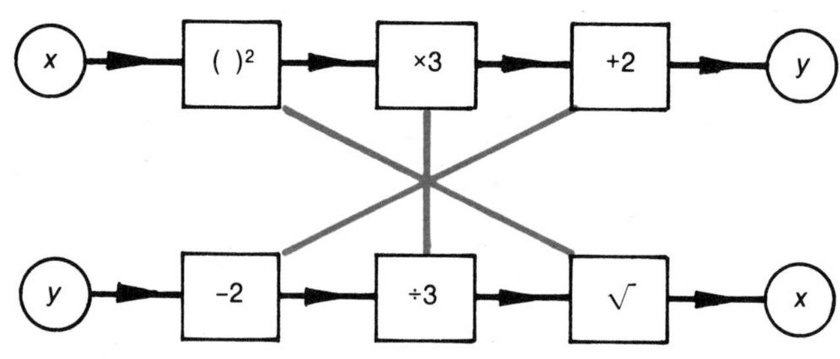

	Program	Inverse	
	x	$y = 3x^2 + 2$	
$(\ )^2$	x^2	$y - 2$	-2
$\times 3$	$3x^2$	$\frac{1}{3}(y - 2)$	$\div 3$
add 2	$3x^2 + 2$	$\sqrt{\frac{1}{3}(y - 2)}$	$\sqrt{\ }$
	y	x	

Exercise 25·4

A Write each of the following below as a program. Find the value of the subject of the formula for the numbers given.

1 $y = 2x^2 - 5 \ldots x = 3{\cdot}7$

2 $y = 2x^2 + 5 \ldots x = 2{\cdot}3$

3 $p = \frac{q}{8} \ldots q = 16{\cdot}8$

4 $y = 2x - \frac{1}{x} \ldots x = 0{\cdot}8$

5 $m = 2n - 5 \ldots n = 3{\cdot}7$

6 $v = \dfrac{4\pi r^3}{3} \ldots r = 16{\cdot}4$

B Use inverse functions to change the subject of the formulae below. Find the value of the new subject for the values given.

1 $I = \dfrac{PRT}{100}$ (i) Make P the subject.
(ii) Find the value of P if $R = 14$ and $T = 5$, while $I = 350$.

2 $S = 4\pi r^2$ (i) Make r the subject.
(ii) Find the value of r if $S = 100$, $\pi = 3{\cdot}1416$.

3 $V = 2gh$ (i) Make h the subject.
(ii) Find the value of h if $V = 200$, $g = 10$.

4 $L = l + kt^2$ (i) Make t the subject.
(ii) Find the value of t if $L = 109$, $l = 106{\cdot}3$ and $k = 0{\cdot}02$.

25·5 Some important formulae

Formulae are widely used in maths and science as convenient ways of remembering and expressing relationships. The list below includes some of the most important formulae concerned with measurement.

Name	Shape	Area	Surface area	Volume
Rectangle	(rectangle, sides l, b)	$A = lb$		
Triangle	(triangle, base b, height h)	$A = \frac{1}{2}bh$		
Circle	(circle, radius r)	$A = \pi r^2$ $\pi = 3{\cdot}1416\ldots$		

Name	Shape	Area	Surface area	Volume
Cuboid	h, l, b		$A = 2lb + 2lh + 2hb$	$V = lbh$
Cylinder	l, r		$A = 2\pi r^2 + 2\pi rl$ $= 2\pi r(r + l)$	$V = \pi r^2 l$
Cone	h, l, r		$A = \pi rl + \pi r^2$ $l^2 = h^2 + r^2$	$V = \frac{1}{3}\pi r^2 h$
Pyramid	h			$V = \frac{1}{3}h \times$ base area
Sphere			$A = 4\pi r^2$	$V = \frac{4}{3}\pi r^3$

Exercise 25·5 (Use the formulae given above)

A

1 Calculate the area of a rectangle, length 7 cm, breadth 10·5 cm.
2 Calculate the area of a triangle, base 14 mm, height 8·8 mm.
3 Calculate the area of a circle, radius 6·32 m.
4 Calculate the surface area and volume of a cuboid whose length is 8·2 cm, breadth 3·1 cm and height 0·85 cm.
5 Calculate the surface area of a cylinder, length 5·2 cm and radius 2·8 cm.
6 Calculate the surface area of a cone, radius 5 cm and height 2·6 cm. (Find l, the shortest distance from the vertex, to a point on the circumference of the base.)
7 Calculate the volume of a cylinder 14 cm long, with radius 1·6 cm.
8 Calculate the volume of a cone, height 12 cm and base radius 2·5 cm.
9 Calculate the volume of a pyramid 14 m high, standing on a square base of side 2·5 m.
10 Calculate the volume of a sphere, radius 2·8 cm.

B

1 The area of a rectangle is 42 cm^2. The length is 12·6 cm, calculate the breadth.
2 Find the height of a triangle whose base is 5 cm and area 12 cm^2.
3 Find the radius of a circle whose area is 10 cm^2.
4 Find the length of a cylinder whose volume is 420 cm^3 and whose radius is 8 cm.
5 Find the height of a cone whose volume is 28 m^3 and whose base radius is 0·82 m.
6 Find the radius of a sphere whose volume is 100 m^3. You will have to find the cube root by estimation.

C All these problems are examples from the real world which use the formulae of measurement.

1 A rectangular house is 14 m long and 8 m wide. What is the floor area of the house?

2 Glass costs £8 per square metre. A piece of glass in the shape of a rectangle is 75 cm wide and costs £6·50. How long is it?

3 An air-sea rescue launch is searching the sea for survivors of a boat which has capsized. The launch sweeps in circles, radius 500 m. What area of sea is covered in each sweep?

4 A water tank is a cuboid 1 m long, 60 cm wide and 40 cm high. Will it hold 1000 litres of water? (1 litre = 1000 cm^3)

5 Another water tank is a cylinder, diameter 1 m and 50 cm deep. How many litres will this tank hold?

6 The great pyramid of Cheops is 137·5 m high. Its base is a square of approximately 220 m. What volume of stone was used in its construction. If stone weighs 3 tonnes a cubic metre, calculate the weight of the pyramid. Does the pyramid weigh more than the whole population of the world? (Count 20 people to the tonne.)

Unit M26 Trinomials: Quadratics

26·1 Negative numbers. Addition and subtraction

In mathematics we find the ordinary whole number system is not enough.
The system is extended to the negative numbers . . . e.g. $^{-}3$, $^{-}7$, $^{-}2$, etc.
and the rational numbers . . . e.g. $\frac{2}{3}$, $\frac{3}{5}$, 1·7, $\frac{^{-}3}{4}$, $^{-}4{\cdot}3$
Rational numbers can be negative.
The basic rule about a negative number is that it is partner to an equal-sized positive number. When the partners are added the result is always zero.

> **Example:**
>
> $^{-}5 + {^{+}5} = 0$
>
> $^{-}3{\cdot}7 + 3{\cdot}7 = 0$, etc.

The partnership enables us to add, subtract, multiply and divide negative numbers.

> **Example:**
>
> $^{-}7 + {^{-}15} = {^{-}22}$ We know that
>
> $^{-}7 + 7 + {^{-}15} + 15 = 0$
>
> so $^{-}7 + {^{-}15} + 22 = 0$
>
> so $^{-}7 + {^{-}15} = {^{-}22}$
>
> $^{-}4 + 9 = 5$* We split 9 into 4 (partner for $^{-}4$) and 5
>
> so $^{-}4 + 9 = {^{-}4} + 4 + 5 = 5$

> **Examples:**
>
> $^{-}7 - {^{+}3}$ is the same as $^{-}7 + {^{-}3} = {^{-}10}$
>
> $2 - {^{-}5}$ is the same as $2 + {^{+}5} = 7$
>
> $^{-}4 - {^{-}9}$ is the same as $^{-}4 + 9 = 5$

Exercise 26·1

A Find the sums of these numbers.

1 $4 + {^{-}3}$	**2** $11 + {^{-}7}$	**3** $^{-}4 + 9$	**4** $^{-}5 + {^{-}8}$
5 $^{-}2 + {^{-}6}$	**6** $^{-}1{\cdot}7 + 2$	**7** $^{-}4{\cdot}9 + 1{\cdot}3$	**8** $^{-}4{\cdot}9 + {^{-}1{\cdot}3}$

* We note that adding a 'partner' has the same effect as subtracting a number. $9 + {^{-}4}$ is the same as $9 - 4$

9 $^{-}5{\cdot}8 + {}^{-}6{\cdot}2$ **10** $^{-}3{\cdot}4 + {}^{-}5{\cdot}5$ **11** $14{\cdot}2 + {}^{-}7{\cdot}4$ **12** $16 + {}^{-}4{\cdot}3$
13 $4 + {}^{-}3 + {}^{-}7$ **14** $^{-}6 + 5 + {}^{-}1$ **15** $^{-}7{\cdot}2 + 3{\cdot}6 + 5{\cdot}1$ **16** $6{\cdot}4 + {}^{-}4{\cdot}2 + {}^{-}3{\cdot}8$

Check on calculator. You will need +/− button. If there is not a +/− on your calculator you will have to find a way of entering negative numbers into the machine, e.g. use [0] [−] [6] for $^{-}6$.

B Subtract the following.

Remember subtracting $\begin{cases} n \text{ is the same as adding } -n \\ -n \text{ is the same as adding } n \end{cases}$

1 $14 - 3$ **2** $17 - 8$ **3** $4 - 9$ **4** $5 - 12$
5 $6 - {}^{-}3$ **6** $8 - {}^{-}2$ **7** $1 - {}^{-}5$ **8** $4 - {}^{-}6$
9 $^{-}3 - {}^{-}2$ **10** $^{-}4 - {}^{-}6$ **11** $^{-}6 - {}^{-}9$ **12** $^{-}5 - {}^{-}11$
13 $^{-}5 - 9$ **14** $^{-}7 - 2$ **15** $^{-}3 - 5$ **16** $^{-}9 - 11$

Check on calculator, use +/−.

C The positive and negative numbers may be shown on a number line

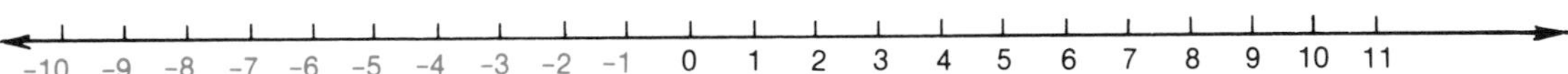

Two of these placed side by side can be used to add and subtract negative numbers.

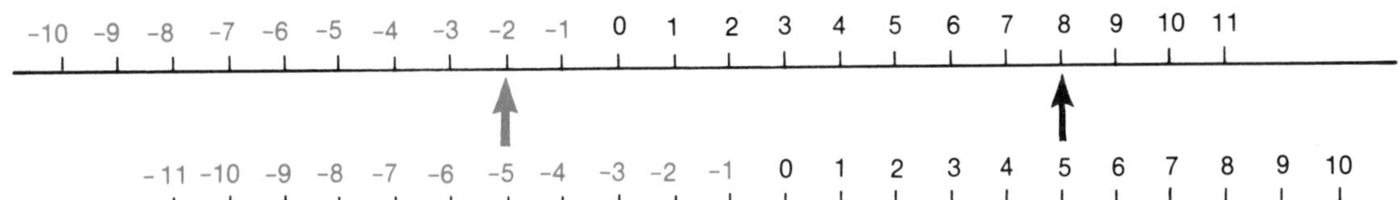

The number lines above show $3 + {}^{-}5 = {}^{-}2$ and $3 + 5 = 8$. (By placing O on the second line against 3 on the first line we can see the result of adding 3 to *any* number.)

Cut out two strips of paper and mark the edges with a number line as shown.

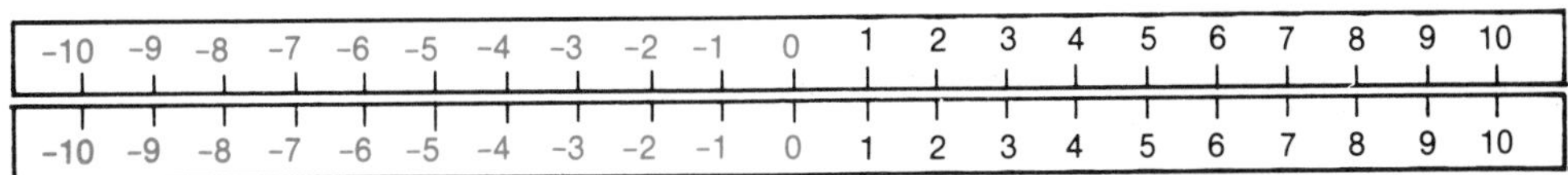

Investigate how the strips can be used to add and subtract numbers including negative numbers. Use the strips to check your answers to question B.

26·2 Negative numbers. Multiplication and division

It is clear that $^{-}5 \times 3$ will be $^{-}15$. We simply add $^{-}5 + {}^{-}5 + {}^{-}5 = {}^{-}15$.

Now $({}^{-}5 \times 3) + ({}^{-}5 \times {}^{-}3)$ will be **zero**, from the distributive law.

$[{}^{-}5(3 + {}^{-}3) = {}^{-}5 \times 0 = 0]$

So $^{-}5 \times {}^{-}3$ must be $^{+}15$.

The **product** of **two negative numbers** is **positive**.

This can also be seen by following the pattern of multiplication below.

$^-5 \times 3 = {}^-15$	I
$^-5 \times 2 = {}^-10$	N C
$^-5 \times 1 = {}^-5$	R
$^-5 \times 0 = 0$	E A
$^-5 \times {}^-1 = 5$	S
$^-5 \times {}^-2 = 10$	I N
$^-5 \times {}^-3 = 15$	↓G

From this table we can also see that:
(i) $^-15 \div {}^-5 = 3$
(ii) $15 \div {}^-5 = {}^-3$
(iii) $^-15 \div {}^+3 = {}^-5$

Dividing one negative by a **negative** gives a **positive** result.
Dividing a **positive** by a **negative** gives a **negative** result.
This leads to the **rules** of signs

$^+a \times {}^+b = {}^+ab$ $\qquad$ $^+a \div {}^+b = \dfrac{a}{b}$ $\qquad$ $^-a \div {}^+b = \dfrac{^-a}{b}$
$^+a \times {}^-b = {}^-ab$

$^-a \times {}^+b = {}^-ab$ $\qquad$ $^+a \div {}^-b = \dfrac{^-a}{b}$ $\qquad$ $^-a \div {}^-b = \dfrac{a}{b}$
$^-a \times {}^-b = ab$

Exercise 26·2

A Multiply these pairs of numbers.

1 $^-3 \times 4$	**2** $^-7 \times 6$	**3** $5 \times {}^-4$	**4** $8 \times {}^-2$
5 $^-3 \times {}^-4$	**6** $^-5 \times {}^-2$	**7** $^-9 \times {}^-8$	**8** $^-4 \times {}^-1{\cdot}5$
9 $^-2{\cdot}5 \times 3$	**10** $^-4 \times {}^-1{\cdot}6$	**11** $^-2{\cdot}3 \times {}^-5$	**12** $^-5{\cdot}2 \times {}^-0{\cdot}7$
13 $^-1{\cdot}7 \times 0$	**14** $0 \times {}^-2{\cdot}8$	**15** $6{\cdot}6 \times {}^-1$	**16** $^-7{\cdot}3 \times {}^-1$

Check on calculator using +/−

B Divide these pairs of numbers.

1 $^-8 \div {}^-2$	**2** $^-8 \div {}^+4$	**3** $^-8 \div {}^-4$	**4** $^-12 \div {}^-3$
5 $14 \div {}^-7$	**6** $14 \div {}^-2$	**7** $3 \div {}^-4$	**8** $^-3 \div {}^-4$
9 $12 \div {}^-0{\cdot}8$	**10** $14 \div 0{\cdot}5$	**11** $^-18 \div {}^-0{\cdot}9$	**12** $^-22 \div {}^-0{\cdot}11$

Check on a calculator using +/−

C Find the result of the following calculations.

1 $3 \times {}^-4 \times {}^-2$	**2** $^-3 \times {}^-4 \times 2$	**3** $^-1 \times 0 \times {}^-5$	**4** $^-2 \times {}^-3 \times {}^-4$
5 $6 \times {}^-2 \div {}^-4$	**6** $^-8 \times {}^-1 \div {}^-2$	**7** $^-9 \times 3 \div {}^-3$	**8** $3 \div (4 \times {}^-1)$
9 $(3 \div 4) \times {}^-1$	**10** $({}^-7 \times 4) \div {}^-2$	**11** $^-7 \times (4 \div {}^-2)$	**12** $^-8 \div ({}^-4 \div {}^-2)$

Calculate brackets first, please!

26·3 Trinomials

When a pair of brackets such as $(x + 2)$, $(x + 5)$ are multiplied out, the result is a trinomial. This is an expression having a term in x^2, a term in x and a pure number.

Example:

$(x + 2)(x + 5) = x(x + 5) + 2(x + 5)$ ... using distributive law

$= x^2 + 5x + 2x + 10$

$= x^2 + 7x + 10$ collecting up the x terms

term in x^2 — *term in x* — *pure number*

Example: (with negative numbers)

$(x + 3)(x - 4) = x(x - 4) + 3(x - 4)$

$= x^2 - 4x + 3x - 12$

$= x^2 - x - 12$

The trinomial may be checked by choosing a value for x and making sure that the product of brackets has the same value as the trinomial.

Example: Let $x = 2{\cdot}7$ $(x + 3)(x - 4)$	$x^2 - x - 12$
$5{\cdot}7 \times {}^{-}1{\cdot}3$	$7{\cdot}29 - 2{\cdot}7 - 12$
${}^{-}7{\cdot}41$	$-7{\cdot}41$
[5] [·] [7] [×] [1] [·] [3] [+/−] [=]	[7] [·] [2] [9] [−] [2] [·] [7] [−] [1] [2] [=]

Exercise 26·3

A Multiply out these pairs of brackets to form trinomials.

1 $(x + 1)(x + 2)$ **2** $(x + 3)(x + 4)$ **3** $(x + 2)(x + 6)$

4 $(x + 1)(x + 1)$ **5** $(x + 2)(x + 2)$ **6** $(x + 3)(x + 3)$

7 $(x + 1)(x - 2)$ **8** $(x + 3)(x - 4)$ **9** $(x + 4)(x - 2)$

10 $(x + 3)(x - 1)$ **11** $(x + 1)(x - 1)$ **12** $(x - 2)(x - 2)$

B Use the value shown to check that the brackets and trinomials are the same.

1 $(x + 3)(x + 5)$ and $x^2 + 8x + 15$ ... use $x = 0{\cdot}75$

2 $(x - 3)(x + 4)$ and $x^2 + x + 12$ ... use $x = 4{\cdot}2$

3 $(x + 4)(x - 1)$ and $x^2 + 3x - 4$ ... use $x = 0{\cdot}84$

4 $(x - 4)(x - 4)$ and $x^2 - 8x - 16$ ... use $x = 3{\cdot}2$

5 $(x - 6)(x + 6)$ and $x^2 - 36$ ... use $x = 4{\cdot}5$

6 $(x + 3)(x - 3)$ and $x^2 + 3x - 9$ ... use $x = 0{\cdot}55$

C

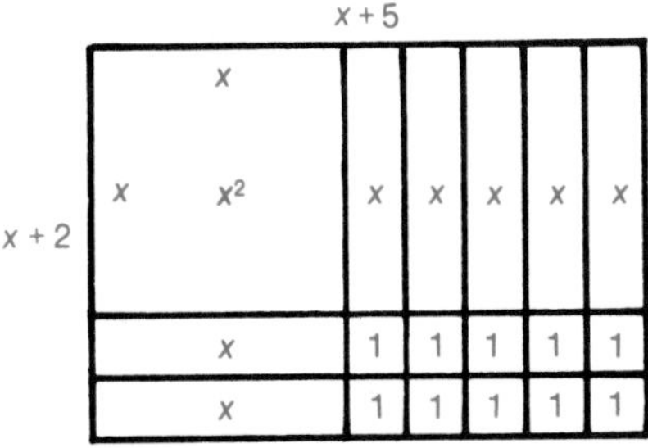

The diagram shows that
$(x + 5)(x + 2) = x^2 + 7x + 10$

The big square x^2 — *7 strips marked x* — *10 unit squares*

Make drawings similar to the above to show ...

1 $(x + 2)(x + 3) = x^2 + 5x + 6$ **2** $(x + 1)(x + 4) = x^2 + 5x + 4$

3 $(x + 2)(x + 2) = x^2 + 4x + 4$ **4** $(x + 1)(x + 5) = x^2 + 6x + 5$

26·4 Factorising a trinomial

Changing a trinomial to a pair of factors in brackets is called **factorising**.

We split the x-term so that part goes with the x^2 and part with the number, and so that a common factor is formed.

$x^2 + 5x + 4$

$x^2 + x \quad + \quad 4x + 4$

$x(x + 1) + 4(x + 1)$

$(x + 4)(x + 1)$

or

$x^2 + 5x + 4$

$x^2 + 4x + x + 4$

$x(x + 4) + 1(x + 4)$

$(x + 1)(x + 4)$

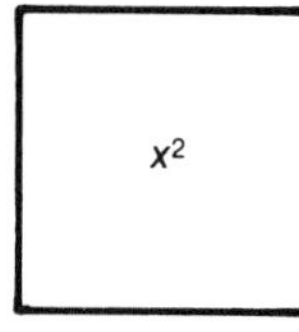

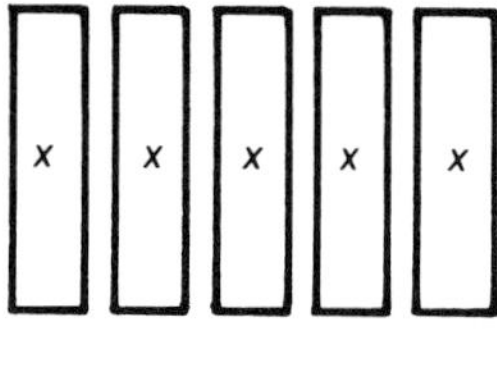

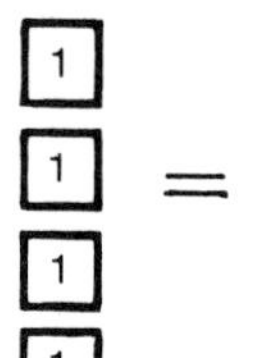

=

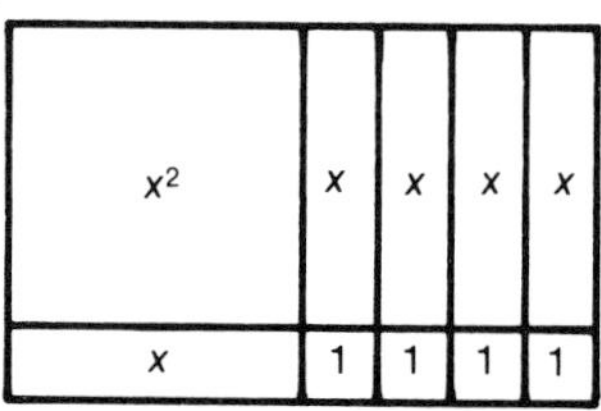

Exercise 26·4

A Factorise the following trinomials

1 $x^2 + 3x + 2$

2 $x^2 + 6x + 5$

3 $x^2 + 4x + 4$

4 $x^2 + 7x + 12$

5 $x^2 + 2x + 1$

6 $x^2 + 10x + 24$

7 $x^2 + 6x + 8$

8 $x^2 + 6x + 9$

B Factorise the following trinomials. Remember that negative times negative = positive

Examples:

$x^2 - 5x + 4$

$x^2 - 4x + {}^-x + 4$

$x(x - 4) - 1(x - 4)$

$(x - 1)(x - 4)$

$x^2 + 2x - 8$

$x^2 + 4x - 2x - 8$

$x(x + 4) - 2(x + 4)$

$(x - 2)(x + 4)$

Note: We split the $2x$ into $4x$ and $-2x$ because $4 \times {}^-2 = {}^-8$

1 $x^2 - 3x + 2$

2 $x^2 - x - 2$

3 $x^2 + x - 2$

4 $x^2 - 3x - 4$

5 $x^2 - 5x + 6$

6 $x^2 - 5x - 6$

7 $x^2 + 2x - 15$

8 $x^2 - x - 12$

C Draw diagrams showing x^2 squares, x strips and unit squares to illustrate the following factorisations.

1 $x^2 + 4x + 4 = (x + 2)(x + 2)$

2 $x^2 + 5x + 6 = (x + 2)(x + 3)$

3 $x^2 + 9x + 20 = (x + 4)(x + 5)$

4 $x^2 + 7x + 12 = (x + 3)(x + 4)$

26·5 Quadratic equations

When a trinomial is equal to 0 we have a quadratic equation.

The equation may be *solved* by factorising. This can be seen in the examples below.

Example:

Solve the equations (i) $x^2 - 5x + 4 = 0$
(ii) $x^2 - 3x - 10 = 0$

Solving an equation means finding the values of x which make the equation true.

(i) $x^2 - 5x + 4 = 0$

$\Rightarrow (x-1)(x-4) = 0$ .... Factorising

$\Rightarrow x - 1 = 0$ .... Because, when two numbers are multiplied and 0 is the result, one of the numbers must be 0

or $x - 4 = 0$

$\Rightarrow x = 1$ *or* $x = 4$

Check: Give x the value 1 in $x^2 - 5x + 4$ The value of the trinomial is 0.

$$\begin{array}{ccc} x^2 & -5x & +4 \\ \downarrow & \downarrow & \downarrow \\ 1 & -5 & +4 = 0 \end{array}$$

Give x the value 4 in $x^2 - 5x + 4$ The value of the trinomial is 0.

$$\begin{array}{ccc} x^2 & -5x & +4 \\ \downarrow & \downarrow & \downarrow \\ 16 & -20 & +4 = 0 \end{array}$$

(ii) $x^2 - 3x - 10 = 0 \Rightarrow (x+2)(x-5) = 0$

$\Rightarrow (x+2) = 0$ **or** $(x-5) = 0$

$\Rightarrow x = {}^-2$ or $x = 5$

Check: put $x = {}^-2$

$$\begin{array}{ccc} x^2 & -3x & -10 \\ \downarrow & \downarrow & \downarrow \\ 4 & +6 & -10 = 0 \end{array}$$

put $x = 5$

$$\begin{array}{ccc} x^2 & -3x & -10 \\ \downarrow & \downarrow & \downarrow \\ 25 & -15 & -10 = 0 \end{array}$$

Exercise 26·5

A Solve the following quadratic equations. Check each value of x.

1 $x^2 + 3x + 2 = 0$ **2** $x^2 - 3x + 2 = 0$
3 $x^2 - 5x + 4 = 0$ **4** $x^2 - 6x + 8 = 0$
5 $x^2 - 2x + 1 = 0$ **6** $x^2 - 6x + 5 = 0$
7 $x^2 + 12 + 35 = 0$ **8** $x^2 + 9x + 20 = 0$

B Solve the following quadratic equations, take care with the − signs

1 $x^2 - x - 2 = 0$ **2** $x^2 - 3x - 4 = 0$
3 $x^2 - x - 6 = 0$ **4** $x^2 - 2x - 8 = 0$
5 $x^2 - 3x - 10 = 0$ **6** $x^2 - 4x - 12 = 0$
7 $x^2 - 2x - 35 = 0$ **8** $x^2 + 3x - 10 = 0$

C Rearrange these equations into trinomials equal to zero. Then solve the quadratics formed. Check that the solutions fit the original equation.

1 $x^2 = 3x - 2$ **2** $x^2 = 2x + 3$ **3** $x^2 = x + 20$

4 $x^2 = 7 - 6x$ **5** $x^2 = 8 - 2x$ **6** $x^2 = 14 + 5x$

Problems

7 If I square a certain number I get the same result as if I doubled the number and subtracted 1. What number did I start with?

8 Four times a number is 12 less than the square of the number. What is the number?

Unit M27 Sin, cos, tan

27·1 The sine ratio

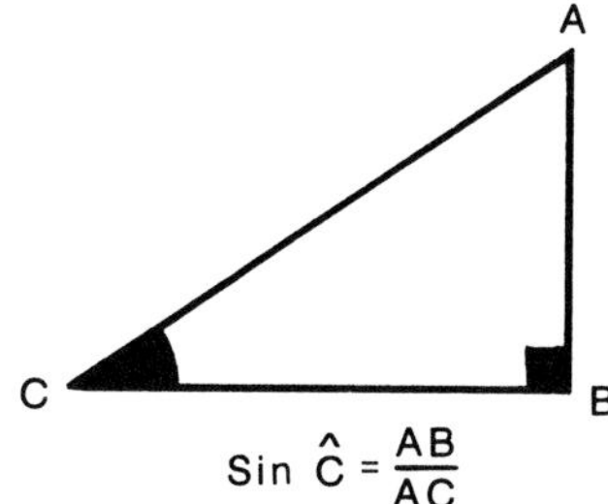

$\text{Sin } \hat{C} = \frac{AB}{AC}$

In right-angled triangle ABC, AC is the longest side. The ratio $\frac{AB}{AC}$ is called the sine of angle C. It is the ratio

$$\frac{\text{length of side opposite angle}}{\text{length of longest side}}$$

The longest side is usually called the hypotenuse of the triangle.

The sine ratio can be found from tables or from the sine function on a calculator, as soon as we know the size of angle $\hat{C}$.

Example:

1 In a right-angled triangle $\hat{C}$ is 42°. What is the value of sin* $\hat{C}$?
(i) From tables, sin 42° = 0·669
(ii) From calculator, sin 42° = 0·6691306 = 0·669 to 3 decimal places

[c] [4] [2] [sin]

2 What angle is $\hat{C}$ if sin $\hat{C}$ = 0·978?
(i) From tables, sin $\hat{C}$ = 0·978 ⇒ $\hat{C}$ = 78°.
(ii) From calculator, using inverse sine, sin $\hat{C}$ = 0·978 ⇒ $\hat{C}$ = 77·95939

[c] [0] [·] [9] [7] [8] [inv] [sin]

The sine ratio and tables are used to calculate the length of side of a right-angled triangle. We have to know the length of the hypotenuse and also the angles of the triangle.

Example:
Find the length of the sides of rectangle ABCD.

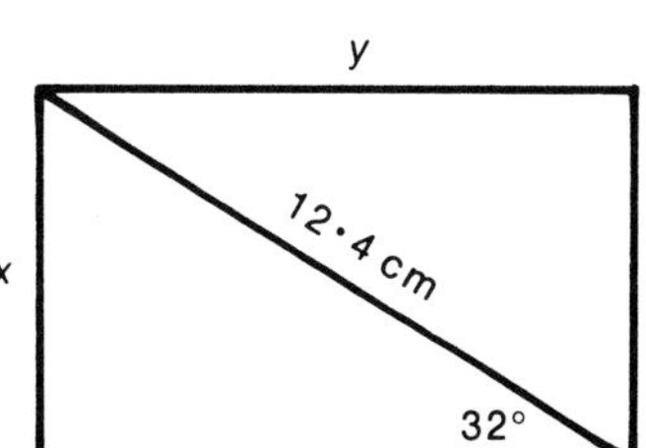

* We drop 'e' off sine when we name an angle.

(i) $\dfrac{x}{12{\cdot}4} = \sin 32° \Rightarrow x = 12{\cdot}4 \times \sin 32°$
$= 12{\cdot}4 \times 0{\cdot}53$
$= 6{\cdot}572$ cm

(ii) $\dfrac{y}{12{\cdot}4} = \sin 58°$ since 58° must be the other angle of the triangle.
$\Rightarrow y = 12{\cdot}4 \times \sin 58°$
$= 12{\cdot}4 \times 0{\cdot}848$
$= 10{\cdot}5158$ cm

Note: Although these lengths can be *calculated* to 3 or 4 places of decimals, this degree of accuracy is *unrealistic*. It takes a remarkably fine ruler to measure 1/100 of a centimetre.

Better answers would be 6.6 cm and 11.5 cm.

Exercise 27.1

A Use tables to look up the following.

1 sin 10°, sin 30°, sin 50°, sin 70°, sin 90°
2 sin 34°, sin 28°, sin 59°, sin 84°, sin 77°
3 sin 6·5°, sin 8·2°, sin 12·8°, sin 14·7°, sin 23·9°
4 sin 78·3°, sin 75·1°, sin 66·6°, sin 54·9°, sin 43·7°

B Use tables to find the angle θ* if

1 $\sin\theta = 0{\cdot}675$ **2** $\sin\theta = 0{\cdot}800$ **3** $\sin\theta = 0{\cdot}452$
4 $\sin\theta = 0{\cdot}115$ **5** $\sin\theta = 0{\cdot}624$ **6** $\sin\theta = 0{\cdot}483$
7 $\sin\theta = 0$ **8** $\sin\theta = 0{\cdot}870$ **9** $\sin\theta = 0{\cdot}707$

C Which of the following are true?

1 For all angles θ, less than 90°, $\sin\theta$ is less than 1.
2 If $\sin\theta = 0{\cdot}5$, θ is 60°.
3 If θ is under 10°, $\sin\theta$ is less than 0·1000.
4 If $x = y$ then $\sin x = \sin y$, where x and y are two angles.
5 If $x > y$ then $\sin x > \sin y$.
6 sin 30° + sin 60° = sin 90°.
7 2 × sin 25° = sin 50°.
8 sin 45° × sin 45° = 0·5 (or 0·49 999 999)

D Use tables (or calculator) to solve these problems.

1 The point X (3, 4) on a graph is joined to a point A exactly 5 cm away (as shown) on the graph. Find the distances AP, XP and work out the coordinates of A and P.

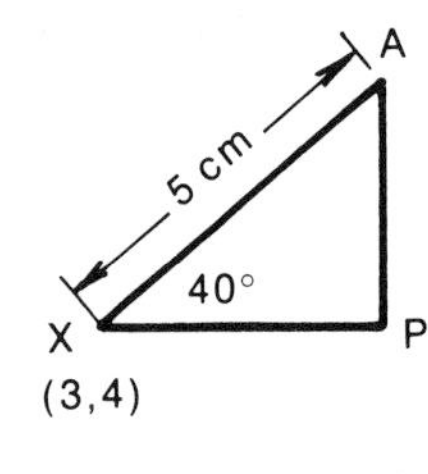

* θ is the greek letter 'theta', used for angles

2 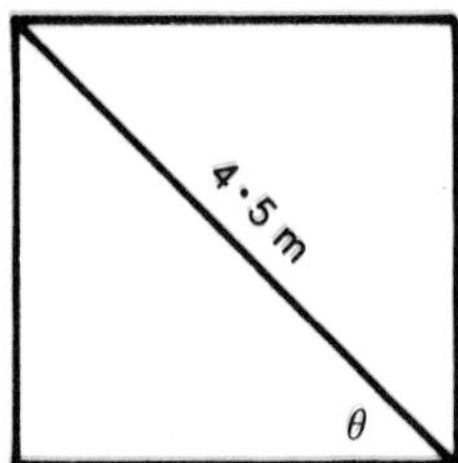

The diagonal of a square is 4.5 m long. Calculate the length of the sides. (Find the value of θ first.)

3 A rectangle has a diagonal 10 cm long while one of the sides is 7 cm long. Find the angle the diagonal makes with the 7 cm side. Find also the length of the shorter side of the rectangle.

4 A pilot measures the distance to a mountain peak as 3.8 km. The angle between his horizontal flight line and the line to the peak is 22° (see figure). Calculate the height above the peak at which the aircraft will pass if it continues its flight without changing height.

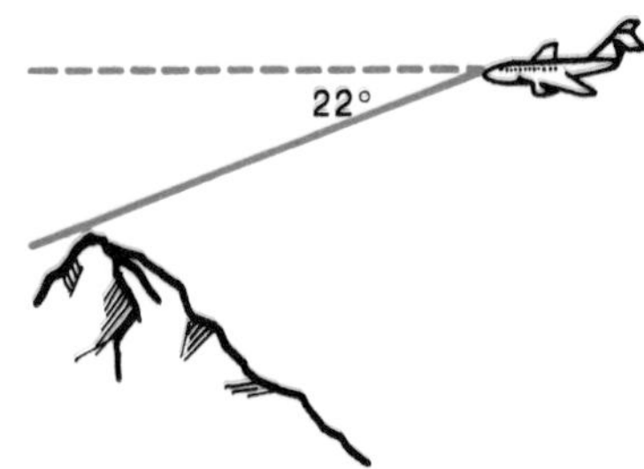

27.2 Co-angles

In a right-angled triangle, the two other angles add to 90°. They are called complementary angles or co-angles for short. To find the co-angle, subtract the angle from 90°.

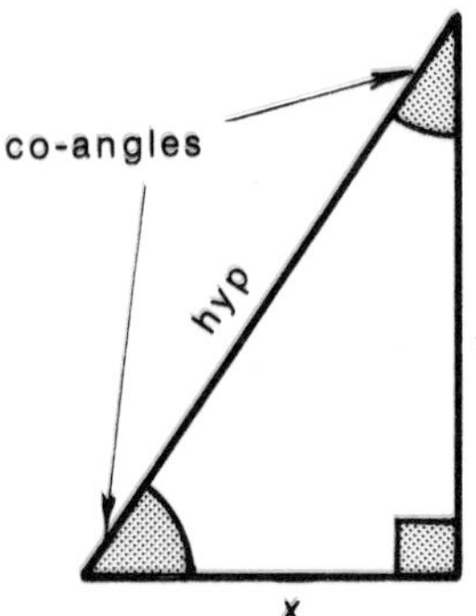

Example:

Angle	*Co-angle*	
42°	48°	. . . since 42° + 48° = 90°
31°	59°	. . . since 31° + 59° = 90°
28·3°	61·7°	. . . since 28·3° + 61·7° = 90°

27.3 Cosine

The sine of a co-angle is called the cosine of the angle.

Thus, in $\triangle$ABC, we have an angle of 52° at B. The co-angle at A is 38° so cosine 52° = sine 38° = x/hyp

Values of cosine are given in tables and as one of the functions of a scientific calculator (cos)*.

From tables, cos 52° = 0·616

sin 38° = 0·616

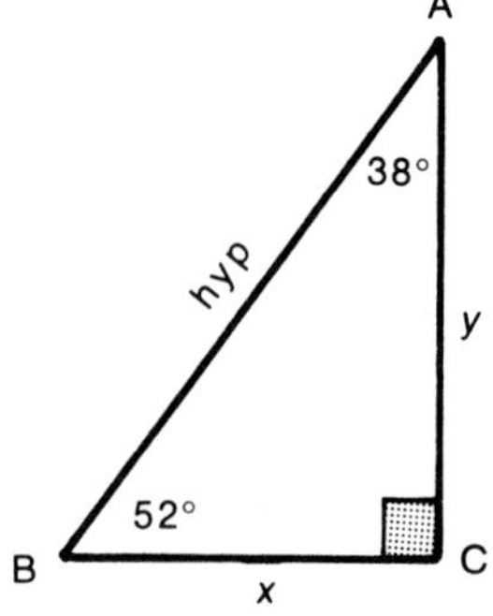

Exercise 27·2

A **1** Write down the co-angle for the following angles.

(i) 40°	(ii) 60°	(iii) 45°	(iv) 90°
(v) 82°	(vi) 76°	(vii) 32°	(viii) 12°
(ix) 28°	(x) 42·5°	(xi) 38·2°	(xii) 4·3°

2 Use tables to find the values of these cosines.

(i) cos 70°	(ii) cos 45°	(iii) cos 20°	(iv) cos 10°
(v) cos 82°	(vi) cos 71°	(vii) cos 44°	(viii) cos 27°
(ix) cos 18·3°	(x) cos 31·2°	(xi) cos 48·5°	(xii) cos 88·7°

3 What angles have the following cosines?

(i) 0·500	(ii) 0·788	(iii) 0·906	(iv) 0·375
(v) 0·999	(vi) 0·992	(vii) 0·951	(viii) 0·791
(ix) 0·384	(x) 0·045	(xi) 0·003	(xii) 0·124

B **1** Use tables to check that the following statements are true.

(i) cos 60° = sin 30°	(ii) sin 60° = cos 30°
(iii) sin 72° = cos 18°	(iv) sin 18° = cos 72°
(v) cos 51° = sin 39°	(vi) cos 39° = sin 51°
(vii) sin 45° = cos 45°	(viii) cos 31·6° = sin 58·4°
(ix) sin 31·6° = cos 58·4°	(x) cos 22·5° = sin 67·5°
(xi) cos 4·2° = sin 85·8°	(xii) cos 85·8° = sin 4·2°

2 Which of the following statements are true? (some are definitely *not* true)

(i) cos θ is less than 1, whatever the size of θ.

(ii) cos θ is more than sin θ, whatever the size of θ.

(iii) cos θ is less than sin θ, whatever the size of θ.

(iv) For all angles over 85°, cos θ is almost 1.

(v) If cos θ = sin θ, then θ must be 45°.

(vi) If cos θ > sin θ, then θ < 45°.

C Find the size of θ in each of the triangles on page 217.

Example:

$$\cos\theta = \frac{4\cdot2}{4\cdot9} = 0\cdot857$$

θ = 31° (from tables)

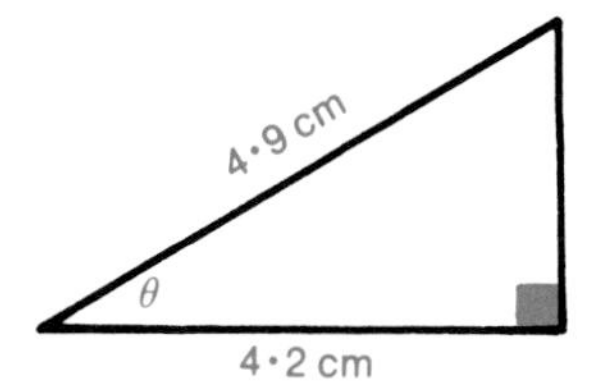

* cos is short for cosine.

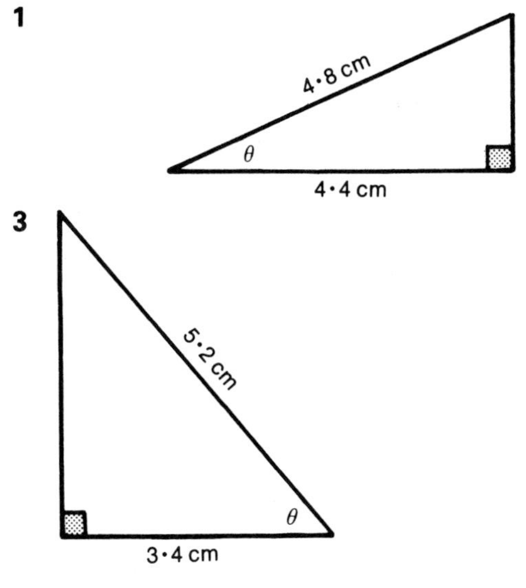

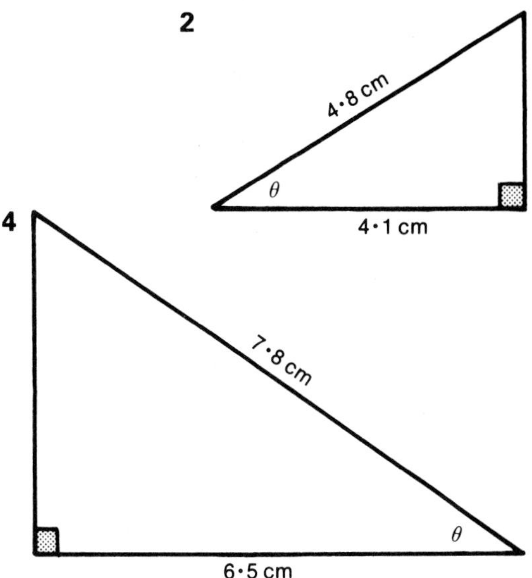

Write down the values of cos θ in the triangles below.

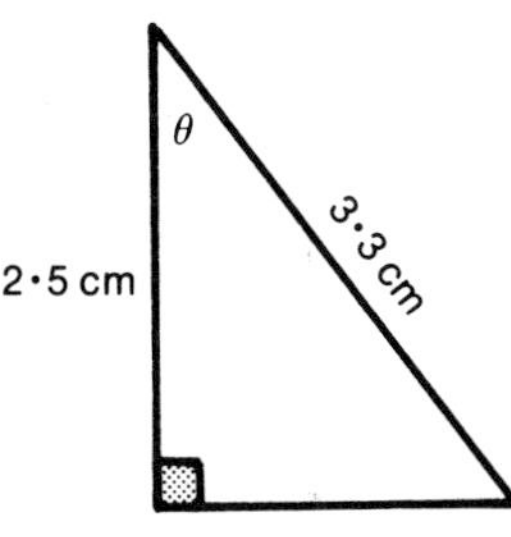

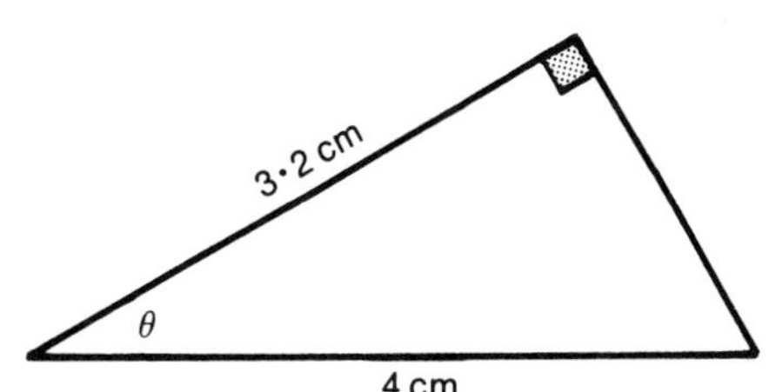

It is sometimes easier to think of cosine as the

$$\frac{\text{adjacent side}^*}{\text{hypotenuse}}$$

but you can always check this by thinking that cosine is sine of the co-angle.

The adjacent side for θ is the opposite side for $90° - \theta$.

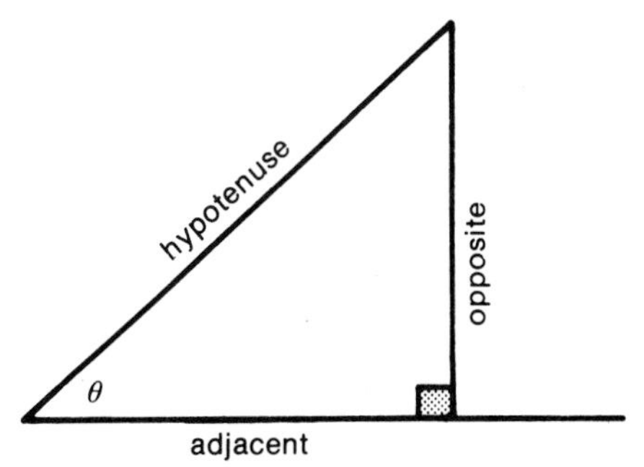

* Or in ordinary language $\frac{\text{the side next to the angle}}{\text{the longest side}}$

27.4 Tangent ratio

The third important ratio in the triangle is

$$\frac{\textbf{opposite}}{\textbf{adjacent}}$$

This is called the **tangent** of the angle. We use this ratio when the length of the hypotenuse is not known. Vaues of tan θ are to be found in the function tables. Scientific calculators will give the value of tan θ if you press **tan**.

Example:

Find the size of the angle marked θ

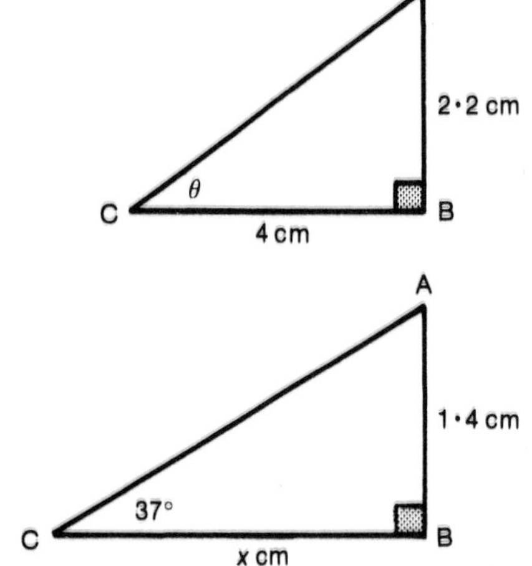

$\tan\theta = \frac{AB}{BC} = \frac{2{\cdot}2}{4} = 0{\cdot}55$

$\Rightarrow \theta = 28{\cdot}8°$ (from tables)

Find the length BC, marked x.

(i) $\tan 37° = \frac{1{\cdot}4}{x} \Rightarrow x = 1{\cdot}4 \div 0{\cdot}754$

$= 1{\cdot}86$ cm

(ii) Using the co-angle = 53°

$\tan 53° = \frac{x}{1{\cdot}4} \Rightarrow x = 1{\cdot}4 \times \tan 53°$

$= 1{\cdot}4 \times 1{\cdot}327$

$= 1{\cdot}86$ cm

Exercise 27.3

A **1** Find the value of the following using tables (and calculator if you have one with functions).

(i) tan 40°	(ii) tan 70°	(iii) tan 45°
(iv) tan 36°	(v) tan 58°	(vi) tan 76°
(vii) tan 12·6°	(viii) tan 19·8°	(ix) tan 60·5°

2 Find the size of θ given that:

(i) $\tan\theta = 0{\cdot}40$	(ii) $\tan\theta = 0{\cdot}78$
(iii) $\tan\theta = 1{\cdot}00$	(iv) $\tan\theta = 1{\cdot}36$
(v) $\tan\theta = 22{\cdot}2$	(vi) $\tan\theta = 5{\cdot}00$
(vii) $\tan\theta = 20$	(viii) $\tan\theta = 75$
(ix) $\tan\theta = 191$	

3 Which of the following statements are true?

(i) tan θ is always less than 1, whatever the angle.

(ii) tan θ is always greater than sin θ, whatever the angle.

(iii) $\tan\theta$ is $> 1 \Rightarrow \theta > 45°$.
(iv) $\tan\theta$ and $\sin\theta$ are almost equal if θ is a small angle (less than 20°).
(v) $\tan\theta = \sin\theta \div \cos\theta$, whatever the value of θ.*

B Write down the value of $\tan\theta$ for each of the following triangles.

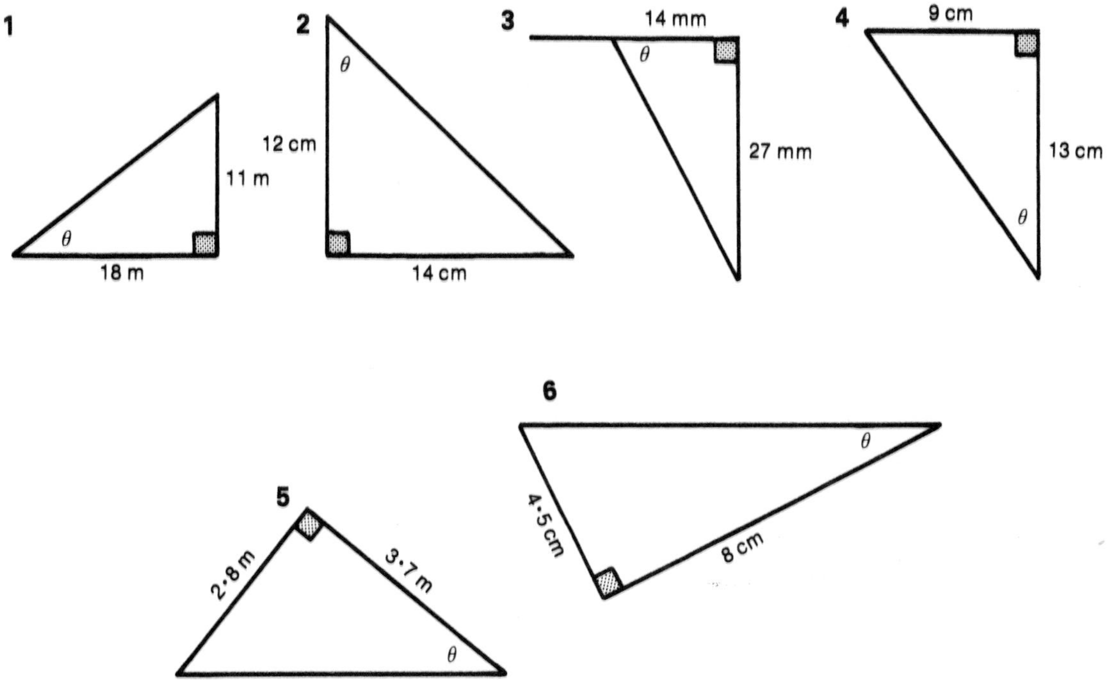

C 1 Use tables of tangent to calculate the side marked x in the following triangles.

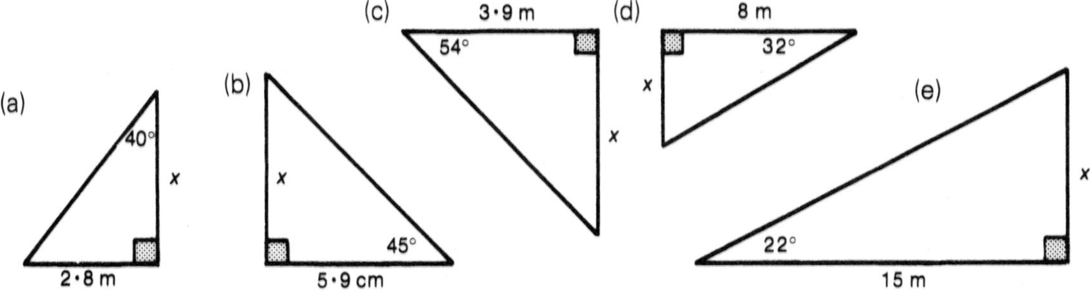

* Allowing for small errors which result from rounding in the tables.

2 Use tables of tan θ to find the size of the angles in each of the triangles below.

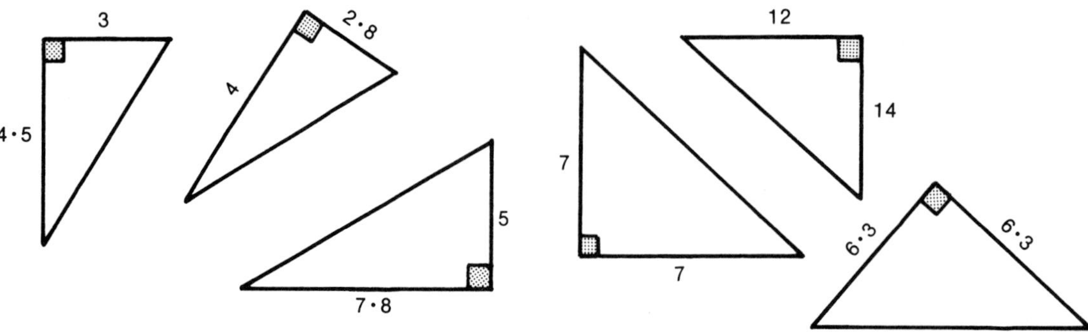

27.5 Applications of tangent ratio

Slope

The tangent ratio is useful when you want to find the angle of slope.

Example:

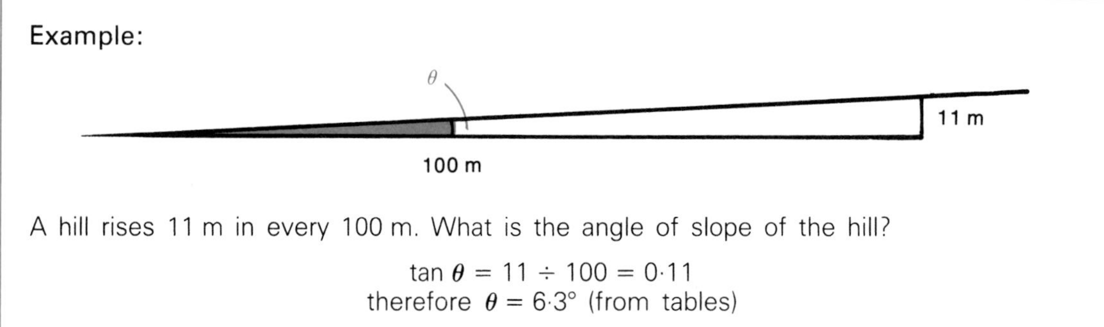

A hill rises 11 m in every 100 m. What is the angle of slope of the hill?

$$\tan\theta = 11 \div 100 = 0{\cdot}11$$
$$\text{therefore } \theta = 6{\cdot}3^\circ \text{ (from tables)}$$

Heights

Heights can be calculated when horizontal distance and angle of elevation are known.

Example:

The angle to the peak of a volcano from P is 12·4°.

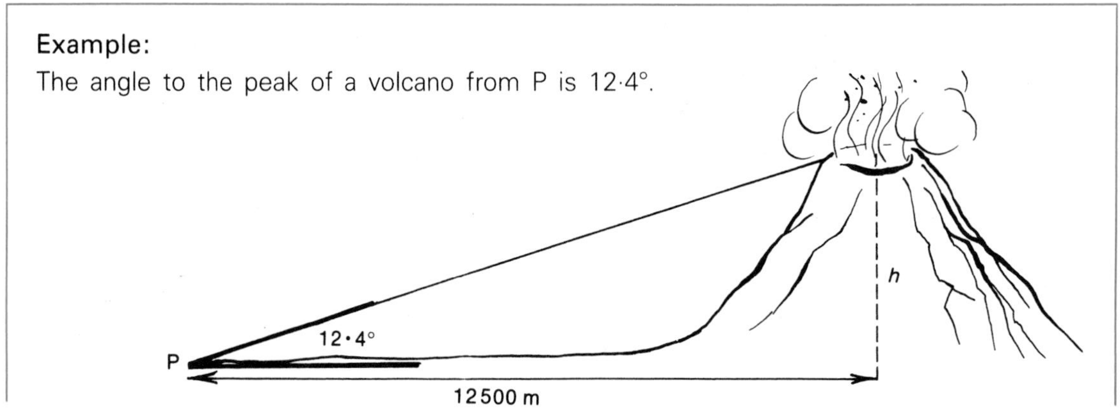

The distance of P from the point directly below the peak, level with P, is 12 500 m. What is the height of the volcano?

$$\frac{h}{12\,500} = \tan 12{\cdot}4° = 0{\cdot}220 \Rightarrow h = 12\,500 \times 0{\cdot}22$$
$$= 2748 \text{ m}$$

Drawing angles

Angles can be drawn very accurately using tangent tables. (Especially if 1 mm^2 graph paper is used.)

Example: Draw a regular septagon in a circle radius 10 cm.

To find seven points equally spaced round a circle, an angle of 51·4° = 360° ÷ 7 is needed at the centre. Once the angle has been drawn the seven points can be marked by 'stepping' with a pair of compasses. The regular septagon can now be drawn and also the seven-pointed star.

We use the fact that tan 51·4° = 1·253 to draw the exact angle in a circle radius 10 cm.

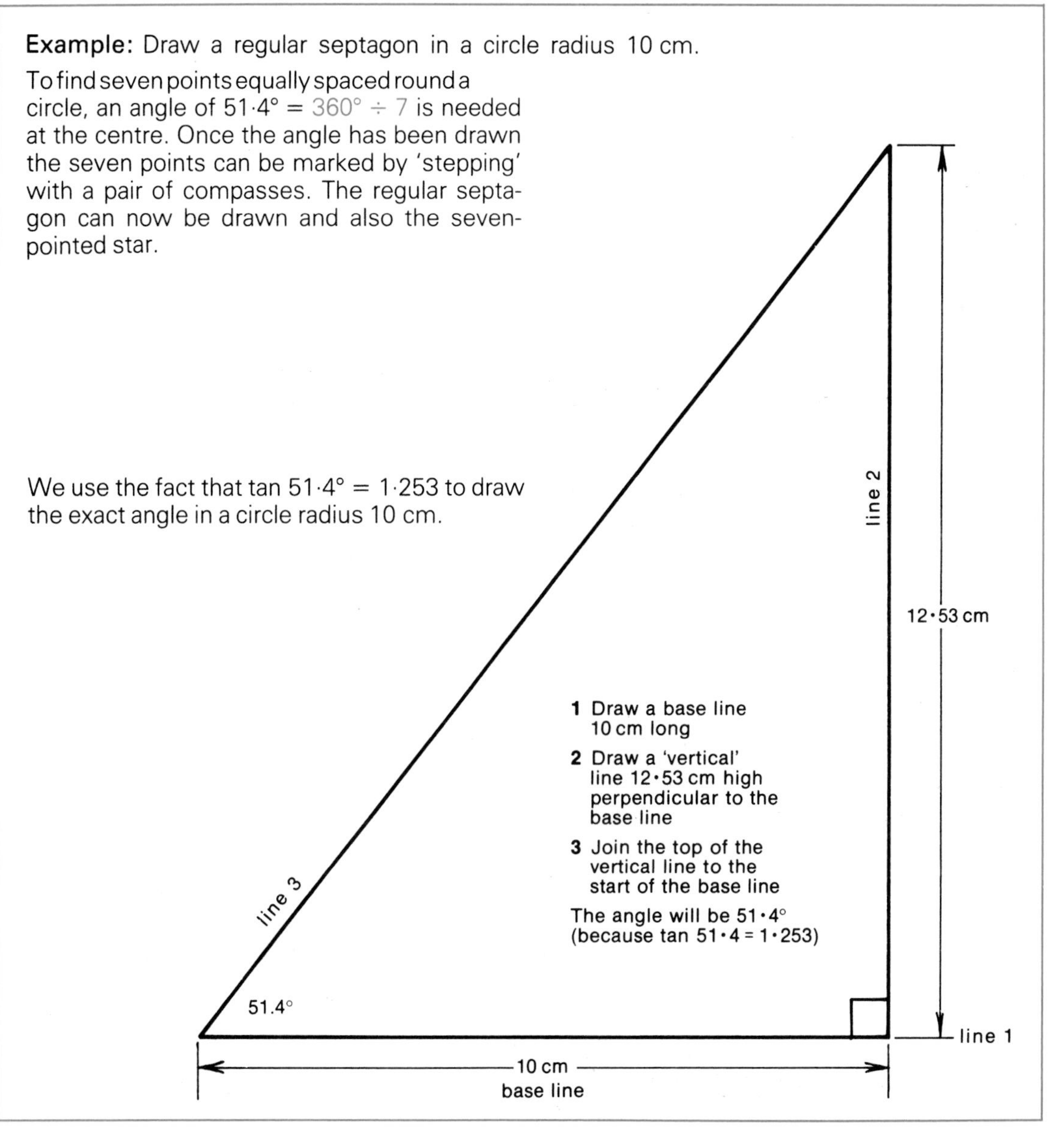

Exercise 27.4

A **1** A railway line climbs 7 m in every kilometre. What is the angle of the slope (to the horizontal)?

2 After take-off a jet climbs in a straight line to a height of 10 000 m. It is then over a point 28 000 m from the runway. At what angle does the jet climb?

3 A steep hill in the English Lake district has a slope of 1 in 3 (one up for three along). What angle is this?

4 The line joining (3, 4) and (5, 7) has a slope of 3 : 2 (3 up for 2 along). What angle does this line make with the x-axis?

5 An aircraft dives from 8000 m to 3000 m while travelling a map distance of 2 km. Calculate the angle between the path of the dive and the horizontal.

6 Each tread of a stairway is 12 cm high and 30 cm from front to back. Calculate the angle of slope of the stairway.

7 Two vertical shafts in a mine are connected by a gallery which has a slope of 12°. If one end of the gallery is 60 m above the other, find the distance between the shafts on the surface.

8 A boy made a 45° set square in metalwork. The sides that were supposed to be equal were in fact 15 cm and 14.7 cm. The right angle was exactly 90°. Calculate the sizes of the angles that should have been 45°.

B Use tables of tangent to find the height of a tree or building in your district. You will need a protractor, tape measure and a wooden board.
Even if you are not able to do the measuring you should explain how it could be done.

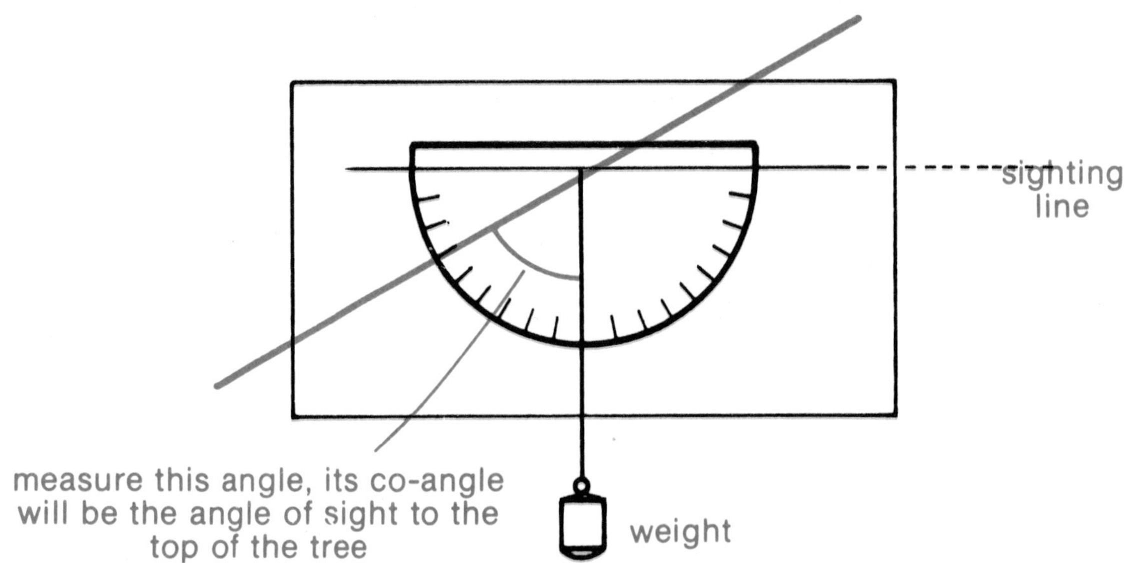

C **1** Use values for tan θ to draw the following angles as accurately as you can.
(i) 45° (ii) 72° (iii) 51·4° (iv) 40° (v) 36° (vi) 24°

2 Use the angles you have drawn to draw the following shapes.
(i) A regular octagon (8 sides).
(ii) A regular pentagon (5 sides).
(iii) A regular heptagon (7 sides).
(iv) A regular nonagon (9 sides).

3 Use angles of 36° and 24° to draw 10-point and 15-pointed stars. You will need some practice before you can make the stars perfectly.

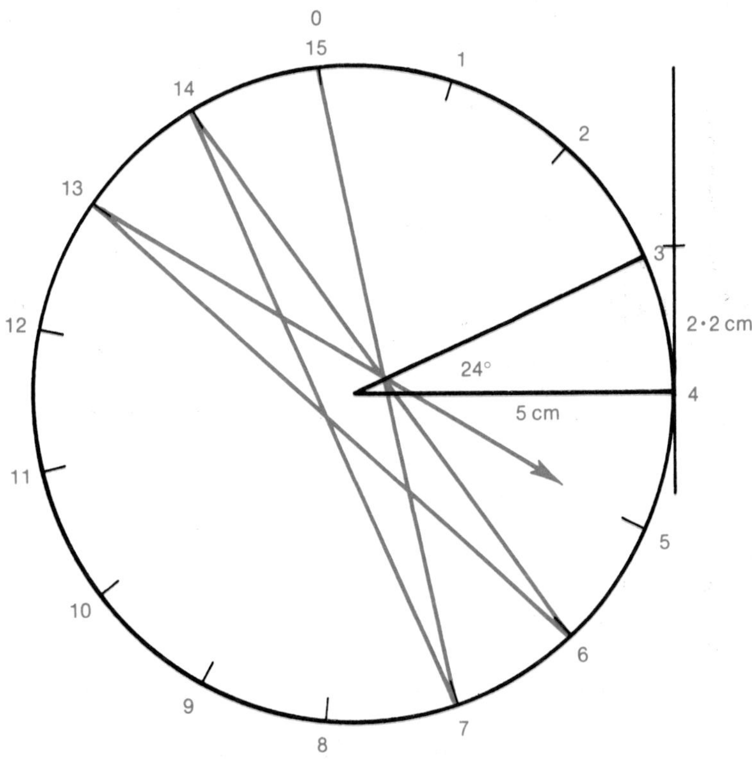

$n \rightarrow n + 7$

1 Start at 15 and count 7 steps to 7. Join the points.

2 Count on 7 more steps (to 14). Join the points again.

3 Continue round the circle until a 15-pointed star is formed.

Other shaped stars can be formed by different mappings.

Unit M28 More trigonometry

28·1 Sin, Cos, Tan

The three trigonometrical ratios for a right-angled triangle are

$$\sin\theta = \frac{O}{H},\ \cos\theta = \frac{A}{H},\ \tan\theta = \frac{O}{A}$$

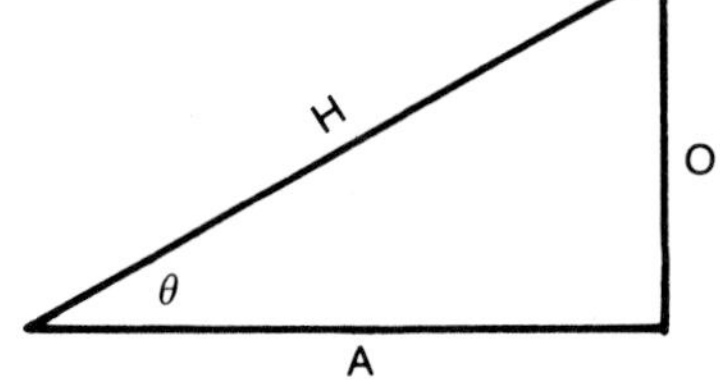

where O = opposite side
A = adjacent side
H = hypotenuse

Some people remember the 'word' SOHCAHTOA to help in finding the ratios. Others make up a sentence like 'Some Old Horses Chase And Hunt Till Old Age'. Some people think it is best to remember

$$\sin = \frac{O}{H}$$

and work out the others from the fact that cos is sine of the co-angle. Tan is easy to remember as the slope or as the other ratio that has opposite over something.

The following relationships are very important:

For all angles . . . $(\sin\theta)^2 + (\cos\theta)^2 = 1$

$$\tan = \frac{\sin\theta}{\cos\theta}$$

$$\sin(90° - \theta) = \cos\theta$$

$$\cos(90° - \theta) = \sin\theta$$

Exercise 28·1

A Work out sin θ, cos θ and tan θ in each of the triangles below (all measurements are in centimetres).

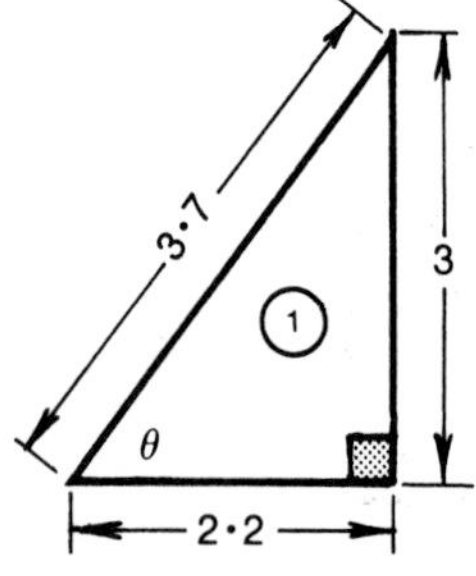

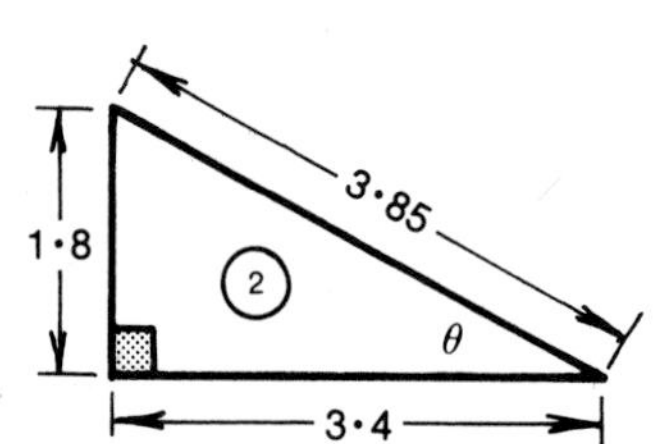

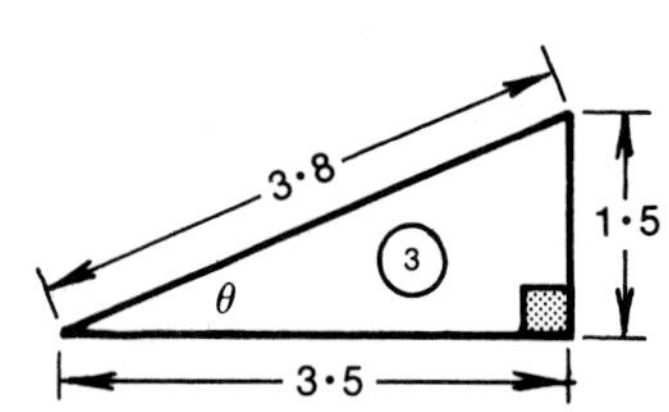

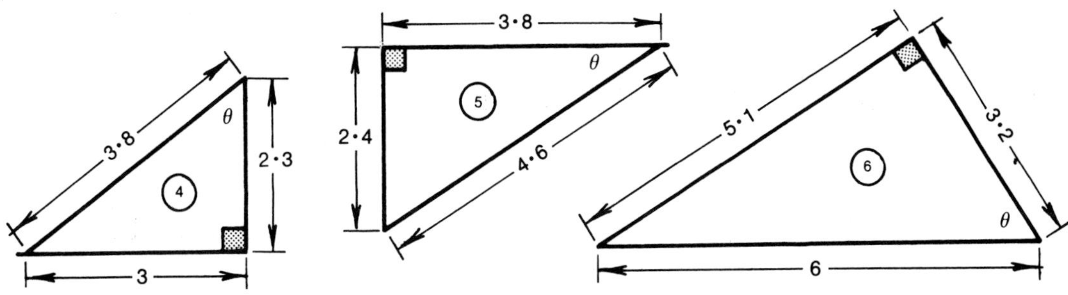

B **1** Use one of the ratios in each triangle above to find the size of the angle marked θ.
2 Does it make any difference which ratio you use?
3 Why would you expect to get slight differences if you used two different ratios to find the angle?

C Check each of the relationships listed below for the angles given.
1 $(\sin\theta)^2 + (\cos\theta)^2 = 1$ . . . check for:
(i) $\theta = 42°$ (ii) $\theta = 75°$ (iii) $\theta = 33{\cdot}4°$
2 $\tan\theta = \dfrac{\sin\theta}{\cos\theta}$ . . . check for:
(i) $\theta = 10°$ (ii) $\theta = 80°$ (iii) $\theta = 45°$ (iv) $\theta = 71{\cdot}3°$
3 $\sin(90° - \theta) = \cos\theta$ . . . check for:
(i) $\theta = 14°$ (ii) $\theta = 75°$ (iii) $\theta = 60°$ (iv) $\theta = 40{\cdot}3°$
4 $\cos(90° - \theta) = \sin\theta$ . . . check for:
(i) $\theta = 0{\cdot}8°$ (ii) $\theta = 15°$ (iii) $\theta = 30°$ (iv) $\theta = 81{\cdot}8°$

D Use tables to search for values of θ in which . . .
1 $\sin\theta = \cos\theta$
2 $\sin\theta = 2 \times \cos\theta$
3 $\sin\theta = \frac{1}{2} \times \cos\theta$
4 $\sin\theta = \frac{1}{2} \times \tan\theta$
5 $\cos\theta = 2 \times \tan\theta$
6 $\cos\theta + \sin\theta = \tan\theta$

28·2 Special triangles

Three special triangles are very useful in trigonometry.

(i) The half-equilateral triangle

The short side is exactly half of the hypotenuse. Its angles are 30°, 60°, 90°.

The third side of the triangle can be calculated by **Pythagoras's** theorem, to be $\sqrt{3}$.

This is known as the 1, 2, $\sqrt{3}$ triangle.

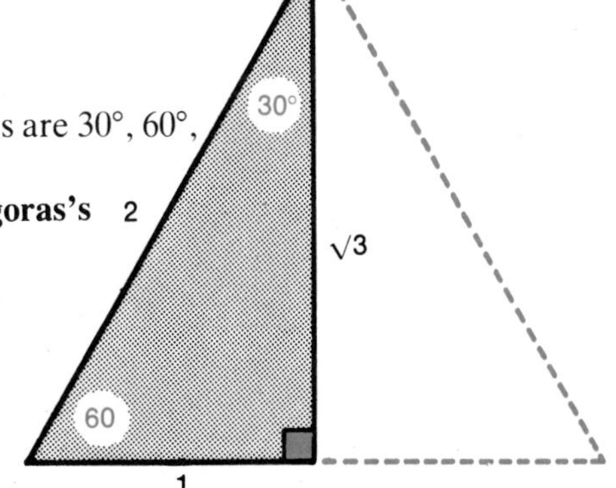

(ii) The half-square triangle

Both short sides are taken as 1 unit.

The hypotenuse is $\sqrt{2}$ by Pythagoras's theorem.

This is known as the 1, 1, $\sqrt{2}$ triangle. Its angles are 90°, 45°, 45°.

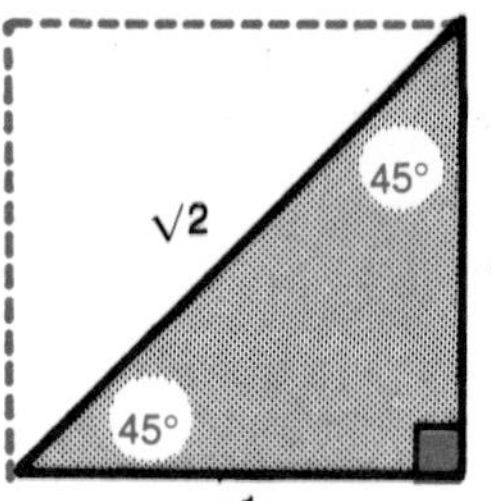

(iii) The 3, 4, 5 triangle

This is the ancient triangle used for drawing exact right angles by the ancient Egyptians. It is the simplest right-angled triangle whose sides are related by whole numbers.

(6, 8 and 10 give a triangle with the same shape. The next simplest is 5, 12, 13)

The numbers 3, 4 and 5 are known as a **Pythagorean triple** because $3^2 + 4^2 = 5^2$.

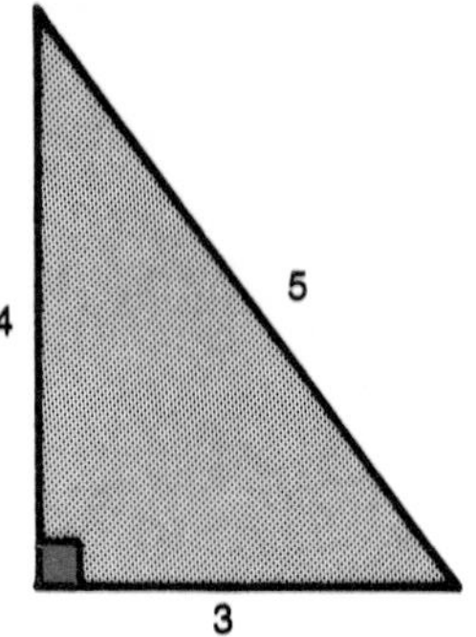

Exercise 28·2

A **1** Draw carefully 1, 2, $\sqrt{3}$ triangles for which the shortest side is:
(i) 4 cm (ii) 5 cm (iii) 3·6 cm (iv) 6·7 cm

2 For each of the triangles above calculate the 'measured' value of ...
(i) sin 30°, cos 30°, tan 30° (ii) sin 60°, cos 60°, tan 60°.

3 How many 1, 2, $\sqrt{3}$ triangles can you find in the figure below?

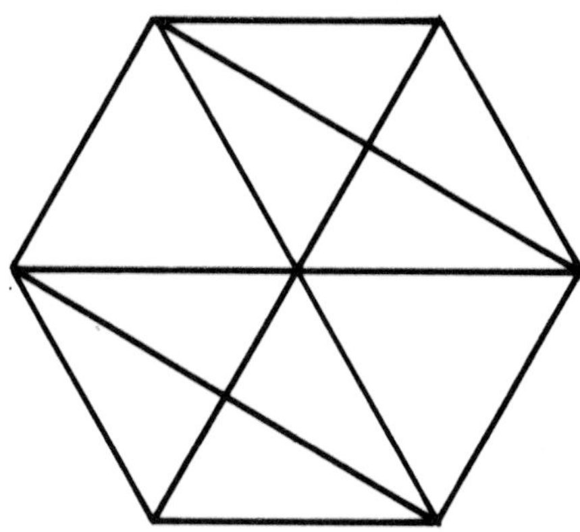

B **1** Draw 45° right-angled triangles for which the short sides are each:
(i) 2·5 cm (ii) 5 cm (iii) 6·4 cm (iv) 10 cm

2 Show that each of the above triangles can be divided into two smaller triangles of the same shape. Can you find any other triangles that have this property?

3 Calculate the length of the hypotenuse for each of the triangles.

4 Use the lengths of side for each triangle to calculate:
(i) $\sin 45°$ (ii) $\cos 45°$ (iii) $\tan 45°$

5 Show that:

(i) $\tan 45° = \dfrac{\sin 45°}{\cos 45°}$ (ii) $(\sin 45°)^2 + (\cos 45°)^2 = 1$

6 Count the 1, 1, $\sqrt{2}$ triangles in the figure below.

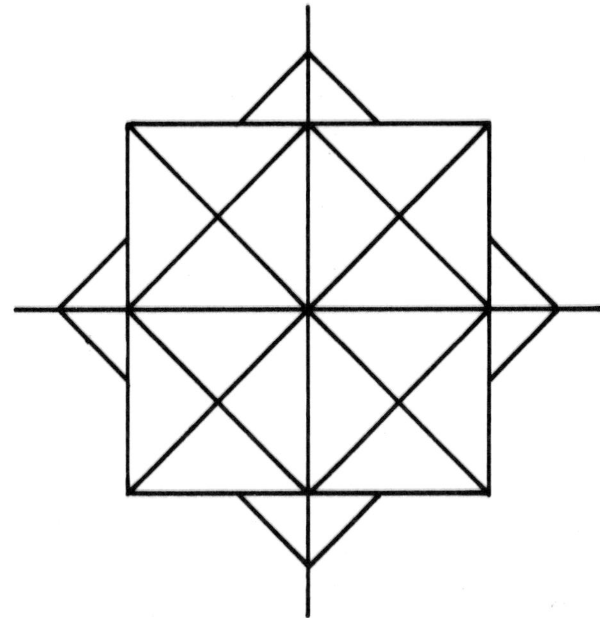

C **1** Draw 3, 4, 5 triangles whose shortest side is
(i) 3 cm (ii) 6 cm (iii) 9 cm long

2 Use tables of sines to calculate the size of the angle θ. Check by measurement in each of the triangles you have just drawn.

3 Divide one of the triangles into four smaller 3, 4, 5 triangles.

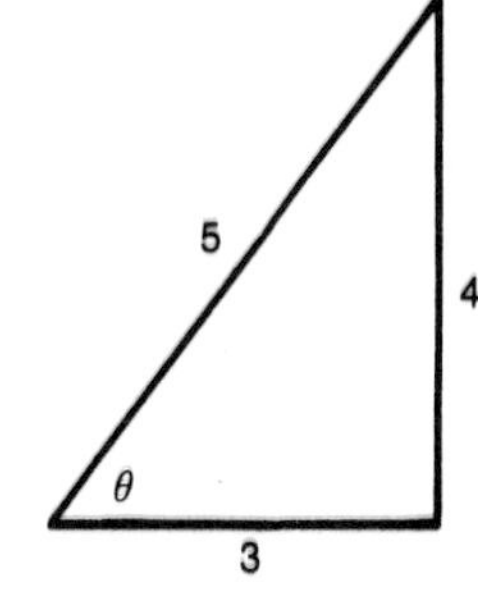

4 Draw a right-angled triangle of any size, but with one angle equal to the 3, 4, 5 triangle (found in question 2). Show that the sides of this triangle are in the same proportion as the (3, 4, 5) triangle.

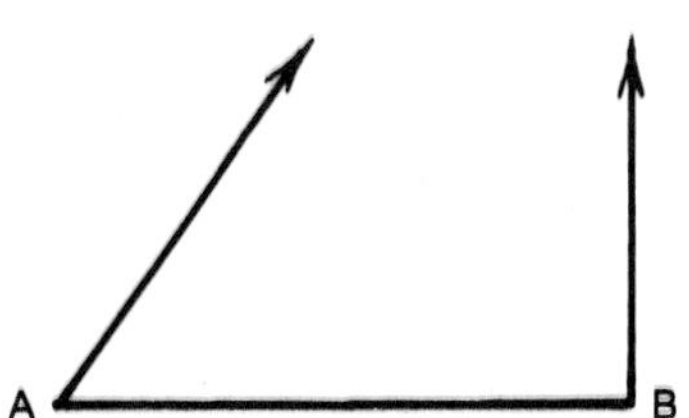

Draw any line AB,
Draw angles of 90° at B and (3, 4, 5 angle) at A. Continue the lines until they meet.

5 How many 3, 4, 5 triangles can you find in the figure below?

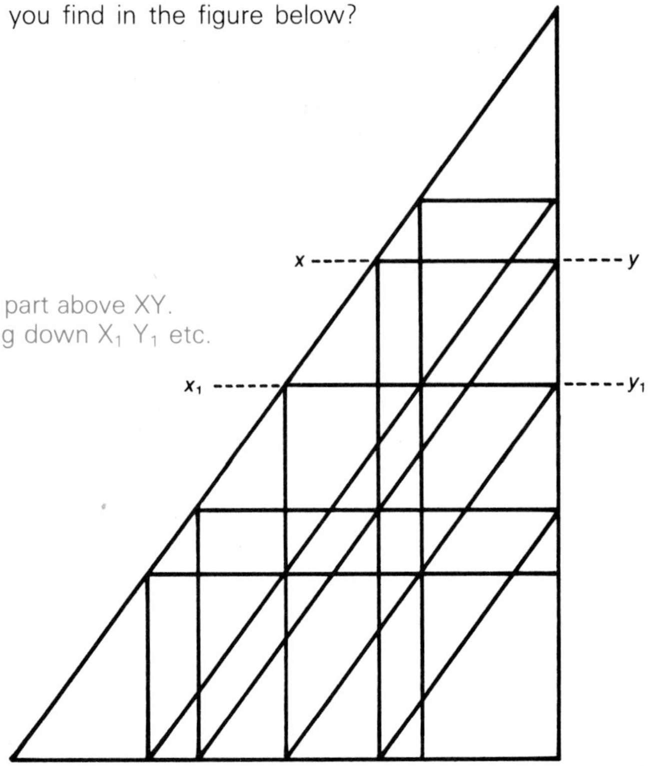

Hint: Find a way of counting the part above XY. This can lead to a way of counting down X_1 Y_1 etc.

28·3 Trigonometrical ratios in the unit circle

All three ratios, sin, cos and tan, can be measured on a unit circle.

XT is a tangent to the circle, that is a line which touches the circle at X.

As P moves around the circles the angle changes. The lengths PQ, OQ and TX also change but PQ is always sin θ, OQ is always cos θ, TX is always tan θ.

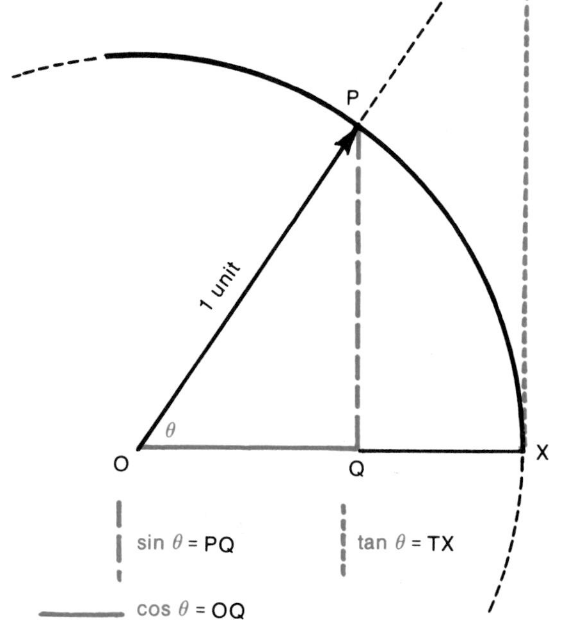

Exercise 28·3

A **1** Measure the lines PQ, OQ and TX on page 228 in centimetres.
2 Calculate PQ ÷ 5, OQ ÷ 5 and TX ÷ 5,*
3 Check that θ measures 57°,
4 Show that $\frac{PQ}{5} = \sin 57°$

$\frac{OQ}{5} = \cos 57°$

$\frac{TX}{5} = \tan 57°$.

B Calculate the ratios PQ/OP, OQ/OP, TX/OP in each of the figures below (having measured the lengths). Use the ratios to obtain sin θ, cos θ and tan θ and use these to find the size of the angle.

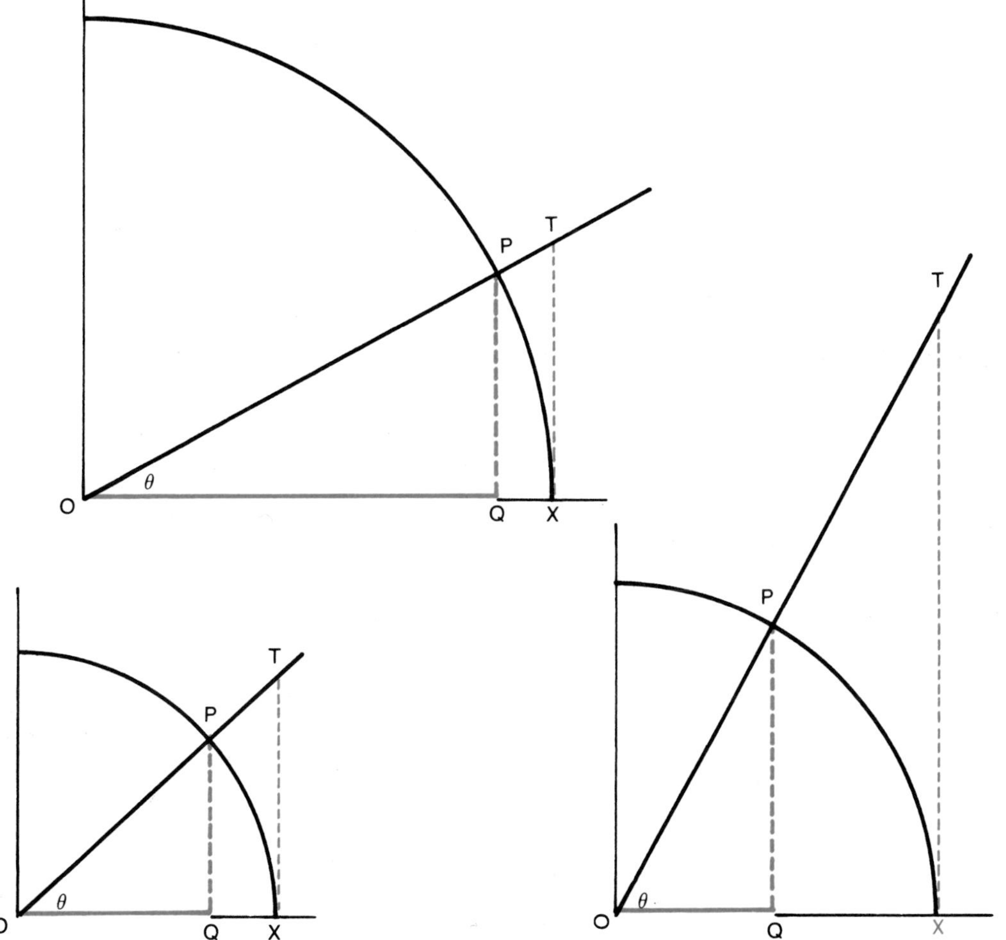

* We divide by 5 because the unit of length is 5 cm.

C Draw a quarter-circle with any radius and choose your own value for θ. Show that it is true that

$$\frac{PQ}{OP} = \sin\theta, \ \frac{OQ}{OP} = \cos\theta, \quad \text{and} \quad \frac{TX}{OP} = \tan\theta.$$

D The line OP represents a *rotating pointer* with O fixed and P moving along the circle from X to Y.

1 Describe how the length PQ changes as P moves round the circle.
2 Describe how the length OQ changes as P moves round the circle.
3 Describe how the length TX changes as P moves round the circle.

28·4 Area of a triangle

The height of the triangle can be found in $\triangle AXB$ using $\sin\theta$

$$\frac{h}{AB} = \sin\theta \Rightarrow h = AB\sin\theta$$

The base of the triangle is BC. So the area of the triangle $= \frac{1}{2} \times AB \times BC \times \sin\theta$.

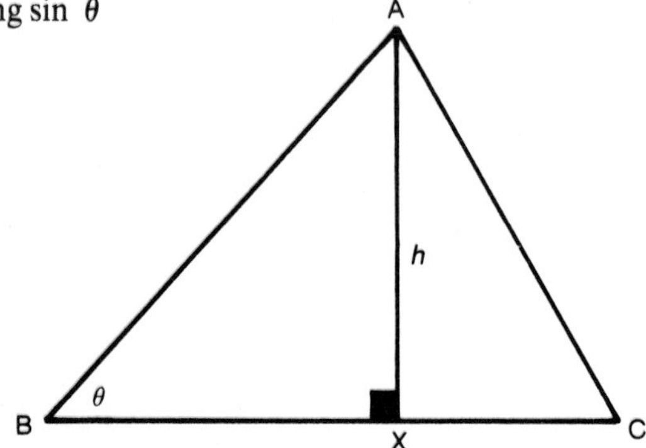

Since we can stand the triangle on any of its three sides . . .
The area of a triangle
$= \frac{1}{2} \times$ product of any two sides $\times$ sine of the angle between them

Examples:

Find the area of $\triangle ABC$

$$\text{Area} = \tfrac{1}{2} \times AB \times BC \times \sin 34°$$
$$= \tfrac{1}{2} \times 3{\cdot}7 \times 4{\cdot}0 \times 0{\cdot}56$$
$$= 4{\cdot}144 \text{ cm}^2$$

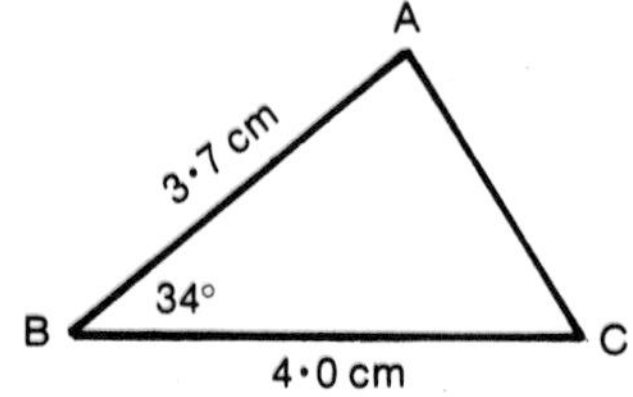

Find the area of $\triangle PQR$

$$\text{Area} = \tfrac{1}{2} \times PR \times PQ \times \sin 44°$$
$$= 0{\cdot}5 \times 3{\cdot}2 \times 2{\cdot}8 \times 0{\cdot}695$$
$$= 3{\cdot}1136 \text{ cm}^2$$

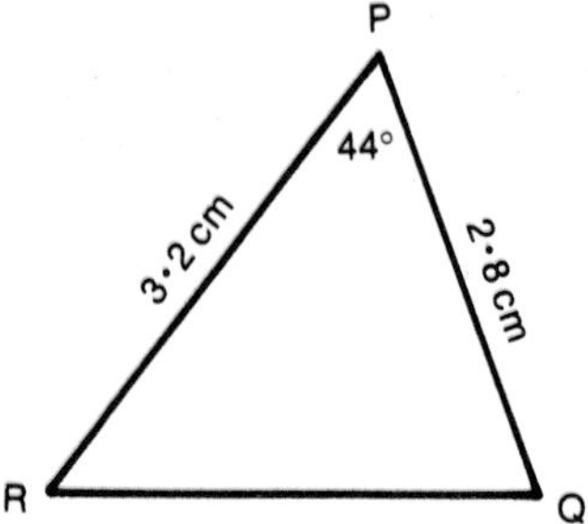

Exercise 28·4

A Calculate the areas of the following triangles.

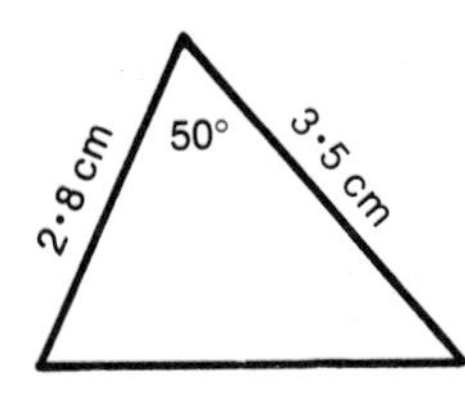

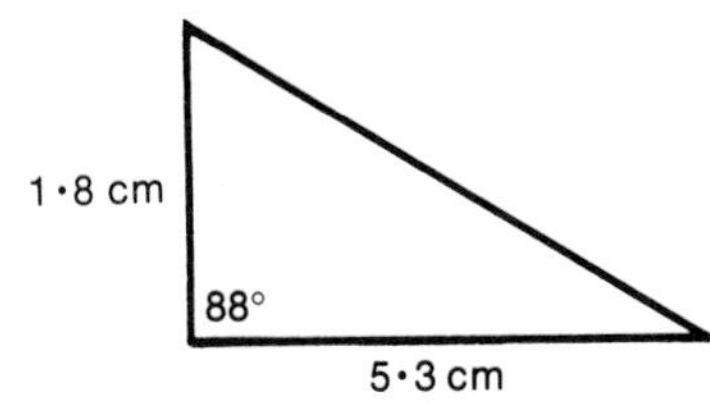

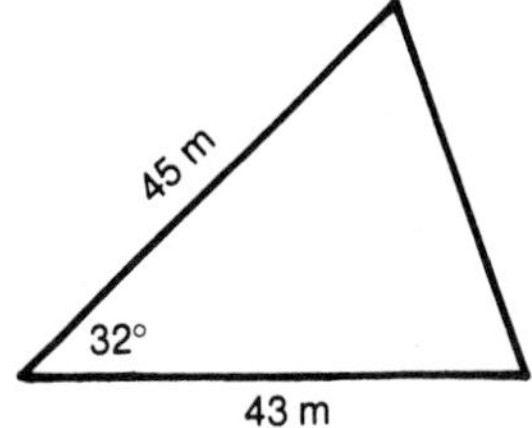

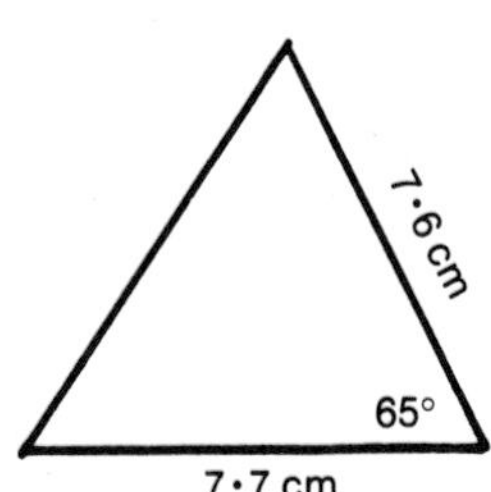

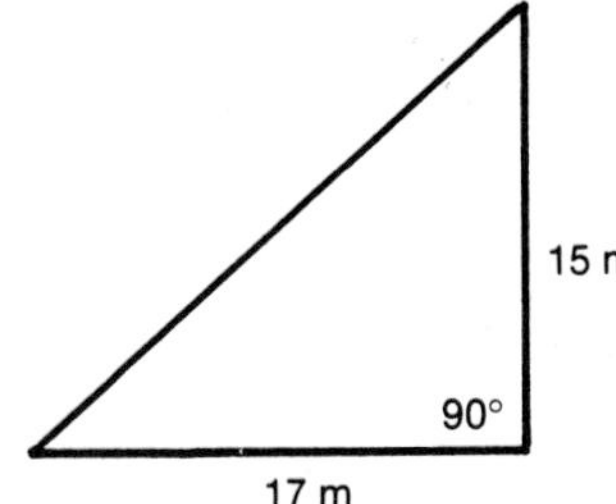

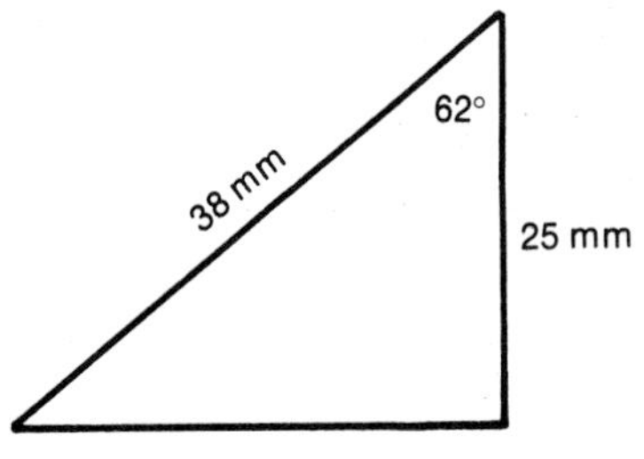

B **1** Use the sine–area formula to find the areas of equilateral triangles whose sides are
(i) 5 cm (ii) 7·6 cm (iii) 8·4 cm (iv) 10 cm (v) 15 cm (vi) 25 cm

2 Show that if you double the length of side of an equilateral triangle, you multiply the area by 4.

3 Show that if two equilateral triangles have sides in the ratio $x:1$* their areas will be in the ratio $x^2:1$.

4 Find the area of 1, 1, $\sqrt{2}$ triangles whose short sides are ....
(i) 5 cm (ii) 3·7 cm (iii) 7·2 cm (iv) 10·8 cm

5 Find the area of 1, 1, $\sqrt{2}$ triangles whose hypotenuses are
(i) 6 cm (ii) 4·8 cm (iii) 7·2 cm (iv) 5·9 cm

You will have to find the short sides first!

C The sides of triangles are usually named by the same letters as the angles opposite.
Calculate the area of $\triangle ABC$ if ...

1 $a = 5$ cm $b = 4{\cdot}3$ cm $\hat{C} = 60°$
2 $a = 6$ cm $c = 4{\cdot}9$ cm $\hat{B} = 44°$
3 $b = 3{\cdot}7$ cm $c = 4{\cdot}4$ cm $\hat{A} = 52{\cdot}3°$
4 $a = 6{\cdot}2$ cm $b = 14{\cdot}3$ cm $\hat{C} = 12{\cdot}2°$

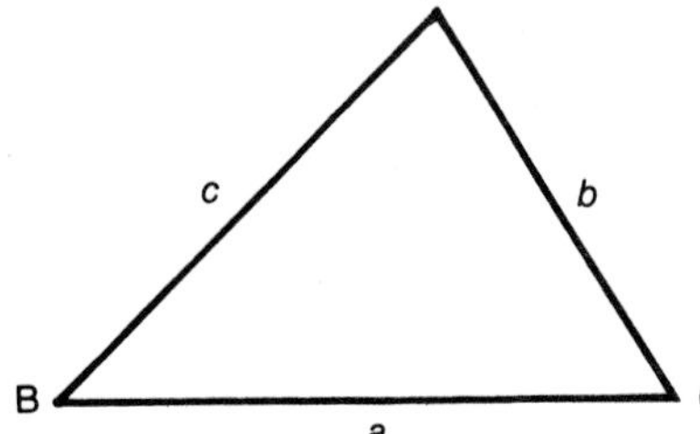

* This means that the sides of one triangle are x times as long as the sides of the other.

D A surveyor measured a piece of land by triangulation. The measurements he took are shown in the plan. Calculate the area of the field.

Measured distances (m)	OA	365	OB	440	OC	388	OD	463	OE	750	OF	542	OG	272
Angles	1	30°	2	21°	3	9°	4	24°	5	26°	6	22°		

You treat the plan as six triangles. In each triangle you know the length of two sides and the angle between them so you can calculate the area.

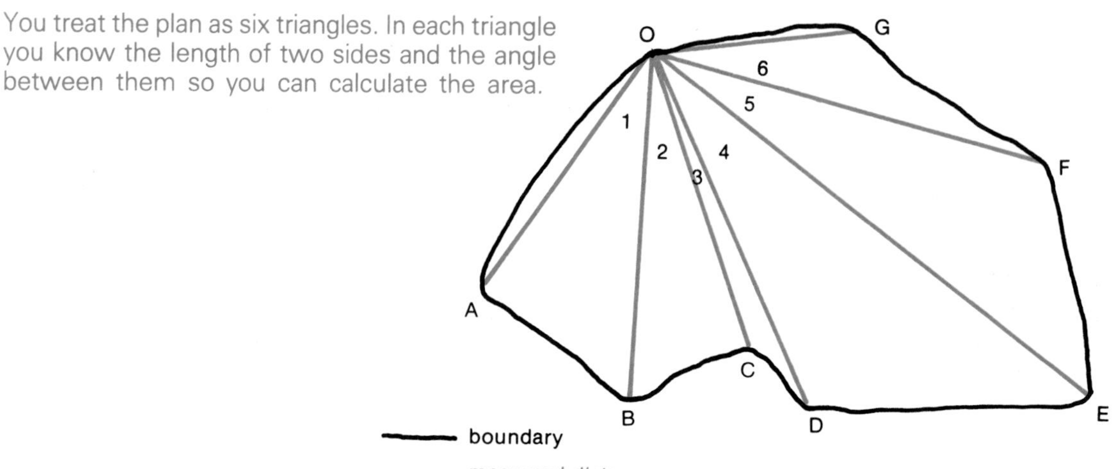

Unit M29 Powers

29·1 What is a power

The product of five 2's all multiplied together is called the fifth power of 2 and written 2^5.

$2 \times 2 \times 2 \times 2 \times 2 = 2^5$ . . . two to the fifth power.

Second powers are called squares.
Third powers are called cubes.

Example:
Write 12 cubed and 3·9 squared as product and as powers.
12 cubed = $12 \times 12 \times 12 = 12^3$
3·9 squared = $3{\cdot}9 \times 3{\cdot}9 = (3{\cdot}9)^2$
Note: It is usual to write a decimal power with brackets.

Exercise 29·1

A Write these powers out as products.

1 4 cubed	**2** 5 squared	**3** 6 to the fifth	**4** 3^8
5 4^4	**6** 5^7	**7** $(1{\cdot}4)^3$	**8** $(2{\cdot}02)^4$
9 $(11{\cdot}5)^3$	**10** $(0{\cdot}65)^5$	**11** $(0{\cdot}21)^3$	**12** $(4{\cdot}37)^6$

B Write these products as powers.
1 $2 \times 2 \times 2 \times 2 \times 2 \times 2$
2 $3 \times 3 \times 3 \times 3$
3 $4 \times 4 \times 4 \times 4 \times 4 \times 4 \times 4$
4 $10 \times 10 \times 10 \times 10 \times 10$
5 $(1{\cdot}2) \times (1{\cdot}2) \times (1{\cdot}2) \times (1{\cdot}2)$
6 $(0{\cdot}3) \times (0{\cdot}3) \times (0{\cdot}3) \times (0{\cdot}3) \times (0{\cdot}3)$
7 $(0{\cdot}01) \times (0{\cdot}01)$
8 $(1{\cdot}45) \times (1{\cdot}45) \times (1{\cdot}45) \times (1{\cdot}45) \times (1{\cdot}45) \times (1{\cdot}45)$

C Write these products in words.
1 12×12
2 $158 \times 158 \times 158$
3 $11{\cdot}6 \times 11{\cdot}6 \times 11{\cdot}6 \times 11{\cdot}6$
4 $0{\cdot}12 \times 0{\cdot}12 \times 0{\cdot}12 \times 0{\cdot}12 \times 0{\cdot}12 \times 0{\cdot}12 \times 0{\cdot}12$

29·2 The value of a power

The value of a power is found by simple multiplication. There are, however, special ways of doing this which depend on the type of calculator in use. Powers may also be found quickly using tables.

Example: (straight multiplication)

Find the value of 3^4

$3^2 = 9$
so $3^3 = 9 \times 3 = 27$
and $3^4 = 27 \times 3 = 81$

Find the value of $(1{\cdot}7)^3$

$(1{\cdot}7)^3 = 1{\cdot}7 \times 1{\cdot}7 \times 1{\cdot}7$
$= 4{\cdot}913$

[C] [1] [·] [7] [×] [1] [·] [7] [×] [1] [·] [7] [=]

Find the value of $(0{\cdot}24)^2$

$(0{\cdot}24)^2 = (0{\cdot}24) \times (0{\cdot}24)$
$= 24 \times 24 \div 100 \div 100$
$= 576 \div 100 \div 100$
$= 0{\cdot}0576$ using tables

Exercise 29·2

A Find the values of these powers by direct multiplication (using head, calculator or tables).

1 2^5 **2** 3^4 **3** 7^3 **4** 10^5
5 100^3 **6** $(3{\cdot}4)^2$ **7** $(2{\cdot}8)^3$ **8** $(0{\cdot}4)^3$
9 $(1{\cdot}3)^6$ **10** $(2{\cdot}6)^5$ **11** $(22{\cdot}4)^4$ **12** $(3{\cdot}06)^7$

B Pick the correct value for the power from the numbers offered.

1 3^4 ... 27, 81, 243
2 5^3 ... 100, 125, 225
3 8^4 ... 409·6, 4096, 40960
4 $(0{\cdot}4)^5$ ... 0·1024, 0·010 24, 0·001 024
5 $(1{\cdot}1)^{10}$ ... 2594, 2·594, 0·02594
6 $(5)^{10}$ ... 976·5625, 9 765 625·0, 97 656·25

C 3^4 can be calculated by finding $3 \times 3 = 9$ and then $9 \times 9 = 81$.
Suggest similar short-cuts to find the values of these powers.

1 4^8 **2** 5^9 **3** 12^6 **4** 6^{10} **5** $(0{\cdot}4)^4$ **6** $(0{\cdot}8)^6$

Show that the short-cut gives the same result as direct multiplication.

29·3 The values of a power. Special methods

Constant multiplier

If your calculator has a 'constant multiplier' program, this can be used to find powers. You may have to look through the calculator booklet to find which buttons to press.
On some calculators, pressing [×] twice sets up the number on display as a constant multiplier.

Example:

	4		4	4k	6	24	5	20				1·2	4·8
[C]	[4]	[×]	[×]		[6]	[=]	[5]	[=]	[1]	[·]	[2]	[=]	... etc.
						↑ 6 × 4		↑ 5 × 4				↑ 1·2 × 4	

To obtain a power, set up the number as a constant multiplier and then keep pressing [=]

Example:

Find the value of: (i) 3^5, (ii) $(2{\cdot}8)^7$

(i) [C] [3] [×] [×] [=] [=] [=] [=]

3 3 3k 9 → 3^2 3^3 3^4 3^5

(ii) [C] [2] [·] [8] [×] [×] [=] [=] [=] [=] [=] [=]

$2{\cdot}8^2$	$2{\cdot}8^3$	$2{\cdot}8^4$	$2{\cdot}8^5$	$2{\cdot}8^6$	$2{\cdot}8^7$
7·84	21·95 . . .	61·46 . . .	172·1 . . .	481·9 . . .	1349·3 . . .

x^y key

If your machine has a key marked x^y, this will give values of powers in one go. The first button you press is the number, then press (x^y), then press the index. Pressing [=] will now give the value.

Example:

Find the value of: (i) 5^7, (ii) $(2{\cdot}3)^4$

(i) [C] [5] [x^y] [7] [=]

5 5 7 78125
or 78124·999

(ii) [C] [2] [·] [3] [x^y] [4] [=]

2 2·3 2·3 4 27·9841

Logarithms

Logarithms can be used to find the value of powers. The logarithms can be found from tables or from a scientific calculator. To find the power of a number, the logarithm of the number is found, multiplied by the index and the inverse logarithm found.

Example:

Find the value of $(3{\cdot}4)^3$ using logarithms.

(i) *Tables* Logarithm of 3·4 = 0·531 using tables.

× 3

1·593

Inv. log of 1·593 = 39·2 (look for 1·593 among the log x values and find the number)

(ii) *Log function*

[c] [3] [·] [4] [log] [x] [3] [=] [inv] [log]

↑ 3 ↑ 3· ↑ 3·4 ↑ 0·5314 ↑ 3 ↑ 1·5944 ↑ 39·3

Note the 0·1 difference in result. The correct result is 39·304.

Exercise 29.3

A Find the values of the following powers by three different methods. Make a note of the differences in the results.

1 8^3 **2** 11^5 **3** $(1{\cdot}6)^4$
4 $(1{\cdot}2)^7$ **5** $(2{\cdot}4)^4$ **6** $(11{\cdot}3)^3$
7 $(48{\cdot}4)^3$ **8** $(2{\cdot}06)^4$ **9** $(3{\cdot}35)^6$

B Decide which is the larger of the following pairs of powers.

1 3^4 *or* 4^3
2 $(1{\cdot}5)^8$ *or* $(1{\cdot}25)^{16}$
3 $(3{\cdot}5)^5$ *or* $(1{\cdot}5)^{10}$
4 $(1{\cdot}1)^{14}$ *or* $(1{\cdot}2)^7$

Note: Put the first result into M then subtract M from the second result. If the answer is a negative number the first value is greater than the second.

C The following powers were worked out by Karen Jones. Check her results. If you feel *sure* she is wrong give the correct value.

	Power	*Value*
1	2^{15}	32 769
2	5^7	390 625
3	$(1{\cdot}4)^8$	147·5789
4	$(1{\cdot}16)^{10}$	3·803

Notes: A power of a positive number is positive.
A power of a number >1 is itself >1.
A power of a positive number <1 is itself <1.
High powers of numbers greater than 1 are very large.
High powers of numbers less than 1 are very small (almost zero!).

29·4 The Laws of Indices

(i) It is easy to see that $2^3 \times 2^5 = 2^8$ by writing the powers out in product form.

$$(2 \times 2 \times 2) \times (2 \times 2 \times 2 \times 2 \times 2) = 2 \times 2 \times 2 \times 2 \times 2 \times 2 \times 2 \times 2$$

(ii) Similarly, for division we can see that $4^5 \div 4^2 = 4^3$

$$\frac{4 \times 4 \times 4 \times 4 \times 4}{4 \times 4} = 4 \times 4 \times 4$$

(iii) It is also easy to see that the cube of 5^2 is 5^6

$$5^2 \times 5^2 \times 5^2 = 5 \times 5 \times 5 \times 5 \times 5 \times 5$$

The above are examples of the laws of indices:

1 $a^m \times a^n = a^{m+n}$ To multiply powers of a number, add the indices
2 $a^m \div a^n = a^{m-n}$ To divide powers of a number, subtract the indices
3 $(a^m)^n = a^{m \times n}$ To 'power' powers of a number, multiply the indices

Exercise 29·4

A **1** Show, by writing out the powers as products, that
(i) $3^3 \times 3^4 = 3^7$ (ii) $2^5 \times 2^3 = 2^8$
(iii) $10^3 \times 10^5 = 10^8$ (iv) $18^2 \times 18^4 = 18^6$

2 Show, by writing out the powers as products, that
(i) $4^3 \div 4^1 = 4^2$ (ii) $5^3 \div 5^2 = 5^1$ (iii) $7^5 \div 7^3 = 7^2$
(iv) $10^8 \div 10^5 = 10^3$ (v) $14^7 \div 14^2 = 14^5$ (vi) $(3{\cdot}4)^{12} \div (3{\cdot}4)^6 = (3{\cdot}4)^6$

3 Show, by writing out the powers, that
(i) $(8^2)^3 = 8^6$ (ii) $(5^3)^4 = 5^{12}$ (iii) $(6^2)^4 = 6^8$
(iv) $(9^5)^2 = 9^{10}$ (v) $(10^2)^3 = (10^3)^2$ (vi) $(16^2)^4 = (16^4)^2$

B Use your calculator to find values for the following powers.
Use the values to test whether the statements are correct.

1 $(1{\cdot}12)^2 \times (1{\cdot}12)^2$ and $(1{\cdot}12)^4$ are equal.
2 $(0{\cdot}35)^3 \times (0{\cdot}35)^2$ and $(0{\cdot}35)^5$ are equal.
3 $(1{\cdot}6)^4 \times (1{\cdot}6)^3$ and $(1{\cdot}6)^7$ are equal.
4 $(0{\cdot}67)^3 \times (0{\cdot}67)^8$ and $(0{\cdot}67)^{11}$ are equal.
5 $(1{\cdot}46)^3 \div (1{\cdot}46)^2$ and $1{\cdot}46$ are equal.
6 $(0{\cdot}36)^5 \div (0{\cdot}36)^2$ and $(0{\cdot}36)^3$ are equal.
7 $(23)^7 \div (23)^3$ and $(23)^4$ are equal.
8 $(3{\cdot}62)^8 \div (3{\cdot}62)^2$ and $(3{\cdot}62)^2$ are equal.
9 $((2{\cdot}2)^2)^3$ and $((2{\cdot}2)^3)^2 = (2{\cdot}2)^6$.
10 $(14^2)^4$ and $(14^4)^2 = 14^8$.
11 $((0{\cdot}45)^2)^2$ and $(0{\cdot}45)^4$ are equal.
12 $((1{\cdot}15)^5)^2$ and $((1{\cdot}15)^2)^5 = (1{\cdot}15)^{10}$.

29·5 Standard form

Any number can be written as . . . a number between 1 and 10 multiplied by a power of 10. This is called standard form.

Example:
(i) 45 can be written as $4{\cdot}5 \times 10^1$
(ii) 265 can be written $2{\cdot}65 \times 10^2$
(iii) 208 000 can be written $2{\cdot}08 \times 10^5$

Numbers less than 1 can also be written in standard form using negative powers of 10.

Example:
(i) 0·38 can be written $3{\cdot}8 \times 10^{-1}$
(ii) 0·0463 can be written $4{\cdot}63 \times 10^{-2}$
(iii) 0·00002 can be written 2×10^{-5}

$\times\, 10^{-1}$ is the same as $\div\, 10$
$\times\, 10^{-2}$ is the same as $\div\, 10^2$
$\times\, 10^{-5}$ is the same as $\div\, 10^5$

The scientific calculator will often present results in standard form. This prevents overflowing the display space for very large or very small numbers.*

> Example:
> 2 960 000 000 would take 10 spaces and overflow
> 2·96 . . . 9 only uses 4 spaces
> 0·000 375 65 would take 9 spaces and overflow
> 3·7565 . . . −4 only uses 7 spaces

* Calculators without S.F. will simply overflow and show *Error*. Such calculators are not reliable above 7 figures.

Exercise 29·5

A Write the following numbers in standard form.

1	275	**2**	4838	**3**	176·4	**4**	16·25
5	65 000	**6**	729 000	**7**	1660 000	**8**	32 000 000
9	0·384	**10**	0·047	**11**	0·000 56	**12**	0·000 006 5

B Write the following standard form numbers in decimal form.

1	$3{\cdot}25 \times 10^{2}$	**2**	$1{\cdot}14 \times 10^{3}$	**3**	$2{\cdot}06 \times 10^{5}$
4	$3{\cdot}58 \times 10^{10}$	**5**	$6{\cdot}5 \times 10^{11}$	**6**	$5{\cdot}2 \times 10^{7}$
7	$1{\cdot}5 \times 10^{22}$	**8**	$1{\cdot}86 \times 10^{5}$	**9**	$2{\cdot}2 \times 10^{-1}$
10	$3{\cdot}5 \times 10^{-3}$	**11**	$4{\cdot}95 \times 10^{-5}$	**12**	$8{\cdot}85 \times 10^{-16}$

C Rewrite each of the following sentences with the numbers in standard form.

1 There are 31 536 000 seconds in one year.
2 There are more than 10 000 000 000 000 000 000 000 molecules in 1 cm^3 of water.
3 A blood cell measures 0·000 000 02 cm.
4 A virus is between 0·000 000 000 1 and 0·000 000 000 001 cm in diameter.

* Calculators without S.F. will simply overflow and show *Error*. Such calculators not reliable above 7 figures.

Unit M30 Applications of powers

30·1 The graph of a power

Since we can find values for powers it is simple to draw a graph of, say, 2^x. We find the values of 2^1, 2^2, 2^3, . . . etc.

All power graphs have the same basic shape. We often use a different scale for x and y.

If 'a' is greater than 2 the y values grow very quickly. If 'a' is below 1·2 the y values grow quite slowly.

Once the graph has been drawn we can use it to **estimate** values of y for a given x. We can also estimate x, given y. This will be clearer from the examples.

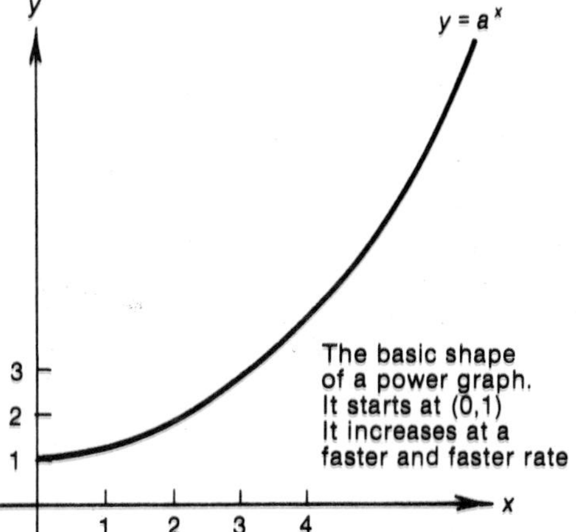

Example:

Draw the graph of $y = 2^x$ from $x = 0$ to $x = 5$. Use your graph to estimate $2^{1\cdot5}$.
First make a table of values of y.
$y = 2^x$. Then draw the graph

x	0	1	2	3	4	5
y	1	2	4	8	16	32

From the graph $2^{1\cdot5}$ is about 3.

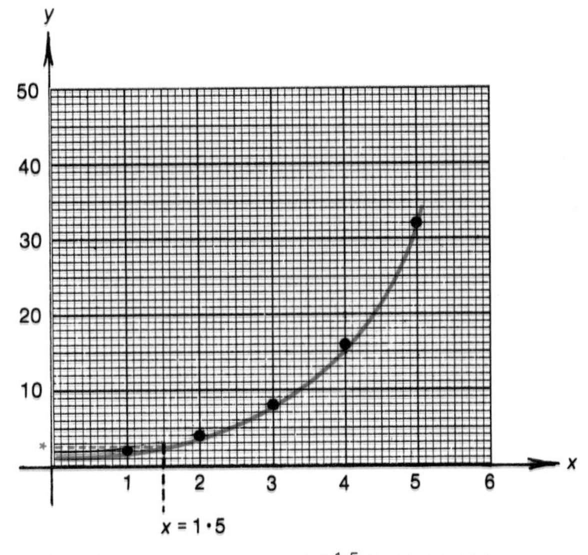

(From the calculator, [c] [2] [x^y] [1·5] [=] we find the exact value of $2^{1\cdot5}$ is 2·8284.)

Example:

Draw the graph of $(1{\cdot}2)^x$ from $x = 0$ to $x = 10$.
Use the graph to estimate
(i) The value of $(1{\cdot}2)^x$ if $x = 3{\cdot}5$.
(ii) The value of x for which $(1{\cdot}2)^x$ is $3{\cdot}5$.

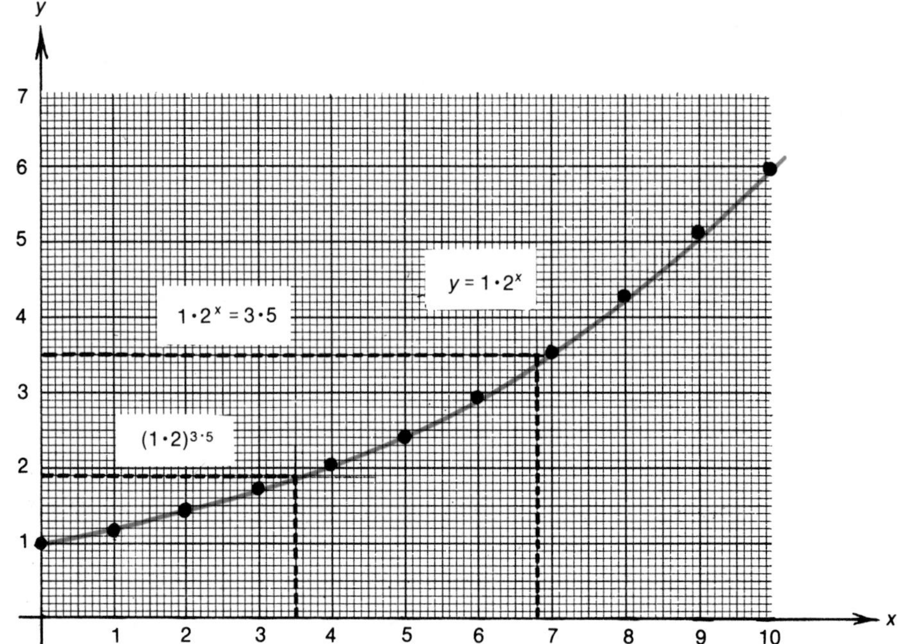

First make up a table of values for y, using a calculator. Then draw the graph. Join the points with a smooth curve, not with straight lines.
$y = (1{\cdot}2)^x$

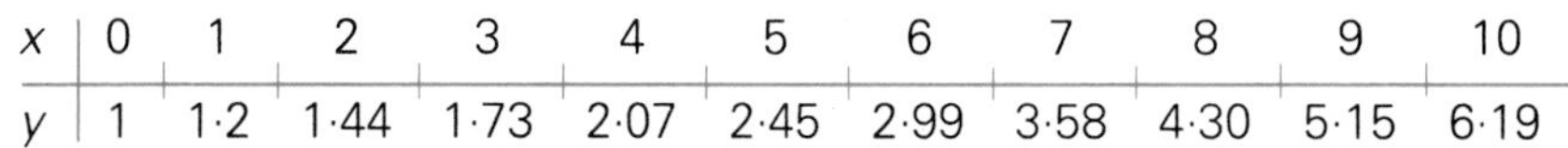

x	0	1	2	3	4	5	6	7	8	9	10
y	1	1·2	1·44	1·73	2·07	2·45	2·99	3·58	4·30	5·15	6·19

From the graph: (i) $(1{\cdot}2)^{3\cdot5}$ is about 1·9.
(ii) if $(1{\cdot}2)^x$ is 3·5, x is 6·8.

Check by calculator: (i) [c] [1·2] [x^y] [3·5] [=] . . . gives 1·89.
(ii) [c] [1·2] [x^y] [6·8] [=] . . . gives 3·45.

Exercise 30·1

A 1 Draw a graph of $y = 3^x$ for $x = 0, 1, 2, 3, 4, 5$. Use 1 cm for 1 unit along the x-axis and 1 cm for 10 units up the y-axis.

2 Use the graph to estimate:
(i) $3^{2\cdot3}$ (ii) $3^{3\cdot5}$ (iii) $3^{0\cdot8}$
(iv) $3^{1\cdot5}$ (v) $3^{2\cdot7}$ (vi) $3^{4\cdot5}$

3 Use your graph to find the value of x if
(i) $3^x = 8$ (ii) $3^x = 20$ (iii) $3^x = 50$

4 Check your estimates using [x^y] on a calculator.

B **1** Draw a graph of $y = (1\cdot5)^x$ from $x = 0$ to $x = 8$. Use 1 cm for each unit along the x-axis and 1 cm for each unit along the y-axis.

2 Use your graph to estimate the value of
(i) $(1\cdot5)^{2\cdot5}$ (ii) $(1\cdot5)^{3\cdot5}$ (iii) $(1\cdot5)^{5\cdot5}$
(iv) $(1\cdot5)^{6\cdot2}$ (v) $(1\cdot5)^{0\cdot7}$ (vi) $(1\cdot5)^{4\cdot3}$

3 Use your graph to find x if:
(i) $(1\cdot5)^x = 2$ (ii) $(1\cdot5)^x = 4$ (iii) $(1\cdot5)^x = 8$
(iv) $(1\cdot5)^x = 3\cdot5$ (v) $(1\cdot5)^x = 2\cdot5$ (vi) $(1\cdot5)^x = 7\cdot5$

C **1** What do you think would be the value of these?
(i) 2^{-1} (ii) $(1\cdot5)^{-1}$ (iii) $(1\cdot2)^{-1}$ (iv) $(0\cdot8)^{-1}$
(v) 2^{-3} (vi) $(1\cdot5)^{-2}$ (vii) $(1\cdot2)^{-4}$ (viii) $(0\cdot8)^{-6}$

2 Check on the calculator using (for example)
[c] [2] [x^y] [1] [+/−] [=]

3 Do you agree that
(i) $2^{-3} \times 2^3 = 1$? (ii) $(1\cdot5)^{-2} \times (1\cdot5)^2 = 1$?
(iii) $(1\cdot2)^{-4} \times (1\cdot2)^4 = 1$? (iv) $(0\cdot8)^{-6} \times (0\cdot8)^6 = 1$?

30·2 Power growth in nature, population

Most things in nature grow by producing new things which themselves produce new things.

sapling (young tree)

sapling produces branches

branches produce branches

and so on

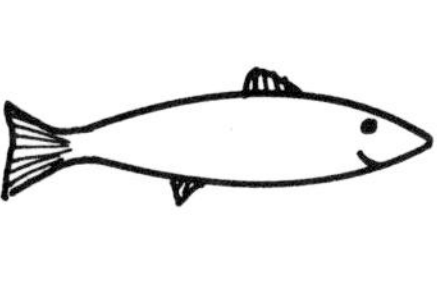
pair of fish

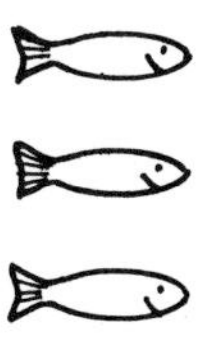
pair produce young fish

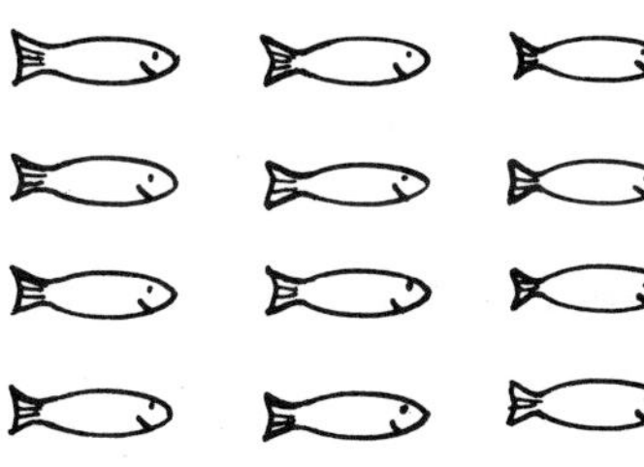
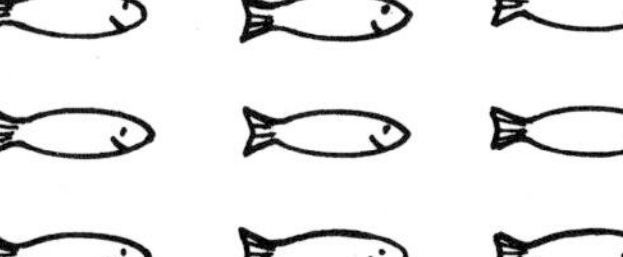
young fish produce more young fish

If conditions are right, animal, plant and insect populations can increase very fast. This leads to plagues of locusts, the overgrowth of land by weeds, etc.
This growth is called **exponential growth.** *

Exercise 30·2

A **1** Terry breeds goldfish. Every six months each pair produces young and on average four of the new fish survive. How many fish will he have in six years if he starts with one pair and keeps all the offspring.

2 The *amoeba* reproduces by splitting in half. If it does this every 24 hours, how many cells will there be after (i) 10 days, (ii) 20 days.

3 When you have an infection it means your body has been invaded by foreign cells which multiply fast. Your body organises defensive cells to fight them but this takes time.
An infection with 1 million cell population grows by 10 per cent every hour ($(1\cdot1)^x$.)
(a) What is the cell population after
(i) 3 hours, (ii) 10 hours, (iii) 24 hours, (iv) 3 days
(b) How long before the population doubles?
(c) How long before the population reaches 1000 million?
(d) Why is it important to treat infections quickly?

B The population of a city is increasing by 6% each year.

1 Draw a graph of the population over the next 10 years if the population is 1 million now. (This will be $(1\cdot06)^x$.)

2 In how many years will the population of the city double at this rate of increase? (Find x if $(1\cdot06)^x = 2$.)

3 What will the population be in 20 years time if the rate of growth continues at 6%?

C In 1979 the following populations and population growths were estimated by the United Nations. Estimate the populations in 1989 and 1999 assuming the growth rate stays the same till then.

	Country	*Population* (10^6)	*Growth rate %*	
1	Ghana	11	3	$(1\cdot03)^x$
2	West Germany	61	0·2	$(1\cdot002)^x$
3	Indonesia	145	2·6	$(1\cdot026)^x$

Note: In 1979 the world population was 4500 million with a growth rate of 1·88% $(1\cdot0188)^x$.

30·3 Compound interest

When money is invested, extra money is produced.
This extra is called interest. The interest itself produces more interest so we have a power growth situation.
The rate of interest tells you how much £1 grows in 1 year.

Example:
(i) 10% interest means £1 grows to £1·10 in 1 year.
(ii) 25% interest means £1 grows to £1·25 in 1 year.
(iii) 6% interest means £1 grows to £1·06 in 1 year.

* Exponent is another word for power.

Since the second year begins with £1 plus interest, $1 + i$, it ends with
$(1 + i) \times (1 + i) = (1 + i)^2$

Example:
£150 is invested at 15% interest for 5 years. What sum of money results? What is the interest earned.
Consider each £1.
Each £1 grows to $(1{\cdot}15)^5$ in five years.
Therefore, resulting sum of money is £150 × $(1{\cdot}15)^5$
= 150 × 2·01136
= £301·70

The interest can be found by subtracting £150 from the final sum.
Interest is £151·70

Calculator: [C] [1] [·] [1] [5] [x^y] [5] [=] [×] [1] [5] [0] [=]

Exercise 30·3

A Find the amount returned from £1 after . . .
1 5 years at 10% interest. $(1{\cdot}10)^x$
2 8 years at 15% interest. $(1{\cdot}15)^x$
3 15 years at 8% interest.
4 4 years at 22% interest.
5 7 years at 14% interest.
Calculate the *interest* earned in each case.

B Find the interest earned when the following sums of money are invested.
1 £500 at 8% interest for 5 years.
2 £70 at 12% interest for 6 years.
3 £900 at 11% interest for 8 years.
4 £350 at 14% interest for 3 years.
5 £650 at 18% interest for 4 years.

C When money is borrowed it has to be paid back with interest. The interest is a charge for the use of the money.

Example:
A man borrows £4000 to buy a car. He pays 22% interest for 3 years and then pays back the loan plus interest. How much does he have to pay back altogether? How much of this is interest?

£4000 at 22% interest becomes £4000 × $(1{\cdot}22)^3$ in three years = £7263·39

He pays back £7263·39 altogether. Of this £3263·39 is interest.

Find the amount which has to be repaid including interest when . . .
1 £500 is borrowed for 4 years at 18% interest.
2 £7000 is borrowed for 3 years at 15% interest.
3 £650 is borrowed for 7 years at 14% interest.

4 £85 000 is borrowed for 20 years at 17% interest.
5 £20 000 is borrowed for 12 years at 8% interest.

30·4 Inflation

When the prices of goods go up every year we say that inflation is happening. The rate of inflation is usually given as a percentage. In 1980 the inflation rate was 16% in the UK.

Usually wages go up to keep up with the price of goods.

Each increase in prices is itself subject to inflation so we have a power growth situation very similar to compound interest.

Example:

In 1980 a new car cost £4000. If the rate of inflation continues at 15% over the years to 1985 what would the 'same' new car cost in 1985?
Each year every £1 cost goes up to £1·15.
New cost after 5 years is £4000 × $(1{\cdot}15)^5$
= £4000 × 2·011 36 (calculator)
= £8045·43

Exercise 30·4

A Assuming a 15% rate of inflation, calculate the probable cost of these objects in 10 years' time.

1 A car costing £4000 now.
2 A kilo of meat costing £3 now.
3 A bicycle costing £80 now.
4 A pair of shoes costing £15 now.
5 A hair-cut costing £6 now.

B Calculate the costs in 20 years' time of each of the things in question A, but at these inflation rates:

1 5% **2** 15% **3** 25%

Why do you think the government always makes such a fuss about 'the problem of inflation'?

C We can expect wages to rise roughly at the same rate as the cost of goods.

1 A secretary earns £80 per week now. What should he/she earn in 10 years' time to keep up with inflation of 16%?
2 A carpenter earns £4·50 an hour now. What would you expect him to earn in 8 years' time if inflation averages 12% a year?
3 My father earned £2·50 per week when he started work 25 years ago. The average rate of inflation has been 8%. What would he start at now?
4 A soldier's pay 20 years ago was £4·20 per week. Inflation has been 8% per year on average. Today the soldier earns £120 per week. Have his wages kept up with inflation?
5 Write a letter to a friend about wages and costs which would be right for 20 years from now. (It might be fun to keep the letter for 20 years and look to see if you were right!)